Geomorphology
of Cold Environments

BY THE SAME AUTHOR

L'Europe Centrale, in collaboration with P. George, in the 'Orbis' Series, Presses Universitaires de France

L'épiderme de la Terre, esquisse d'une géomorphologie appliquée, in the 'Évolution des Sciences' Series, Masson, Paris

Traité de Géomorphologie, in collaboration with A. Cailleux, S.E.D.E.S., Paris:
Vol. I Introduction à la Géomorphologie Climatique
Vol. II modelé périglaciaire
Vol. III modelé glaciaire
Vol. IV modelé des régions sèches
Vol. V modelé des régions chaudes, savanes et forêts

Principes et méthodes de la Géomorphologie, Masson, Paris

Geomorphology of Cold Environments

JEAN TRICART
Director of the Centre of Applied Geography
Professor of the Faculté des Lettres, Strasbourg

translated by
EDWARD WATSON
Senior Lecturer in Geography
University College of Wales, Aberystwyth

MACMILLAN
ST. MARTIN'S PRESS

First published in 1969 *by*
MACMILLAN AND CO LTD
Little Essex Street London WC2
and also at Bombay Calcutta and Madras
Macmillan South Africa (Publishers) Pty Ltd Johannesburg
The Macmillan Company of Australia Pty Ltd Melbourne
The Macmillan Company of Canada Ltd Toronto
St Martin's Press Inc New York
Gill and Macmillan Dublin

Library of Congress catalog card no. 77–84839

Printed in Great Britain by
R AND R CLARK LTD
Edinburgh

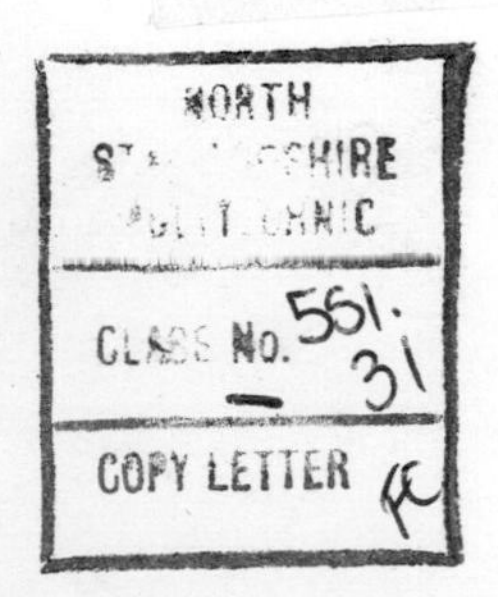

Preface to French Edition

THE writing of this book has been made possible only by the help and encouragement of many other people. It presents in a condensed form the material contained in the two volumes of *Traité de Géomorphologie* (S.E.D.E.S., Paris). The formulation of the ideas presented here has taken place over the last fifteen years, as a result of collaboration with A. Cailleux, in discussions, excursions together and through the exchange of innumerable letters. On all fundamental points agreement has been reached between us. Nevertheless I accept all responsibility for the views expressed and for the shortcomings of this book.

It owes a great deal to many colleagues whose hospitality in France, Germany, Holland, Belgium, Sweden, Scotland, Spain, Morocco, Italy and Peru enabled me to collect a wealth of observations during many visits to these countries, to exchange ideas and acquaint myself with work hitherto unknown to me. To them all, I offer my sincere thanks.

I am also indebted to J. Dylik who has kindly provided several Russian publications and made available summaries of many others, and to M. Roger, the energetic founder of the C.E.D.P., later Head of the Service d'Information Géologique de B.R.G.G.M., for translation of Russian works, which, owing to limited means, were unfortunately fewer than had been hoped.

Finally, I would like to thank Madame A. R. Cloots, née Hirsch, my research assistant, who carried the heavy burden of responsibility for references and summaries and for proof reading. Without her help, the amount of teaching, research and administration of a large department would probably have prevented this book from being written.

Preface to English Edition

Géomorphologie des Régions Froides, which first appeared in 1963 is an abridged form of two parts of the *Cours de Géomorphologie: Modelé glaciaire et nival* and *Le modelé périglaciaire* produced in collaboration with Professor A. Cailleux. Professor Tricart revised the text and bibliography for this translation in 1968.

Acknowledgements

In addition to the author, the publisher wishes to thank the following who have kindly supplied original photographs:

Mr. Bradford Washburn, Director of the Museum of Science, Boston: Plate 3
C.I.M.: Plate 2(a)
National Air Photo Library, Department of Energy, Mines and Resources, Ottawa, Canada. (Photo No. T469R – 156) Plate 4
Beekert: Plate 5
Institut Géographique National: Plate 6
Professor Fritz Müller, McGill University. Photograph from Ph.D. thesis: 'Beobachtungen über Pingos, detailuntersuchungen in Ostgrönland und in der Kanadischen Arktis' *Meddeleser om Grønland*, Copenhagen, No 3. and the National Research Council of Canada's English translation: 'Observations on Pingos' *Technical translation 1073*, by D. A. Sinclair, Ottawa: Plate 9(b)
The United States Navy Department, Washington: Plate 10
Mr. Bradford Washburn, Director of the Museum of Science, Boston: Plate 11

Contents

Introduction

GREAT frozen expanses of the ice sheets, the chaos of *séracs* on mountain glaciers, snow and névé fields which last through the summer in sheltered hollows of slopes, ground which is by turns soft, marshy, and hardened by the frost of the tundra, flows of sodden earth, great unvegetated debris slopes, peculiar geometrical patterns of stones – these are the pictures called to the geomorphologist's mind by the term 'cold environments'. Though found repeatedly over vast polar areas, these features are not confined to such regions. A large proportion of them may be met outside their normal environment, on high mountains in very different latitudes. Above a certain altitude, precipitation in all parts of the world takes the form of snow and nourishes glaciers; the temperature becomes low enough to inhibit the growth of a dense vegetation cover and to cause frequent freeze–thaw cycles.

There is, therefore, a cold *latitudinal* zone and a cold *altitudinal* zone which may be grouped together under the term '*cold environments*'. They have many features in common, such as a scanty vegetation, or even the absence thereof, soil-forming processes that go with this, and the frequent conversion of moisture to ice. There are, however, important differences: the mountain climate is not identical to the polar climate, it is due to a deterioration with altitude in the zonal climate of the neighbouring lowlands, and it retains many of the features of the latter. The pattern of temperature oscillation at 5000 metres in the Andes of Ecuador is essentially diurnal, while that of Lappland, the Taimyr Peninsula or Grahamland is annual. Though the purely physical processes are intrinsically the same (e.g. the mechanical properties of ice, the effects of frost), they function in a different way. The ice of a valley glacier near melting point has not the same viscosity as that at the centre of the Greenland ice sheet, which is subjected to temperatures several tens of degrees below zero. The effects of ground frost are not the same in the tundra, where the winter is long and severe and wind sweeps away any snow, as in a mountain valley in middle latitudes, where the snow survives to form a protective cover. The geomorphological context in which they occur also differs. The strong relief of the mountains favours processes which operate on steep slopes, such as scree formation, and inhibits those operating on gentle slopes, such as solifluction. In spite of a basis of common processes, the morphogenetic systems differ.

The emphasis should therefore be placed on processes common to all cold environments, though operating differently in space. On this basis, cold environments may be defined as those in which *the conversion of water to the solid state plays a predominant geomorphological role.* They therefore include:

(i) Glaciated areas where water is most often in a solid state so that it flows in the form of glaciers,

(ii) Areas with intense seasonal frost or frequent diurnal freeze–thaw cycles, with or without permanently frozen ground.

Their delimitation is a complex problem and can no more be done by surveyed lines than that of other morphoclimatic regions. The ecology of relief forms, like that of plants, depends on a combination of different factors and on frequency rather than averages. The distribution of phenomena due to cold on the face of the earth will be dealt with at length and forms the content of Part I. Yet, although cold environments as defined above form 25% of the land surface, their geomorphological importance is appreciably greater than this figure indicates. Indeed, as a result of the climatic fluctuations of the Quaternary, the geomorphological effects of cold extended over large areas in the temperate zone where they made a distinctive imprint, often still clearly visible, even when they do not form a major feature in the landscape. For this reason a chapter will be devoted to the former distribution of phenomena due to frost climates.

The great practical importance of the study of the geomorphological effects of frost climates is due to this two-sided distribution: first, the present-day phenomena of high altitudes and high latitudes, and secondly, the surviving features from the cold phases of the Quaternary, in those parts of the temperate zone which are economically most advanced. It makes a valuable contribution to the solution of many problems of applied geology concerning morainic, proglacial, and alluvial deposits in much of Europe, the Soviet Union, Canada and the United States. In these countries soil conservation often means the protection of periglacial deposits, such as loess or glacial deposits, against accelerated erosion caused by agricultural exploitation, for soil has developed on these deposits on a relief inherited from the final cold phase.

The present frost climate zone is also economically one of the most important pioneer areas, hitherto undervalued because of the difficulties of development. Its exploitation is now being vigorously pursued, especially in the Soviet Union and in Canada, mainly for its mineral wealth. Towns are mushrooming alongside industrial establishments and lines of communication have to be constructed to provision a population which is rapidly increasing. Finally, rivalry between the United States and the Soviet Union gives the polar regions great strategic value: important bases have been constructed there for defence. All this requires a better knowledge of the environment, including the morphogenetic processes which are powerful enough to threaten any economic development failing to take them into account. In the last thirty years, knowledge of the frost climate zone has made giant strides: because the practical problems of its development are so great it is becoming the most studied of all zones in climatic geomorphology.

This is the result of a long process of evolution, for scientific interest in at least part of the problem goes back some time. Glacial phenomena were the first to be studied: since the end of the eighteenth century, contacts between the academic worker and the mountaineer led the former to postulate that the area covered by ice was once much greater than at present. It was a Swiss, Kulin, who in 1787 demonstrated this from the distribution of erratic blocks. His work remained unnoticed and the idea was taken up again by Venetz, then Charpentier and finally by Agassiz, who from 1836 became the great proponent of the theory, eventually convincing the scientific world. He brought together the scattered observations of Bernhardi in Germany, Esmark in Norway and Hutton in Scotland, showing the widespread nature of the glaciation and proposing the term 'glacial epoch' for the Quaternary. He succeeded in convincing the British that the erratic blocks in their islands were not brought by icebergs, as Lyell supposed, but were remnants of moraines. The term *drift* survived none the less. During the first years of the second half of the nineteenth century, Geikie in Great Britain, and Torrel in Scandinavia, made an important contribution to the knowledge of the Quaternary glaciation.

As part of geology, the study of glaciers profited from a general enthusiasm for exploration and discovery, and the investigation of existing ice. The rivalry to reach the pole led to several Arctic expeditions which collected abundant data, if somewhat haphazardly. From the closing years of the nineteenth century, the development of hydro-electric power and the Alpine tourist industry focused attention on Alpine glaciers, which were the first to be systematically studied, especially by Forel. From these studies has sprung glaciology, a discipline which embraces all aspects of glaciers: regimen, dynamics and morphogenetic activity. It was only later that scientific polar expeditions made similar studies of polar ice, especially those expeditions associated with Hobbs, Tyndall and Wegener.

At the same time, the study of glaciers by geologists such as Heim and Richter went on. Towards the end of the nineteenth century, Penck and Brückner developed their chronology of the Alpine glaciations.

Glaciology made its greatest advances after the First World War, when team work became common. When, at the beginning of the twentieth century, it was realised that geomorphologists, especially de Martonne, had developed a theory of glacial erosion in ignorance of the mechanics of ice flow, attention was directed mainly to processes. Physicists began the study of ice crystals and the properties of ice; they even attempted to apply to its flow the theory of mechanics. The study of glacier regimes progressed vigorously in the Alps, Scandinavia, Alaska and Greenland. The scientific exploration of Antarctica was also organised, and this, one must remember, represents nearly 90% of the ice in the world today. The development of sedimentology made possible a systematic analysis of glacial deposits, especially in Germany, Scandinavia, Holland and more recently, in the Soviet Union, Switzerland, the United States and Poland.

From the point of view of methodology, the evolution of glacier study shows two interesting points:

(1) The first is derived from the concept of sediment correlation. Since the end of the eighteenth century, the former extent of glaciation has been deduced from its morainic deposits. The study of the deposit to interpret its form, developed in practice into a reconstruction of the Quaternary glaciers, considerably before this method had been formulated as a principle. The work of Geikie, for example, has shown from a study of boulder clays that these were deposited directly by ice, as Agassiz believed, and not by icebergs as Lyell thought. This is one of the earliest examples of the reconstruction of a process from the study of a deposit. Again, at the end of the nineteenth century, Penck and Brückner showed the importance of palaeosols as a method of geomorphological dating, by using the ferretto zone as a criterion for old moraines. Because it remained outside the Davisian conspectus, the study of glaciers has provided modern geomorphology with some of its chief methods of research.

(2) The study of glaciers began with the reconstruction of Quaternary phenomena, and then was directed mainly towards mountain glaciers. First Wegener, and then the French Polar Expeditions, began the glaciological exploration of Greenland, while that of Antarctica has only recently got under way. As a result, our understanding of glacier mechanics is very incomplete; it is derived from a single category, the temperate valley

glacier of the Alpine type, which is almost an exception, from the world viewpoint. From this, much has been extrapolated, probably too much, since many of the geomorphological concepts founded on this one type have proved faulty. A thorough revision of our ideas is taking place at the present time, as a result of new data yielded by the study of polar glaciers and the analysis of the materials left by the Pleistocene ice sheets.

The study of the other geomorphological effects of frost climates, conveniently grouped under the heading of periglacial phenomena, had scarcely begun at the end of the nineteenth century. From the early nineteenth century, however, the existence of solifluction deposits was recognized in Great Britain. These were generally near the surface and called *head* because they formed the top or head of exposures. Little attention was paid to them. Quaternary study fell into two parts forming a diptych: glacial deposits and diluvium. What is now attributed to periglacial phenomena might, after a fashion, be included in the latter. Belgrand found in the coarse alluvial gravels of the Seine, with their blocks carried by ice floes, an argument in favour of the Deluge. Others have held loess to be an interglacial deposit, 'diluvial'. The Davisian concepts worked against an appreciation of periglacial phenomena; they operated within the field of 'normal' erosion and attributed to senility alone landforms which have been subdued by solifluction. This refusal to take into account the influence of climate on relief could only result in a failure to study forms which are essentially climatic. Nevertheless, between 1880 and 1920, polygons, block streams and striped ground were discovered. Students fell into two groups:

1. The Davisian school regarded these as minor forms, relegated to the status of curiosities, without any real importance in the evolution of relief. In order to avoid upsetting the scheme of 'normal erosion', they were attributed to the work of snow, making them a sort of appendage to the 'climatic accident' which the glaciers constituted. Such was the position of de Martonne.

2. Those who had been little influenced by Davis made a serious study of them. The two fundamental works were those of Anderson on solifluction, and of Högbom on the action of frost, both appearing at the beginning of the twentieth century. Their most faithful followers were the Germans: Salomon in 1916 demonstrated the role of Quaternary periglacial activity in the relief of the mountains of central Germany.

Research on periglacial processes thus remained marginal to Davisian geomorphology which could not assign to them their proper role. As in glaciology, this was done by students with varying backgrounds:

1. German geomorphologists, trained in climatic geomorphology, made

a large number of observations both at home and during their numerous expeditions to polar regions. This is also true of the Poles who followed Lozinski, the inventor of the term 'periglacial'. Steeger described periglacial ground structures in the Rhine alluvium in 1925. Büdel demonstrated the origin of block streams. Many studies were devoted to patterned ground.

2. The geologists, less influenced than the geographers by Davis, and the prehistorians, made similar advances. With Leffingwell and Eakin, an American school developed in Alaska. In France, the forerunners were Abbé Breuil, Milon, Dangeard, Bigot, followed by Patte and Cailleux. In the Soviet Union, the systematic exploration of the Arctic with a view to its development, led to the accumulation of a large body of data.

3. The engineers were faced with the problem of frost damage to roads and sometimes buildings. The development of road transport, especially between 1919 and 1939, led to organized research, especially in Germany, and later in the United States. In Russia, this assumed an even greater importance and the first works on the problem were published there.

For the reasons given above, the study of periglacial phenomena received a great impetus after the Second World War. Specialized institutions have been devoted to it in the U.S.S.R. (Leningrad) and North America (Montreal). The establishment of the I.G.U. Commission on Periglacial Geomorphology in 1949 has provided a focus for coordinated recording and research. In almost every country, the role of Quaternary periglacial activity is being defined and it appears to be considerable down to the latitude of the Mediterranean.

This field of study is undergoing a very rapid evolution. Countries such as France, Switzerland and Italy are making up for a late start in recording data and studying processes. Ideas are in a state of constant change. The realization of the significance of periglacial phenomena in landform development is one of the major recent advances in geomorphology. Many points remain to be clarified, but at least we are conscious of their significance.

PART ONE

Extent of Frost Climate Phenomena

THE area covered by a glacier is precise; it may be delimited on a map, even a large scale one, by a line. This is not true of periglacial phenomena. For the former, the movement of water on the land surface in a solid form is a simple criterion; in the latter, the dominance in morphogenesis of freeze–thaw is a much more variable mechanism, which is influenced not only directly by the climate and indirectly by the intervention of the vegetation cover, but also by the rocks, which are susceptible to frost weathering to a greater or lesser degree. Frost weathering and *cryoturbation* (movement of soil particles under the effect of freeze–thaw), are the dominant processes in periglacial climates, but not the only ones. Running water and wind also take part as transporting agents. Screes accumulated by gravity occur on all sufficiently steep slopes. The limits of these processes are more blurred than is the case with glaciers, in which only ice and, to a large extent, meltwater take part.

The periglacial mechanisms become steadily less effective as the climate becomes less rigorous and the vegetation more dense. There is no clear boundary between the periglacial and the temperate zone, comparable with the ice margin, but rather a transition which is sometimes very gradual and very complex, like that bounding other morphoclimatic zones.

The concept of the cold but unglaciated region is not easy to define; as a result, it has been formulated relatively late in spite of the distinctiveness of some the phenomena which characterize it. This also accounts for the nature of the term used to describe it, 'periglacial'. The word was introduced by Lozinski (1909), who was the first to observe the part played by the cold conditions of the Quaternary in the relief of the sandstone plateaux near Cracow, and relate this to the proximity of the ice front. The term proved simple and useful, and was adopted in turn by the Germans, Americans and French. Recently, it has been strongly criticized by Guillien as inadequate. Nevertheless, even if glacier tongues do penetrate the forest, it is still valid whatever the setting of the mountains, for periglacial phenomena occur in the immediate vicinity of the ice, on the slopes overlooking it and on the upper slopes around the snowline. This is just as true on a world scale. The ice forms a number of large masses in high latitudes and periglacial features occur between them and around them. It was the same in the Quaternary. In certain conditions, such as in Siberia, there exist areas without glaciers which are colder than some of the glaciers, but this is an exceptional situation. To justify its use, a term must fit the general case and the term periglacial does just this. It is up to us not to stultify it by extreme interpretations. Good tools can be rendered ineffective by bad workmen.

The area subject to very cold conditions has varied considerably in the recent past. The disappearance of the Scandinavian ice sheet took place just 8000 years ago. As in the advances and retreats of the Quaternary, the glaciers have recently advanced and are now in retreat. The periglacial zone has kept pace. These changes are somewhat complicated because the speed of readjustment of the two is not the same. The build-up of an ice sheet takes much more time than the destruction of the vegetation, the freezing of the ground and the establishment of frost weathering and solifluction. Though the melting of the ice was more rapid than its accumulation, it was nevertheless slower than the stifling of periglacial processes by the readvance of the vegetation once the climate improved. Changes in the climate of the Quaternary resulted in processes of readjustment much more complex than those of the present day.

It seems logical to divide Part I into two chapters: one devoted to the present extent of these phenomena and their relation to climate, the other to their extent during the Quaternary, and a reconstruction of its climate based on the conclusions derived from present-day distribution.

CHAPTER 1

Present-day Extent

SINCE the delineation of the area covered by ice presents few problems, we shall begin with an attempt to define the climatic factors favourable to the accumulation of ice; it is the interplay of these factors which leads to the development of the different types of glaciers. We shall then examine the areas displaying periglacial features and try to define these in terms of climate.

(A) AREA COVERED BY GLACIERS

Greenland and Antarctica make up about 97% of the area, and 99% of the volume, of ice in the world. In spite of the great theoretical and practical importance of the mountain glaciers, situated as they often are, near the world centres of population, it is the ice sheets (the inlandsis), that form the core of the study. Beside them, the mountain glaciers are really an exception to the general rule. This is equally true of the cold phases of the Quaternary. Glaciation is zonal and the ice sheets occupy some of the coldest regions of the globe.

Minor exceptions to this occur. In the middle of glaciers, even in ice sheets, rocky ridges project through the ice, with surfaces that are too steep for snow to lodge. These are the *nunataks* of the inlandsis. Because the colour of their surface is darker than that of the snow, they thaw from time to time in spite of air temperatures being below zero. They are more or less subject to periglacial processes, especially frost shattering. Valley glaciers descend below the snowline into other climatic regions where they slowly melt; outlet glaciers of the Greenland ice sheet and, more strikingly, valley glaciers in the Alps, sometimes reach the forest zone. The Lower Grindelwald Glacier, then at a maximum, reached 933 m above sea level in 1818 when the mean annual temperature was 5·4°C. Even today, the Upper Grindelwald, Trift and Aletsch Glaciers end at about 1400 m. On all counts, these glaciers belong to the zone of snow and ice; their extension below the snow line is due to the peculiar behaviour of glaciers.

(1) Conditions Favouring the Existence of Glaciers

For a glacier to form, part of the winter snowfall must fail to melt the following summer. The snow then accumulates from year to year and its physical characteristics are modified: it becomes first névé, then ice. The line which encloses such a region, the *glacio-nival* zone, is the snowline.

Two factors account for the formation of glaciers: the amount of snowfall and the rate of melting (or *ablation*). The snowline marks the unstable, constantly changing equilibrium between them.

(a) Accumulation The geomorphological importance of snow is not limited to nourishing glaciers, though this is its most important function. Outside the permanent snow belt, seasonal snow banks have secondary effects which must not be overlooked, the work of snow meltwater, avalanches, snow pavements and *niveo-aeolian* processes.

Snowfall measurement: in climatology, several methods are used to record snowfall. All are not of equal interest to the geomorphologist.

The *number of days* with snow indicates the average number of days in the year on which snow falls. There is no direct relation between this figure and the occurrence of glaciers; the number of days with snow approaches 100 in Quebec and yet there are no glaciers.

The *depth of snow* is the thickness of fresh snow measured at the end of each fall or of each 24-hour period. It is measured on a snow table, a flat surface of one square metre lying horizontal and well exposed. When it is windy, the results are misleading. Individual measurements are added to give the annual snowfall. Even where no melting occurs and the snow piles up fall upon fall, the actual deposit never reaches the recorded annual snowfall. It might appear that the greater the snowfall, the longer it takes to melt and the greater the chance of forming névé fields and glaciers. In actual fact, the annual snowfall is only moderate on the great ice sheets and much greater in the mountains of middle latitudes, so that there is an important difference between mountain glaciers where snowfall plays an essential role and the majority of ice sheets which are situated in areas of low precipitation.

The *intensity of snowfall* is the annual fall divided by the number of days with snow. It is therefore the average snowfall on each day with snow; a light fall is one under 30 mm, a heavy fall between 60 and 100 mm. This is a factor of great importance in the dynamics of snow and ice. It plays a fundamental part in the initiation of avalanches and the stratification of névé, which in turn influence the flow of ice. Again, the figures for ice sheets are much smaller than those for mountain glaciers.

The *water-equivalent* of snow is obtained by weighing: 1 kg of snow equals 1 litre of water. The same comments apply to these measurements as to those of snowfall.

The *nivometric coefficient* is the ratio of snowfall to total precipitation, assuming the reduction of snowfall to water-equivalents. A coefficient of 1 obviously implies a precipitation entirely of snow.

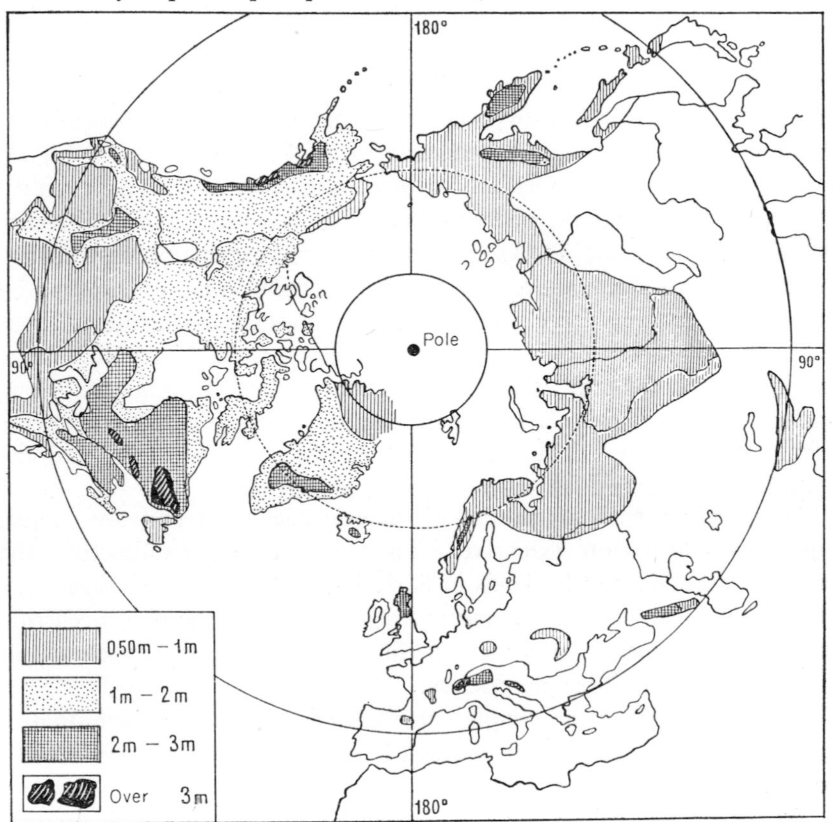

FIG. 1 Snowfall in the northern hemisphere (*after Péguy*)

Note the moderate total on the Greenland ice sheet, compared with the heavy fall in Labrador where glaciers are significant. Only in Alaska does a large total produce extensive glaciers, on account of the considerable fall in temperature with altitude.

Regional patterns of snowfall: The two main points are the nivometric coefficient and the annual precipitation. The types suggested below are arranged in decreasing order of importance.

(i) Regions with a nivometric coefficient approaching unity, and large annual totals, provide the best conditions for nourishing glaciers. They are fairly rare and of limited extent for they combine the two generally opposed conditions, of being at once cold and humid. They occur in the oceanic parts of the Arctic and at high altitudes in humid regions. These are always mountainous areas and include the very high Alpine areas of 3000-3500 m. Spitzbergen, especially North East Land, appears to be of similar altitude, though precipitation is clearly lower. Southwest Greenland, as Corbel has shown, is another good example.

(ii) Regions with a nivometric coefficient approaching unity, and low annual totals, are much more extensive and form by far the most common polar type. The whole Antarctic ice sheet, and most of the Greenland sheet, fall into this category. The influence of altitude (2000–3000 m) merely reinforces the regional characteristics of climate.

(iii) Regions with a medium nivometric coefficient and high annual totals are humid regions, where the role of snow is less important because of heavy summer rain. Heavy snowfall and rapid melting occur, resulting in conditions unfavourable to glacier development. The area covered by this type is not very large because it also implies the opposed conditions of high rainfall, found only in maritime climates, and a temperature range which is likely to occur only in a continental climate. To this type belong mountain massifs with a large precipitation, because of their maritime situation. At lower altitudes, the nivometric coefficient falls, and the geomorphological role of snow decreases in importance.

(iv) Regions with a medium nivometric coefficient and low annual totals are much more extensive. This association exactly describes the continental climate of lowlands in fairly high latitudes, which combine a large annual range of temperature with a moderate rainfall, occurring mainly in summer. A large part of Siberia belongs to this type and, although very cold, it has no glaciers.

There is therefore no simple correlation between the distribution of snow and the area covered by glaciers. In summary, there are two limiting cases:

(i) Moderately cold regions, with positive but not very high summer temperatures, and with a heavy snowfall, such as southwest Greenland (Corbel), the mountains of Norway and southeast Alaska.

(ii) Very cold regions, with a total of summer positive temperatures in degree-days approaching zero, with little or no rain and a small annual snowfall, such as Antarctica, most of Greenland and the islands north of Siberia.

The largest ice-covered areas (more than 80% of the total) are situated in regions where snowfall is moderate but the nivometric coefficient is high. The same seems to have been true of the Quaternary, although some moderately cold and very snowy mountain areas played an important part in the growth of the ice sheets (e.g. southwest Norway in the formation of the Scandinavian ice sheet).

(b) **The Snow Line** The lower limit of permanent snow occurs where summer or mid-day heat is just insufficient to melt the mass of snow formed by precipitation. It thus depends on two factors: snowfall, which is the 'constructive' element, and the calories received at ground level, which form the 'destructive' element.

The first element is directly recorded in meteorological observations, the second is not. Figures for average air temperatures only are available, not those for ground temperatures. These figures indirectly record insolation, but there is, more often than not, a great difference between the temperature of the air and that of the soil, which warms and cools more quickly under the influence of the sun's rays. The difference is at a maximum in climates with clear skies and at a minimum in foggy climates, and is of the order of several degrees.

This difference causes important local anomalies which are related to the character of the ground, aspect and site conditions.

The character of the ground: Snow and ice, being white, reflect heat and warm up slowly. Dark rocks absorb heat. Dry, porous, well-drained soils warm more rapidly than cold, moist, heavy soils.

Aspect: This involves the classic distinction between *l'adret* or sunny slope and *l'ubac* or shaded slope. This difference becomes less important at very high latitudes where every 'day' in summer the sun makes a complete circuit a little above the horizon. It is also of little importance in equatorial regions, where the sun shines almost vertically.

Site conditions: The snow must be able to stay on the ground. On steep slopes it cannot lodge, so steep rocky features project through the névés and glaciers. This influence of topography must not be isolated from its climatic context, for on this also depends the degree to which the snow lodges. In the equatorial zone for example, direct condensation in the form of ice (hail, hoar-frost) leads to glaciers on steep rocky slopes (40° and more) if the orientation is favourable.

Generally speaking, it is difficult to fix the snowline precisely and it is particularly uncertain in rugged areas. The best results are obtained from direct observation which alone is able to take into account the considerable variations from year to year, and the fact that it is really a transition zone.

In a general way, however, the position of the snowline varies with two factors: snowfall and insolation.

(i) Differing amounts of snowfall result in its rising in altitude from humid to dry regions, where there is less snow to melt in the warm season.

In the temperate zone, it rises from the western margin of the continents towards their centre and falls again to its lowest level on their eastern margin. In the west, the climate is humid but temperate, because of the warm convection currents on the eastern margins of the oceans. The centres of the continents are dry, with a very continental climate: this includes a low snowfall, and a low rainfall occurring mainly in summer, which with high summer temperatures accelerates melting. On the eastern side, humidity is comparable with that of the west, but cold ocean currents lower the winter temperatures and cause atmospheric disturbances associated with heavy snowfall.

In the tropics, the snowline falls from the western margin of the continents, which is dry, to the wetter eastern margin.

(ii) Insolation causes the snowline to rise from the poles to the Tropics of Cancer and Capricorn where it reaches its maximum elevation because of the dry climate. There are, however, appreciable differences between the two hemispheres. In the northern hemisphere, the distribution of the land masses in the various latitudes is more even, so that there is a more regular increase in its elevation with latitude from the pole to the tropic. In the southern hemisphere, the large proportion of sea in temperate latitudes cuts insolation by increasing the cloud cover, thereby lowering the snowline as compared with the northern hemisphere.

The difference between the two hemispheres is slight in very high latitudes, where the northern hemisphere is also largely sea, and at its greatest in middle latitudes between 40 and 45°, where the southern hemisphere is almost completely water. This difference is inverted at the tropics because of the existence of the main alpine area of the southern hemisphere, the Andes, on the arid western continental margin.

(c) The Glacier Budget Glaciers, with the exception of those which terminate in the sea, must be compared with rivers in arid regions, which come down from well watered mountains and lose themselves in the desert. The area they reach depends not only on their supply but also on the losses they suffer along their course.

(i) Techniques of study. It is almost impossible to obtain exact measurements of *accumulation* and *ablation*, because some features are difficult to measure. As far as accumulation is concerned, it has already been pointed out that snowfall figures for windy areas are only approximate. Measurements of ablation of a similar order of accuracy. It is possible to gauge the meltwater stream at its origin, but its flow represents only part of the ablation process for it omits the effects of sublimation and evaporation on the glacier surface. The former, involving the direct transformation of ice to water vapour, occurs even at very low temperatures and plays a decisive part on ice sheets, except in the north of Greenland (Peary Land) and some parts of Antarctica. It is not possible to arrive at an exact glacier balance-sheet from analytical measurements but once the budget is known, they may be used to define certain elements of it. Recourse must be had to synthetic, bulk measurements. These consist of estimating the thickness of snow deposited on a glacier at a given point, during a given period, or conversely the thickness of a bed which has disappeared. From the density, which may be measured at the time, the water equivalent may be calculated. The methods in use are simple: for short period measurements, a narrow vertical hole is dug in the snow, and its depth is periodically measured. Surface ablation is measured by the reduction in the depth of the hole. To measure accumulation and surface ablation at the same time, snow scales are used. These are stakes fitted with equidistant transverse bars, which are sunk in the snow to a given depth. Along them the level of the glacier surface is measured. Recently, methods of radioactive determination have been developed: radioactive particles falling with the snow subsequently disintegrate. Knowing the initial relation between the proportion of these unstable particles and that of the stable particles which accompany them, the time that has elapsed since their fall, and consequently the age of the ice, may be determined.

The glacier mechanism. A number of fundamental principles have been formulated by Ahlmann:

(i) The glacial regime is the sum of the masses of water represented by accumulation and ablation.

(ii) The glacial budget is the algebraic sum of accumulation and ablation. If it is positive, the glacier is increasing in volume; if negative, it is decreasing.

(iii) The budget year begins at the end of the ablation period in autumn and continues to the end of the ablation period in the succeeding year. It is based on the accumulation–ablation cycle, making it possible to calculate whether a particular year has a surplus or a deficit.

Accumulation is primarily a function of snowfall. There are secondary sources, however, rain may be changed to glazed frost on the surface of the glacier or infiltrate into snow and freeze at depth; hoar frost may be formed by direct condensation of atmospheric moisture in contact with the glacier; and finally, there is hail. The amounts involved vary, like snowfall, and the differences over the earth's surface are great. The centre of the Greenland ice sheet receives the equivalent of 200 mm of water, the glaciers of North East Land in Spitzbergen 520 mm, compared with almost 2500 mm in southwest Greenland. It should be pointed out that, leaving aside ice sheets and ice caps, part of the accumulation occurs indirectly, by snow avalanches and slides bringing down the snow which has fallen on the rock faces above the glacier. This may be very considerable at the foot of cirque walls and avalanche chutes.

Ablation is much more complex, with a large number of factors in operation. It may be considered as two main processes which differ greatly in importance. Melting, which causes losses in the form of water, measurable by gauging the meltwater stream if there is no loss by percolation into the bedrock or deposits, and secondly, evaporation, which may be measured directly. The latter results in the loss of water vapour, sometimes rapidly, as, for instance, on a hot summer day in the mountains, and sometimes slowly, as in the sublimation of snow. Glaciers in which evaporation is dominant are very few. One such example is the valley glaciers of New Swabia, in Antarctica, which end on rock with no sign of meltwater.

Generally, the two main sources of heat: radiation and convection, operate under different conditions. Radiation is at a maximum with a clear sky, light winds and dry air; it plays an important part at low temperatures. Convection, which increases the exchange of heat by conduction between the air and the glacier, is on the other hand favoured by strong winds and high temperatures. Ablation is strongly affected by the thickness of the morainic cover, a dust particle accelerates melting, but not a dust cover several metres thick.

On glaciers outside the polar zone, the temperature increase in spring transforms the surface of the névé into melting snow and drops of water penetrate the underlying cold névé. When they reach the zero isotherm, they refreeze, releasing their latent heat which warms the adjacent ice. It is only when the entire mass of névé or ice reaches 0°C that the whole of the meltwater can escape. In such conditions, rain may filter through the névé or ice without contributing to the growth of the glacier. If the meltwater which has helped to warm up the névé is retained by it, the amount ought to be deducted from the estimated ablation.

The amount of ablation varies very much with variation in climate. Indeed, the conditions of ablation much more often determine the extent of glaciers than conditions of accumulation. Thus, the two great ice sheets occur in areas of little accumulation, areas as dry as southern Algeria, but owing to a low rate of ablation (which does not exceed a few millimetres in the centre of Greenland because of the intense cold), the budget over large areas shows a surplus. The Greenland ice is also due to glacier survival: it accumulated when temperatures were lower than at present. In the whole of central Antarctica, present-day accumulation is virtually nil, because of the combination of a low precipitation with strong winds. The latter drive the snow towards the edges of the ice cap which are consequently well supplied. This process serves to increase the glaciers which descend from the ice cap through the gaps in the mountains or which spread out widely to form the shelf ice. Everywhere else the role of temperature is highlighted by the rhythm of ablation. In Iceland two-thirds of the annual ablation occurs between June and August, compared with only 3% between December and February.

In general, it may be said that ice sheets owe their existence mainly to low temperatures, while mountain glaciers (Iceland, Alaska, Alps, etc.) owe it to a high snowfall which offsets large-scale ablation. Knowledge of this fact is essential to an understanding of present-day oscillations of glaciers, and their former extent during the Quaternary. It has still more far-reaching consequences: it affects the dynamics of glaciers and their geomorphological effects. It is therefore fundamental, though many authors have neglected it.

(d) **Present Variations in the Volume of Glaciers** Even in a short period, variations in meteorological conditions from year to year are clearly sufficient to modify the glacier budget as it depends on a very sensitive balance. There are constant changes in glacier volume, with important geomorphological effects.

These oscillations are measured in several ways. As a long-term project, the most accurate method is to compare detailed topographic surveys. For a short-term study another method is used, First, a detailed plan of the glacier tongue is made; this includes the position of reference points on the solid rock flanking the glacier, which are used as sighting beacons. Two precise transverse profiles of the glacier surface are then plotted, these are traced on blocks on the ice by means of lines of differently coloured markers. Each year the distance from the glacier snout to each of these profiles and its width on each of them is measured.

Variations in the size of the glacier tongue reflect changes in the glacier budget over a longer or shorter time. When there is a surplus, the glacier tongue grows and advances; when there is a deficiency, it shrinks and retreats. The size of the oscillations is roughly proportional to the size of the glacier. At present few glaciers are advancing. These are mainly in

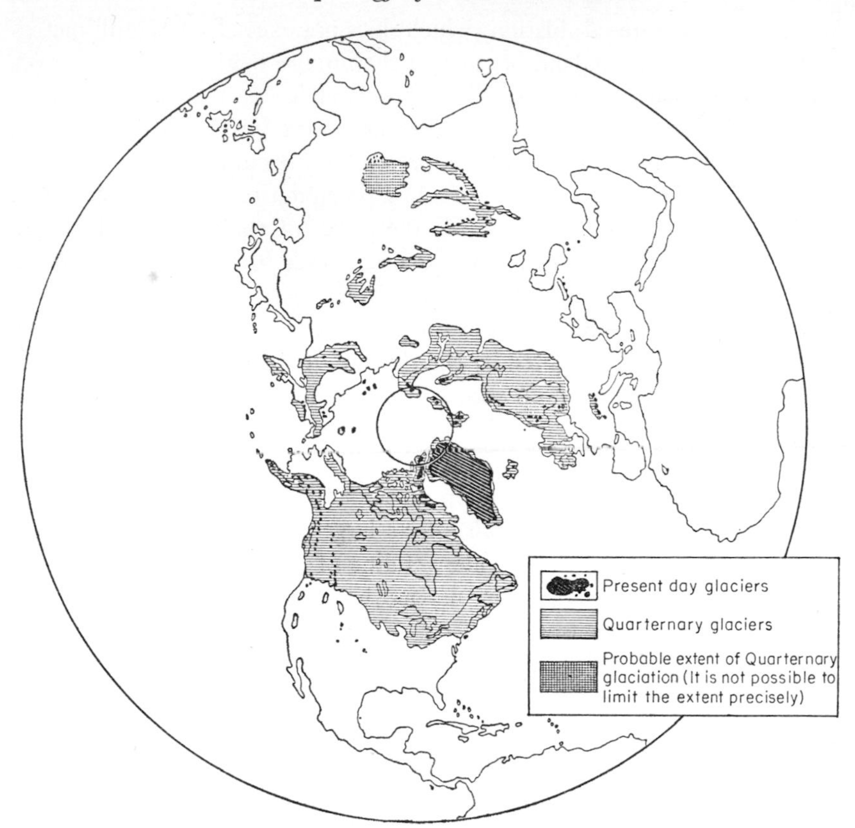

FIG. 2 (a) Area covered by glaciers in the northern hemisphere (*after Flint*)

Alaska, where advances are taking place at considerable speeds, explicable only partly by the size of the glaciers involved. The overall picture is that the majority of the world's glaciers have been in retreat for several decades. Advances are rare and of short duration. Excess of ablation particularly affects the tongue as it is at a maximum there. Reduction in thickness occurs mainly in the lower part and is naturally accompanied by a reduction in width because the flanks are rarely vertical. With the tongue thinning and narrowing, the front retreats all the more rapidly. In the Alps, the last few years have been marked by budget surpluses but the effects have not yet been felt at the snout.

Oscillations of the ice front are not synchronized with, nor are they strictly proportional to, the climatic fluctuations which cause them. There is a time lag which varies with the form of the glacier and the cause of the fluctuation. There is also a threshold effect and the phenomenon of

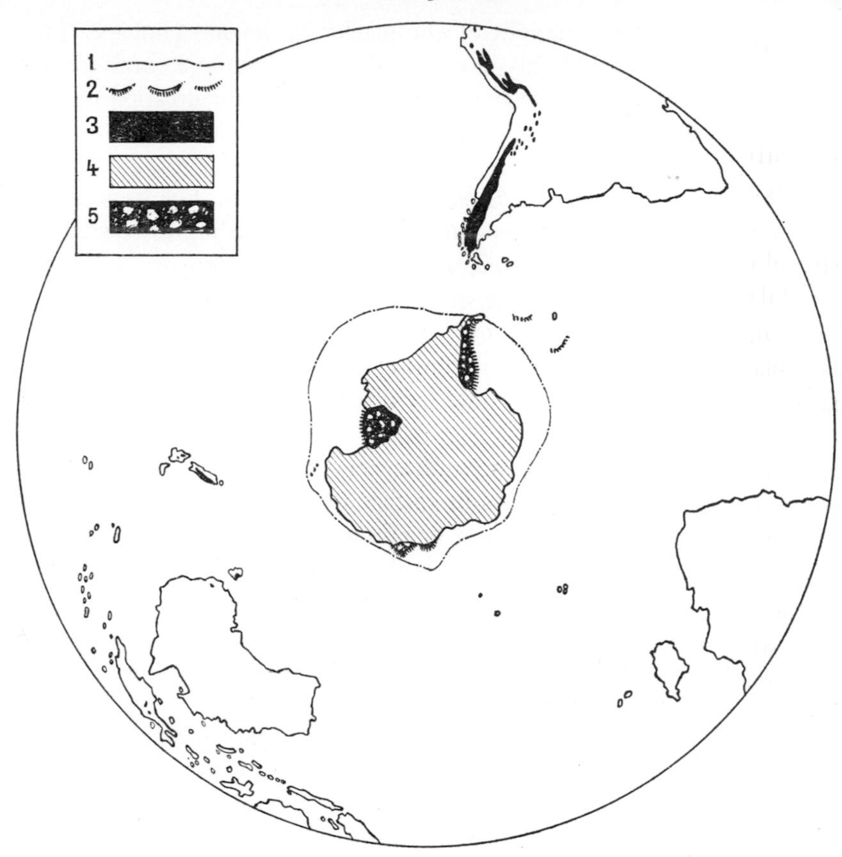

FIG. 2 (b) Area covered by glaciers in the southern hemisphere (*after Flint*)

1. Present-day limit of pack ice during the southern winter
2. Ice cliffs bounding the shelf ice
3. Areas glaciated in the Quaternary
4. Existing Antarctic ice sheet
5. Existing shelf ice on the borders of Antarctica

amplification. A slight rise in temperature may produce a marked retreat owing to the collapse of masses of ice at a steep front. An increase in the volume of ice at the head of a glacier may set up a dynamic wave which moves down as a rapid advance.

(2) The Various Types of Glacier and their Distribution

Glaciers are complex and it is possible to classify them according to several criteria which are not necessarily found together, e.g. the physical state of the ice, the dynamics of the glacier or its morphology. This association varies considerably in time and space. Even in a single glacier system the variations are sufficiently great to require the creation of subdivisions.

(a) **Features of Glaciers** *The physical state of the ice.* The basic factor is the temperature of the upper part of the ice. According to Avsiouk of Russia, who continued the work of Ahlmann of Sweden, the following types of glacier may be distinguished:

(i) Glaciers formed entirely by recrystallization, or dry polar glaciers. The temperature at the surface is continuously below zero, so no melting takes place and the ice forms only by direct recrystallization in a solid state.

(ii) Glaciers formed by recrystallization and infiltration, or humid polar glaciers. A temporary rise in surface temperature above 0°C leads to a slight infiltration of meltwater or rain which is recrystallized.

(iii) Glaciers formed by limited infiltration. A higher summer temperature allows more abundant meltwater to percolate into the glacier, but the water is completely trapped by freezing and does not form meltwater streams. It does not descend below the surface zone, so all precipitation is stocked in the glacier.

(iv) Glaciers formed mainly by infiltration, or maritime glaciers. The whole surface is raised above 0°C by meltwater and winter temperatures are not low enough for the cold thermal wave to penetrate to the lower ayers. In summer the whole glacier is at melting point. Streams of meltwater can circulate through the whole mass of ice.

(v) Glaciers formed by infiltration and freezing, or continental glaciers. Summer meltwater is retained in the surface layer, which is shallower than that penetrated in winter by sub-zero temperatures. Thus in summer the deeper part remains below freezing point and streams of meltwater are limited to the surface layer of the ice.

Three of these types predominate: the dry polar, which includes the bulk of ice sheets, the maritime, and the continental.

Glacier dynamics. In terms of movement, which influences strongly their geomorphological actions, glaciers may be divided into three classes: active, passive and dead.

(i) Active glaciers are those in which ice flow is most rapid so that the removal of debris is most efficient. Rate of flow is partly dependent on thickness. These represent an important proportion of glaciers, and occur in regions of good snow supply.

(ii) Passive glaciers are those in which the ice flows slowly. Most of them have been declining for a long time. As the ice thins, the rate of movement decreases. The removal of debris is inefficient and moraines tend to get thicker. Geomorphological results are landforms of retreat, in whose development meltwater plays a very important part.

(iii) Dead glaciers are those which no longer have a supply of ice. They continue to exist because of the slow rate at which ice melts. They are relict forms whose main geomorphological role is to produce meltwater.

Morphology. This depends on two main factors: the topography which existed before the glacier and controls the conditions of ice flow, and the supply of snow, which decided the extent to which this topography is blanketed by ice. Glaciers cannot be satisfactorily classified on grounds of topography. The amount of ice must be taken into account.

(b) **Geomorphological Classification** A combination of criteria, with morphology as the most important, leads to a classification consisting first of ice sheets (inlandsis), then piedmont glaciers, mountain or alpine glaciers in their many forms (cirque, valley and plateau glaciers), and finally masses of stagnant or dead ice.

Ice sheets: These differ very greatly in scale from the other types. The Antarctic ice sheet covers 13 000 000 and that of Greenland, 1 650 000 sq km. For this reason, they are described as areas of regional glaciation, as opposed to areas of local glaciation, which include all the other types. This fundamental difference in size is reflected in the distinctive character of ice sheets, which in turn affects their other properties. The enormous volume of ice multiplies the time lags and gives them a great amplitude. Ice sheets are primarily due to low temperatures. This readily explains their distinctive geophysical character; they belong exclusively to the polar type.

They have the form of a flattened dome and reach considerable heights, the Greenland ice sheet reaching about 3240 metres above sea level. Because of their great thickness they completely bury the relief on which they lie, so that projections of the bedrock surrounded by ice, or *nunataks*, are few and of small area. The surface form of the ice sheet is largely independent of the underlying topography.

The combination of high altitude and high latitude gives these ice sheets a distinctive climate: they are very cold and very dry. This results in anticyclonic conditions, with outflowing winds which have great geomorphological significance. The temperature of the ice is very low and only increases below the surface layer. The temperature regime of the ice sheet is not related to present-day climate but is inherited from a colder period.

Towards the margins of the ice sheet the surface changes to that of the humid polar type. The smooth ice cap passes into a less regular form, *nunataks* are more numerous, and the ice divides into tongues occupying the valleys. Meltwater is abundant, flowing in steep-sided canyons in the ice which restrict access to the ice cap. These seem to form repeatedly in the same place. The water in them disappears into subglacial caverns, down shafts or *moulins*, such as occur on a smaller scale on local glaciers.

The outlet glaciers of the ice sheets may reach a considerable thickness. In Antarctica, the Beardmore Glacier, which descends into the Ross Sea, is 22 km long and 40 km wide.

Local glaciers: These, in contrast to ice sheets, are closely dependent on relief which, in conjunction with climate, controls their size.

(i) Piedmont glaciers are valley glaciers whose supply is large enough to allow them to extend out on to the foreland of a mountain range. They consist of several parts: the upper is formed by a system of ice-filled tributary valleys ending in cirques at their head. The main glacier, filling a valley below the snowline, is similar to ordinary valley glaciers of comparable size, reaching 30 to 50 km in length and 3 or 4 km in width. The expanded ice foot is typical: it spreads out from the mountain foot in the form of a semi-circle, like a large alluvial cone at the mouth of the valley. Piedmont glaciers imply an abundant supply of snow, as their distribution shows; they are found in humid subpolar areas, especially Alaska and southern Chile. During the Quaternary, the great Alpine glaciers were of this type. They need in addition to a cold humid climate, mountains whose summits rise high above the snowline.

(ii) Valley glaciers. These lack the expanded lobate snout because they end within a mountain valley, very often at the top of a more steeply sloping stretch on which retreat has been more rapid because of the thinning of the ice. They are frequently smaller in size than piedmont glaciers. The longest valley glacier is the Fedschenko Glacier in the Pamir, with a length of 77 km. Valley glaciers are found in mountain chains where the height difference between the snowline and the summits is less than in piedmont glaciers, or else when the supply of snow is only moderate. This explains their occurrence in two clear-cut groups. One is in certain polar areas where snowfall is relatively light (parts of Spitzbergen, Novaya Zemlya, Franz Josef Land), the other is the very high mountain chains of the temperate zone (Alps, Central Asian ranges, and the Rocky Mountains).

The complexity of the form of valley glaciers depends on the abundance of snow and the height difference between the snowline and the crest line. When snow is abundant, many tributary ice streams converge on the main glacier from the high-lying cirques and this convergence often leads to a congestion of ice. This type has been called the composite Alpine. If, on the other hand, the snow supply is small, the glacier is shorter and convergence occurs near the snout (e.g. Gorner Glacier). Where the supply is large, ice from the higher areas reaches the trunk glacier from all directions, with cases of diffluence and branching arms. Rocky ridges may be enclosed by a veritable net of glaciers (e.g. the glacier on Clavering Island on the east coast of Greenland).

(iii) Glaciers without a valley tongue. These are simple forms which extend over a small difference in elevation, never more than a few hundred metres. They are confined to areas where the altitude difference between crests and snowline is at a minimum. They are widespread on the earth's surface, occurring just as often in polar areas, where they occupy low dry areas, as in temperate or sub-tropical mountains. They are the only forms which can exist in mountains where conditions are unfavourable to glaciation, especially in arid regions such as northern Chile.

In the tropics, the snowline is very high, and the mountains are rarely high enough to offer an extensive area or varied relief above it. The only mountain chain to do so is the Himalaya which receives a large precipitation from the monsoon; it alone harbours large composite glaciers.

As a group, elementary glaciers may be divided into two main types, each depending mainly on relief.

(i) Ice caps with divergent flow. These have a domed centre in a topographically dominant position so that ice flows towards the margins. Ice without a névé cover occurs only around the periphery where ablation is dominant. Where the snow supply is abundant, the outline of the margin becomes more complex; divergent tongues appear and there is a transition to glaciers of the composite class. Ice caps with radial flow are found on areas of little dissection, on plateaux of various sizes or the summits of volcanic cones; the erosion surfaces of ancient massifs which extend only two or three hundred metres above the snowline offer ideal conditions for their development. When the relief is greater, this is no longer the case, outlet glaciers form and flow down the entrenched valleys. In the tropics it is usually only volcanoes which are high enough to rise above the snowline. High because of their recent formation, these constructional landforms have a relatively undissected surface, suitable for an ice cap, while climatic conditions are unfavourable to the development of outlet glaciers and a complex pattern. Alpine ice caps occupy flattened summits well above the snowline, but the steep surrounding slopes do not allow the snow to lodge.

Glaciers with convergent flow never occupy summit positions, but occur in depressions and are overlooked by rocky uplands, they are sometimes far below the highest summits of the upland in which they occur. They result from peculiar conditions of supply: the greater part of their snow reaches them in the form of avalanches where they are overlooked by steep slopes and in wind-blown drifts when they occupy depressions in a plateau. They may occur well below the snowline on well shaded slopes facing away from the sun. The result is a cirque glacier of very rounded form, overlooked by peaks, without an outflowing tongue because the snow supply is only moderate.

Decadent forms: Some present-day glaciers are found in sites in which, if they once disappeared, they could not re-form under present conditions. Such are the glaciers situated entirely below the snowline, they are generally relict forms which have been able to persist because of very unusual conditions. They may be divided into two main types:

(i) Glaciers due to an accidental excessive supply sometimes called, regenerated glaciers. These survive on account of abnormal supplies of snow, most of which is brought indirectly by avalanches or drifting. They always occur in hollows amid very strong relief, at the foot of cirque walls or narrow rocky chutes and usually their location is controlled by orientation. In cirques, these relict glaciers cannot spread far, they are merely cones of ice built against a steep rocky face whose top coincides with the mouth of an avalanche chute. Depending upon local relief, one may distinguish simple cones, compound cones (where two avalanche chutes are close together), and ice glacis (where they are further apart). Ice cones are particularly frequent in dry mountains of the Alpine type which rise only a little above the snowline: eastern Italian Alps, southern French Alps.

(ii) Glaciers due to delayed melting or relict forms. These differ from the above by an absence of an adequate snow supply. They survive below the snowline where special conditions impede the melting of the ice, these conditions being almost always the burial of the ice beneath moraines. They are more or less motionless bodies of dead ice, whose volume is slowly decreasing. In mountainous areas, the supply of debris from the slopes may be sufficient to bury the ice completely, so that its melting is checked and it may advance below the snowline. Ice movement in this case is not due to the pressure of the névé, it is entirely due to gravity. This type of glacier has been called a rock glacier, when the ice completely melts and only the heap of rock debris remains, it becomes motionless. They occur especially in dry sunny areas of very fissile rocks such as Morocco, the southern Rocky Mountains and the southern French Alps (at Chambeyron, for example).

(B) World Distribution of Frost Climates

The polar or mountain areas where frost plays a geomorphological role of primary importance are found in three main climatic regions.

(1) Dry Climates with Severe Winters

This is the continental Arctic climate which in essentials coincides with the polar zone of the northern hemisphere. It is especially characteristic of those parts of central Siberia which face the Arctic Ocean between the Kara Sea and the Chukchee Peninsula, of the north Canadian archipelago and the northern limit of America between the Behring Sea and Hudson Bay, and finally of part of the interior plains of Alaska and Yukon Territory.

This type of climate is modified by two influences. Towards the south, progressively higher summer temperatures are recorded, though there is no improvement in the winters. The transitional seasons are almost non-existent. It is only in the warm summer months that days of partial frost occur; as their number decreases, geomorphological processes change. In such regions, relict permafrost is found. Towards the oceans, namely the North Atlantic and the Behring Sea, there is a steady change to a moist climate with severe winters.

Its characteristics are very low winter temperatures which last for most of the year. Between the very short summers, the ground becomes deeply frozen. Temperatures are very variable with sharp changes of weather and a large daily temperature range. The result is frequent alternations of frost and thaw in spring, summer and autumn. Moreover, the small amount of heat received in summer (which is too short and in very high latitudes too cold), does not allow the complete thawing of the layer frozen in winter and leads to the formation of permafrost. This climate is the climate of contemporary permafrost.

Another feature is the low precipitation, around 200 mm for the more typical stations. It increases towards the south as the summers get warmer. Precipitation takes place at all seasons, even in winter when it occurs as snow. But the snow cover is very thin, easily blown away by the wind and it offers the soil no protection against frost or wind deflation. In this dry climate, the soil dries out easily and is attacked by wind, even when frozen. This climatic region experiences very stong winds at all seasons, due to depressions in which air masses of very different temperatures are superimposed in the lower levels of the atmosphere, both in winter and summer. In summer, these winds cause renewed attacks of

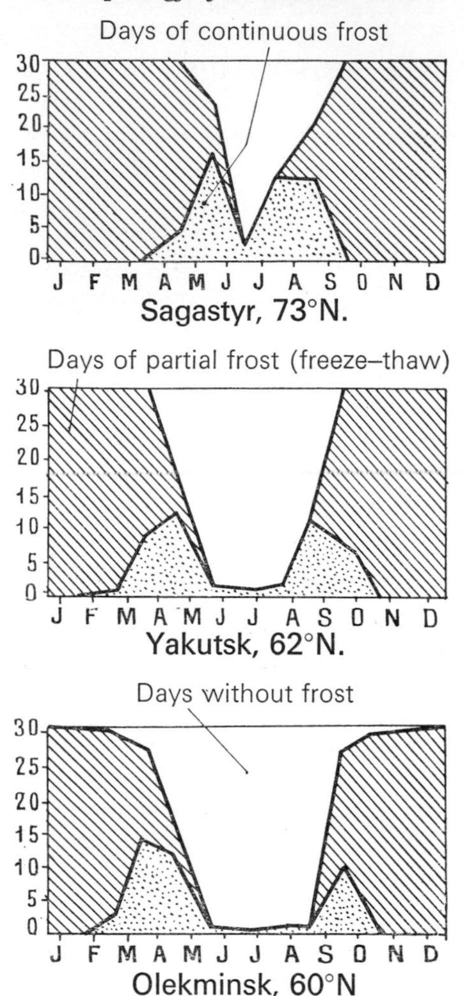

FIG. 3 Number of days of frost at some periglacial stations (*after Troll*)

frost which have a particular geomorphological significance, for in winter the snow is swept away in blizzards, Dry climates with severe winters are characterized by a morphogenetic system in which frost plays the dominant part. A lesser, almost negligible, part is played by running water, but wind action is quite important.

(2) Humid Climates with Severe Winters

These fall into two types: the arctic and the mountain, the latter being an adjustment to altitude, of the humid temperate climate.

(a) The Arctic Type This is transitional between the dry climate with severe winters and the Arctic climate without marked seasons. It corresponds to part of Köppen's ET climates, the wettest part without definite seasons. Its boundaries are difficult to fix, particularly on the continents, where it grades into the preceding type which itself becomes less typical towards the south. Some of its characteristics occur, to a less marked degree, as far south as the narrow coastal fringe of northern Siberia and Arctic Alaska, in the form of marked changes of temperature

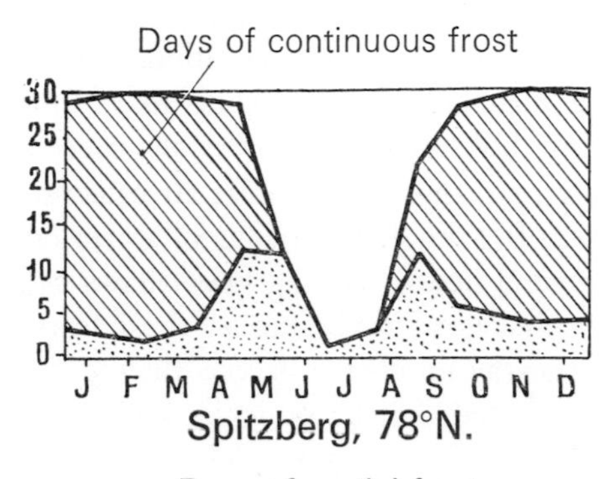

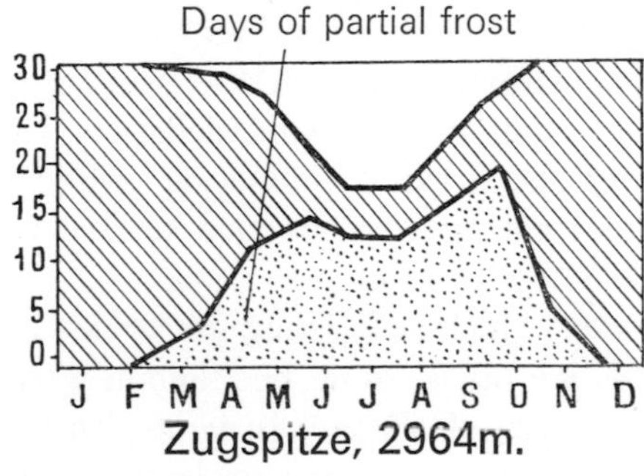

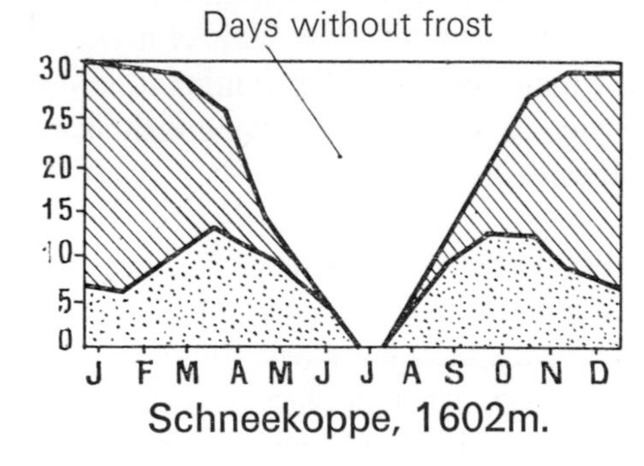

FIG. 4

and fog but with a decreased morphological significance. Its southern limit passes through the glacial Arctic Ocean north of Norway, but it is typical of Spitzbergen and the middle latitudes of Greenland.

Its characteristics are less easy to deduce from climatic means than those of the previous climate. Indeed its average temperatures do not differ greatly from them, but there is always a tendency towards a smaller annual range. The summers are marked by three or four months above 0°C, so that there is a seasonal thawing of the ground. Nevertheless, winters are cold enough for the mean annual temperature to be below 0°C so that there is permafrost.

Very marked variations are, however, hidden by these averages. In coastal parts, the climate is more variable because of maritime influences; strong winds during the passage of depressions cause sudden changes of weather. In summer, streams of cold polar air cause sharp drops in temperature, with frost. In winter, incursions of warm oceanic air raise the temperature for several hours, causing brief thaws called *ottepeli* by the Russians. The morphological importance of these features is considerable because they increase the number of freeze–thaw cycles.

It should also be noted that humidity is higher that in the previous type of climate. Annual totals are almost always in excess of 300 mm and are better distributed over the year as the temporary warm spells of winter are marked by precipitation. In winter there is an appreciable snow cover which reduces the importance of wind deflation. In spring the snow melts and saturates the ground, promoting solifluction. In summer, rainfall is sometimes adequate to produce surface run-off over frozen ground.

Fog, sometimes very thick and lasting for weeks, is another aspect of this climate. Winds are often strong but their morphological activity is less than in the dry type of climate. In winter the thicker snow cover protects the ground better; in summer the rain checks the drying of the surface of the soil and hence deflation. This climate produces a morphogenetic system in which freeze–thaw is dominant, and wind action secondary. Running water in the form of slopewash is also secondary but nevertheless significant.

(b) **The Mountain Type** This belongs to lower latitudes, where low temperatures are due to altitude. It corresponds to the zone immediately below the snowline in the temperate belt. Its character is broadly similar from Norway to the Alps, though there is a gradual modification with latitude. In Norway, especially in the north, it scarcely differs from the climate of moist polar regions. In the Alps, the lower latitude introduces appreciable modifications and orientation plays a very great part. As an illustration of this type, the Alps and Central European mountains will be considered, as they are better known than most areas.

Monthly temperatures show variations which are similar to those of the arctic type. For six or seven consecutive months, the monthly average is below 0°C, so that a continuous severe frost alternates with a seasonal thaw, usually from May to September. There are, however, significant differences and the mean annual temperatures are lower. The summer maxima are similar to those of the arctic type but winters are less cold. The essential difference between them is the degree of winter cold, and because of the less rigorous winters, permafrost is exceptional.

Precipitation is much higher than in the arctic type, exceeding 1 m everywhere. Aspect is of much more fundamental importance than in the Arctic. On south-facing slopes snow may melt in winter during sunny days but frequently freezes again at night, whereas on north-facing slopes patches of snow may survive late into the summer and prevent the ground from thawing. Relief is also important. It may favour or hinder the survival of snow, which forms a protective screen, reducing the number of freeze–thaw cycles, and it may modify the angle of the sun's rays and so influence the warming of the ground. Peaks and isolated summits have a microclimate which is less extreme: they cool less rapidly at night and warm more slowly during the day. They therefore experience fewer freeze–thaw cycles. The bottoms of open valleys with rocky walls are more extreme and liable to temperature inversions; they have a greater number of freeze–thaw cycles.

Conditions vary a great deal from place to place, so that generalizations must be treated with caution. Yet, looking at this climate as a whole, the morphogenetic action it induces is characterized by:

(i) the importance of frost action, which is, however, different from that of the arctic type in that there is no permafrost and frost penetrates the ground less effectively because of the snow;

(ii) the importance of running water because of the high precipitation. Its action, though seasonal, is important because the water efficiently removes the debris of frost shattering;

(iii) the relative unimportance of wind action, which is checked by the snow cover and the humidity, while the relief prevents winds becoming strong and constant over large areas.

Areas with this type of climate are never large. Periglacial processes operate only locally, affecting slope development and surface soils, but not the evolution of regional relief, which depends on glaciers and streams.

(3) Climates with a Small Annual Range

Like other periglacial climates, these have a mean annual temperature around 0°C but in this case the monthly means differ little from the annual and frost may occur in any month. These climates are found in two geographically separate regions: some oceanic regions in high latitudes, and high-lying areas in the tropics (which like the lower elevations in the tropics have a low annual range).

(a) Island Climates in High Latitudes These occur in small land areas in high latitudes in seas free of ice, and have the characteristics of a cold oceanic climate. First, the mean annual range is of the order of a 10°C and seasonal differences are negligible. As a result of relatively light

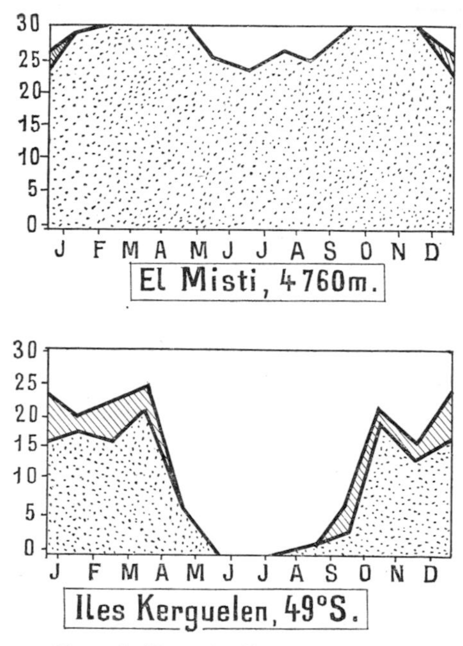

FIG. 5 (For shading see Fig. 4)

frosts, there is no permafrost. Secondly, the weather is very changeable at all seasons and it is mainly the relative frequency of the various types of weather which marks the seasons. During winter, cold waves may bring on a sudden and intense frost for several days, separated by temporary thaws: conditions which are very favourable to frost shattering. In summer, it is never very hot, and cold waves may cause short spells of frost. Thus, the variability of climate, combined with a low annual

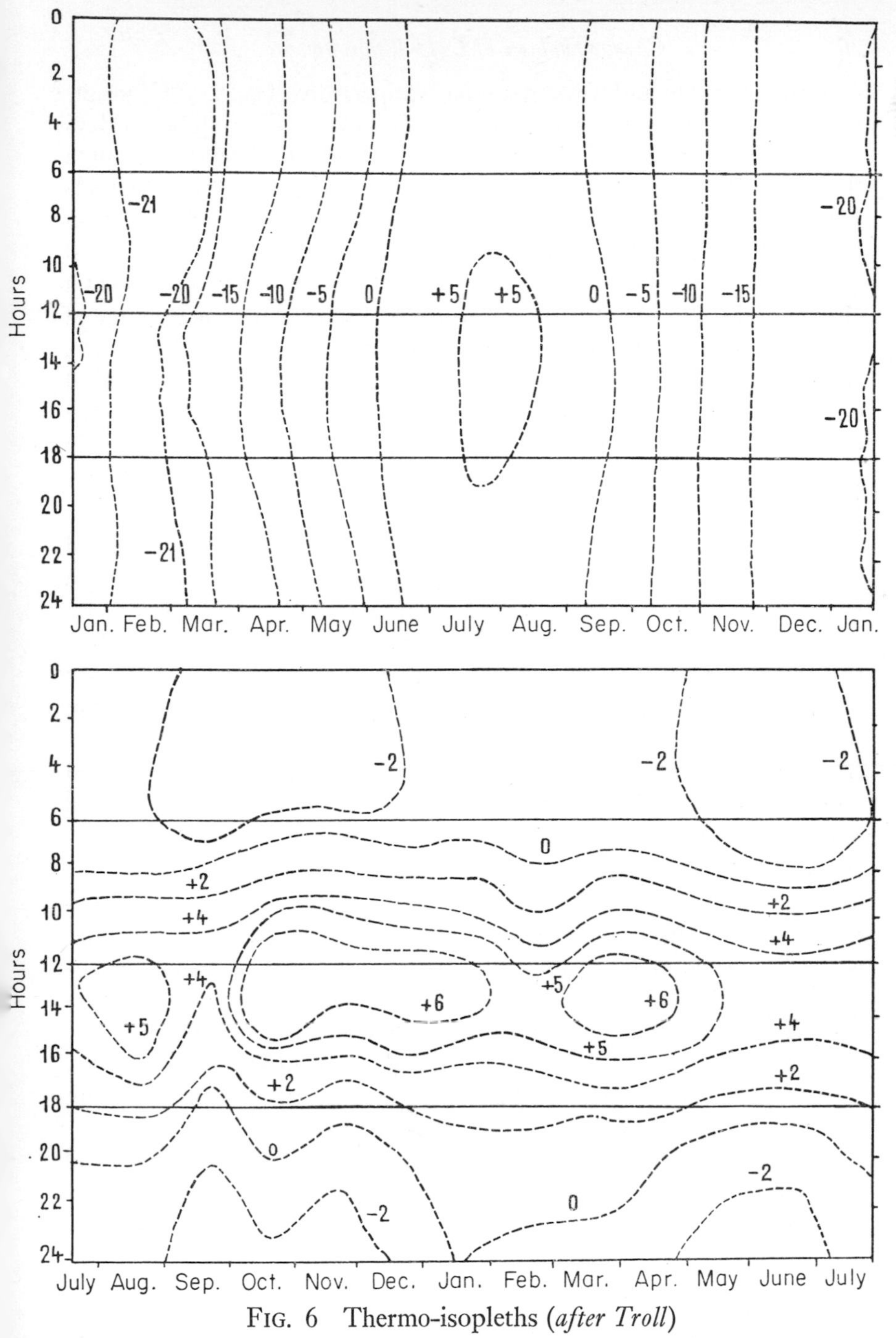

FIG. 6 Thermo-isopleths (*after Troll*)

The pecked line joins points of equal temperature and shows both diurnal and annual fluctuations.

(a) *Green Harbour*, Spitzbergen, 1912–16. Large annual range (horizontal), very small diurnal range (vertical).

(b) *El Misti*, Peru, lat. 16° S. at 4760 m. 1894–5. Small annual but large diurnal range.

temperature range and a mean annual temperature close to 0°C, means that frost may occur for short periods at all seasons. The number of days of partial frost is large. In the Kerguelen Islands, the only season with frost-free days is the southern summer, from mid-December to mid-February. A final feature is the considerable humidity which results in thick and persistent fog, especially in summer, and rain and snow at all seasons. The snow does not lie, but melts within a few days because of a change in the weather, it does not protect the soil but acts as a source of moisture. Rain keeps the soil continuously wet; at the same time it is subjected to freeze and thaw. The rain accentuates the geomorphological effects of the latter, producing a series of wet freeze–thaw cycles. On the other hand, the rain largely eliminates the action of wind however strongly it blows (and frequent squalls accompany the sharp changes in temperature).

From the geomorphological viewpoint this climate is essentially one of frost action, with frosts of short duration and shallow penetration but a large number of freeze–thaw cycles per annum.

(b) **Mountain Climates of Low Latitudes** These are due to the effects of altitudes in normal tropical climates, which has two main results. On the one hand, the temperature rhythm of equatorial and tropical climates is preserved: there are no thermal seasons in true equatorial climates and they are weakly marked in tropical climates. It appears that the annual range at 2000 to 3000 m is less than at sea level; above that level it increases and at about 4000 m returns to the range for low altitudes. The daily range is large, much larger at all seasons than the annual range, and this is what determines the incidence of frost. The second major feature is the frequency of frost, that essential characteristic of mountain climates. This climate of the periglacial zone of mountains in low latitudes gives rise to morphological processes characterized by:

(i) considerable frost action due to many days of partial frost;

(ii) slight penetration of ground frost; because of its short duration, permafrost has never been recorded in these regions;

(iii) high humidity which eliminates wind action and promotes soil movements, except of course in arid regions.

These climatic conditions favour ice formation by exudation (needle ice or pipkrakes), whose geomorphological role is considerable. Aspect also plays a part. Snowfall usually occurs at night and the survival of this snow on east-facing slopes exposed to the morning sun is short-lived, while fresh snow melts in a few hours. The snowline is highest on these slopes, and periglacial processes intense (frost shattering, needle ice formation).

On slopes reached by the sun only in the afternoon the snow survives better, for the air remains cold and ablation occurs mainly through the direct effects of radiation. In Venezuela, where equatorial convection causes cloud formation even during the morning, slopes exposed to the southwest, west and northwest rarely receive the warmth of the sun. Snow is persistent enough to form glaciers at the snowline. This has also been observed by Dollfuss in Peru.

In the periglacial zone of mountains in low latitudes, the frost cycle is essentially diurnal.

However, the direct influence of climate is not the only factor in periglacial morphogenesis; the vegetation, although only moderately developed, also plays a part. Yet, since the cold is the chief limiting factor, the main types of vegetation growth follow the climates which have just been defined. In the areas which are coldest or subject to particularly frequent frosts, the vegetation cover is absent and where conditions are slightly better, it is limited to isolated tufts of small plants, which are incapable of modifying the mechanical processes of morphogenesis. The result is the frost-debris desert, a feature found in high mountains as well as in polar regions. When heat increases, and especially when there is a 'warm' season, the tundra appears. In continental climates with such a summer, the tundra may form a fairly close damp grassland which checks the penetration of frost into the ground and favours the survival of permafrost. It modifies the processes of frost shattering and solifluction. Finally, in large areas in central and eastern Siberia, in Alaska and in the Canadian Northwest, boreal forest or taiga occurs on permafrost sometimes more than 100 m thick. This is due to the same cause as the apparently anomolous temperature curves recorded in several bores in the Greenland ice sheet, where the ice at depth is at a much lower temperature than the present-day annual mean. Both phenomena are relict, survivals at depth of a cold which penetrated to that level during a comparatively recent period when the climate was more severe. To understand contemporary phenomena cold environments, it is essential to look to the past and determine the part played by palaeoclimates.

CHAPTER 2

Frost Climate Phenomena of the Quaternary

ALTHOUGH features due to present-day intense cold are found in more than a quarter of the land surface, landforms inherited from the cold of the Quaternary are much more widespread. Glaciers alone, during their maximum extent, covered 45 to 50 million sq km, or almost a third of the continents. The fringe of periglacial action extended beyond their margins to occupy another 10 million sq km at least. A total of about 40% of the land areas was subjected to the cold conditions of the Quaternary. These areas are amongst the most densely populated and most intensely developed on the earth. They included all Europe except for the Mediterranean lowlands, at least two-thirds of North America, almost the whole of the Soviet Union, a large part of China and Japan, much of the mountainous areas in low latitudes, New Zealand, the southeast of Australia and the southern part of South America.

As at present, glacial and periglacial processes were associated, as they are both the result of the same climatic conditions, but from the geological and palaeogeographical point of view it is glaciation that plays the most important part. While the effects of periglacial phenomena were limited to the areas in which they occurred, glaciation had world-wide repercussions. Melting of present-day ice sheets, which occupy just under 10% of the land surface, would release water equal to a layer 60–80 m deep. Allowing for isostatic readjustments, sea level would rise between 30 and 53 m. The Quaternary glaciations were of very short duration on a geological time scale. The great ice sheets of the Würm disappeared in 10 000 years whilst the length of the Pliocene is estimated at 10 million years, the Eocene at 20 million. The Pleistocene was a virtual cataclysm, causing sharp breaks in the geodynamic equilibrium. The transfer of water to the continents in the form of ice caused a large-scale and rapid lowering of sea level which changed the development of coasts and part of the river valleys. The transfer of the load represented by this water from the ocean basins to the continents, during glaciation, and in the opposite direction during deglaciation, subjected the deformable crust of the earth to intense and sudden stresses which led to the extremely rapid isostatic movements. These are one of the outstanding features of the Quaternary period. The post-glacial uplift of Fennoscandia was much more rapid than all other known tectonic movements, with the exception of movements of certain fault blocks in New Zealand, which are almost as rapid.

The glaciations are, from the geological point of view, the most important part of the Quaternary. They have caused large-scale geomorphological changes and led to the formation of extensive and thick deposits. These, the principal Quaternary beds, have been affected by rhythmic tectonic deformation and, far from the ice, by innumerable changes in sea level. This justifies the use of the glacial sequence as the stratigraphic column of the Quaternary, the 'Glacial Epoch' of Agassiz.

Although they played a dominant part, glaciations are not the only evidence for the cold climate of the Quaternary. Periglacial action accompanied them and if its consequences do not extend to the whole of the earth, they are none the less fundamental to the morphogenesis of the regions which have been affected. The rocks have been shattered by frost; solifluction has spread a wide mantle of unsorted debris which has often choked rivers and forced them to build terraces; wind has deposited beds of fertile loess or fashioned fields of dunes. All these features survive over wide areas today as a result of the recent and sudden nature of the last climatic change. Many of the soils which produce our daily bread have been developed from material broken down by periglacial action. Many of our most urgent problems of soil conservation are concerned with the protection of these precious remnants from the rainwash erosion which is resulting from cultivation. Over much of the globe, the problems of applied geomorphology demand a first-hand knowledge of the features due to the Quaternary, both periglacial and glacial.

We shall now examine the fluctuations of the Quaternary glaciation, methods of collecting data, the succession and extent of the various glacial phases, their after-effects and finally the associated periglacial effects.

(A) Succession of Cold Periods

The establishing of a Quaternary stratigraphy presents particular difficulties demanding special techniques whose principles must be briefly explained.

(1) Methods of Investigation

Glacial formations almost all consist of detritus of terrestrial origin, poor in fossils, always of very local distribution, subject to frequent changes of facies, and very often with gaps in the sequence. The application of classical methods of stratigraphy based on changes in fauna and flora is difficult because few new species appeared in such a short time, and equally few became extinct. Quaternary palaeontology still presents many difficulties and agreement is far from being reached as to what is a warm or a cold fauna. Moreover, truly glacial deposits are usually completely devoid of fossils. The Swedish oceanographer Peterson has succeeded in taking deep cores from the sea floor in different parts of the world (the Mediterranean and the Caribbean Seas, etc.). The study of the foraminifera in them has made it possible to distinguish eleven alternations of warm and cold fauna. It is nevertheless very difficult to relate these palaeontological data to the palaeogeography. The correlation of foraminifera with particular glacial phases is far from easy. The high rate of reproduction and scattering of marine micro-organisms makes them sensitive to quite short-lived changes in environment. Indeed it is possible that some successions of cold and warm fauna correspond to simple secular oscillations of the kind which affect glaciers at the present time. Because of possible changes in current direction, the marine environment can be very sensitive to small-scale climatic changes, as is demonstrated today by the migration of cod and seals northwards along the west coast of Greenland. A most useful palaeo-thermometer has been developed by Urey. This is based on the proportion of isotopes of O^{18} and O^{16} in organic calcium, principally foraminifera. The ratio of the two isotopes is a function of the temperature of the water in which the organism lived. Cores of pelagic deposits from the ocean floors record the succession of cold and warm periods as far as the Equator, where the fluctuations are less marked than at latitude 65°. At the Equator the surface temperature of the sea has fluctuated between 21–22°C and 26–27°C, giving a fall in temperature of some 5°. It is thus possible to speak of 'cold periods' over the whole world. Unfortunately the poverty of the data rules out correlations with the stratigraphic succession on land.

Emiliani has tried to use ratios of sedimentation to date these climatic fluctuations, but these rates probably vary, the temperatures influencing the biological deposits, and variations in climate influencing the detrital and chemical accumulations. Further results are needed before it will be possible to correlate submarine cores with the stratigraphy of land areas and great care is necessary.

The methods used to establish Quaternary stratigraphy, some of which are applicable to sedimentary sequences of any age, may be divided into two groups based on their exactness.

(a) **Very Precise Methods** These apply mainly to the most recent period, the last glaciation and post-glacial period.

(i) *Radioactive method* This is based on the disintegration of the C^{14} isotope and used for the most recent Quaternary. It is accurate to within 2000–3000 years, which is of a high order. But its field of application is limited: in practice, it has so far given precise results only for the last 20 000–25 000 years. It is, at the moment, useful only for the late-glacial and post-glacial periods.

(ii) *Varves* This technique, developed by the Swede, de Geer, uses proglacial lake sediments. In lakes situated close to glaciers and fed by their meltwater, clay and silt is deposited by settling out from suspension. In summer, abundant sediment is supplied by the ice and the deposition of detrital material is rapid, micro-organisms are present only in low concentrations. In winter, because of reduced melting, inorganic material is greatly reduced, while autumn sees a rapid accumulation of micro-organisms. The resulting deposit consists of beds a few millimetres thick which show an alternation of pale, thicker layers (the predominantly inorganic detritus of summer), and dark thinner layers (the organic material of autumn and winter). The two layers together make a varve, which is annual. This means it may be used for dating.

(iii) *Pollen-analysis* This is one of the methods most widely used by geologists and botanists. It consists of estimating the frequency of the various kinds of plants in a given period by counting the pollen contained in its deposits. Suitable deposits are peats, organic muds and peaty soils. The results are more satisfactory in some areas than others.

(b) **Less Precise Methods** The existing subdivisions of the Quaternary have been established by these methods, which, unlike those just dealt with, may be applied to any area with deposits.

(i) *The prehistory method* Since the time of Boucher de Perthes, the founder of the study of prehistory, prehistorians have studied the fossil remains of man and other clues to his activity. As time went on, an ordered sequence which gives relative dating was deduced, but with a margin of error which increases with age. In the same period men with different industries may have lived side by side, or the same people may sometimes have been able to make tools using two methods and two different techniques.

(ii) *The pedological method* This was used on a large scale for the first time by Penck to unravel the sequence of glaciation in the Alps. When a moraine or proglacial sediment has been deposited, it gradually becomes covered by vegetation, its surface becomes weathered and develops a soil which varies with climatic conditions. The length of time required for this is of the order of several thousand years. The depth of weathering depends upon the climate and the time available; frequently the soil has subsequently been removed completely. In general, soils developed on early Quaternary moraines are thick and mature and pebbles of easily weathered rock formerly present in them have disappeared; they indicate climates different from those of the present day.

To this pedological method must be added the study of cryopedological data. In very cold climates, the action of frost produces characteristic structures in the ground (festoons, plications, involution, polygons, injections, etc.), which remain after the cessation of the conditions which produced them. These affect only the uppermost layer, 1–3 m usually, but sometimes as much as 6 m. Like any other bed, periglacial palaeosols may be buried under more recent deposits and can be used to date the bed in which they have developed. Thus, in the area affected by Scandinavian ice, the Saale moraines frequently contain periglacial palaeosols which developed during the last glaciation, whilst the moraines deposited during the latter (the Weichsel Glaciation) do not contain them, except in the extra-marginal zone (e.g. Jutland). A series of beds at Tarzymiech in Poland has as its base varved silts with Dryas pollen and cryoturbations representing tundra lake deposits, with progressively colder conditions producing finer and finer varves. Towards the end of this phase of deposition, ice wedges formed indicating the period of maximum cold. A subsequent amelioration of climate is indicated by reworked loess deposited by streams, and containing molluscs and plant remains; this fills the ice wedge casts. Sandy fluviatile deposits of a cool dry climate, which became progressively colder, overlie them and show cryoturbations at their top. A final return of warm conditions produced muds in which the calcium carbonate content decreases by half.

(iii) *The correlation of deposits* This depends in detail on a variety of factors. Over most of the earth, the Quaternary is marked by a tendency for rivers to deepen their beds by downcutting. This results in the older deposits being found at a higher elevation than the more recent ones, which were laid down in the more deeply sunk valley. Along the river courses, flights of terraces were produced. In periglacial regions these terraces usually coincide with part of the cold periods; some of them contain cryoturbations, others are associated with periglacial slope deposits. The study of these alluvial deposits is a valuable part of the investigation of palaeoclimates, as the Tarzymiech example shows. It is necessary, however, to distinguish very carefully between syngenetic cryoturbations formed during the period of deposition, and postgenetic cryoturbations, which formed subsequently. Penck relied on this method to distinguish between four successive glacial periods. The oldest deposits form the highest beds, and are most frequently preserved on the interfluves (*Deckenschotter*). The most recent deposits, on the other hand, form terraces in the valleys with much thinner and less fully developed weathered horizons. The use of relative heights to fix the order of Quaternary deposits is by no means the only method. Use has also been made of another kind of correlation, the relationship between glacial deposits and interglacial marine deposits corresponding to a glacio-eustatic rise in sea level. Similarly, the study of periglacial phenomena in coastal areas is of great significance, for it may also provide a correlation between the glacial periods and changes in sea level. Very frequently, frost structures and solifluction sheets extend below raised marine deposits, and in the case of the most recent, beneath the present sea level. They thus date periods of marine regression, especially the most recent: the pre-Flandrian regression. The relations between glacial deposits and loess may also provide a means of correlation.

(iv) *Methods of sedimentary petrography* These study the deposit itself to obtain information of two types, the first to reconstruct the environment in which deposition occurred, the second to get evidence on the origin of the material. Strictly speaking, neither of these constitutes a method of dating. They consist of indirect information, which in the absence of other criteria helps to fit a deposit into a stratigraphic sequence. Petrographic studies give indications of the geographical origin of the material by taking account of the percentage of fragments of different rock types of a given size, the variation of this percentage as a function of size, the suite of heavy minerals, etc.

(2) The Occurrence of Cold Periods

(a) The Contemporaneity of the Glaciations One of the great problems of Quaternary morphogenesis is that of the contemporaneity of its different glacial phases throughout the world. If they had not coincided in time, the volume of water locked up by the ice in the Quaternary would have been much less variable and the glacio-eustatic lowering of sea level would have decreased. Furthermore, they would not necessarily have risen from a general cause but might have been due to local fortuitous events.

Several workers have shown that the great glacial advances were indeed contemporaneous. It is now known that the retreat of the Scandinavian ice sheet, the North American ice sheet and the great glaciers of Patagonia occurred at the same time. Submarine investigations show that the surface waters of the sea in which the foraminifera live were affected by the cold as far as the Equator. The contemporaneity of the ice sheets is a proven fact.

In detail, synchronization is not exact. Valley glaciers seem to have melted more rapidly than ice sheets. The formation of the moraines of the Pomeranian stadial is dated at about 16 000 years ago, as is the departure of the ice from Lake Michigan. Yet various estimates lead to the conclusion that the ice left the great sub-Alpine lakes about 25 000 years ago. Thus the decline of the Alpine glaciers seems to have slightly preceded that of the ice sheets.

Local glaciers and ice sheets appear to have been even more out of phase during the advance stages, The small supply of snow to the ice sheets, compared with their great bulk, must have led to their forming only very slowly. Furthermore, several American authors have suggested that climatic fluctuations could have different effects, even opposite effects, on different glaciers. Valley glaciers are influenced rapidly and directly, but not Arctic ice sheets. Ewing and Donn have put forward the theory that a climatic amelioration, by melting the sea ice of the Arctic, would promote the glaciation of the neighbouring land masses because of increased precipitation. This in turn would cool the sea again and check the growth of the ice sheets. In Antarctica, the intense cold checks accumulation. A climatic amelioration sufficient to increase precipitation but not enough to seriously increase ablation, would produce a glacier balance sheet with a greater surplus and lead to an expansion of the ice sheet, to the extent that has been shown to have occurred in the Quaternary. In this case, the fluctuations of the Antarctic ice sheet would be the converse of those of other Glaciers, especially the ice sheets of the northern hemisphere. At the moment this is only a possibility, but one worth keeping in mind.

(b) **The Number of Cold Periods** The terms cold period and glaciation must not be confused, although the two are related since the cooling of climate allowed the considerable growth of ice sheets which are the basic feature of the Quaternary. According to the mode of growth of the ice sheets or large regional glaciers, a given area may or may not be reached by them during a given cold period. Likewise, the time-lag in the reaction of glaciers to climatic change may cause complications on a regional or local scale.

CORRELATION OF THE DIFFERENT ICE SHEETS

North Germany	*Alps*	*European Russia*	*Siberia*	*North America*
WEICHSEL (Pomeranian, Brandenburg)	WÜRM	MOSCOW (Valdai, Moscow)	SARTAN	WISCONSIN
Eemian	Riss-Würm			Sangamon
SAALE (Warthe, Saale)	RISS	(Moscow?) DNEPR	SYRJANKA	ILLINOIAN
Holstein	Mindel-Riss			Yarmouth
ELSTER	MINDEL	LIKHVIN	OLDER?	KANSAN
	Günz-Mindel			Aftonian
	GÜNZ			NEBRASKAN

The number of major cold periods for the Alps was put at four by Penck in 1901; his writings popularized the nomenclature based on certain Bavarian rivers, Günz, Mindel, Riss and Würm, in chronological order. Minor fluctuations of the ice front took place within these periods whose duration was estimated at several tens of thousands of years, and which were separated by warm interglacial phases, the Günz-Mindel, Mindel-Riss and Riss-Würm. Within the Würm, different authors distinguish two or three secondary advances, in the Riss, two. The geomorphological importance of these fluctuations varies in the periglacial zone. They sometimes leave clear evidence, as at Tarzymiech, in the type of alluvial deposits. In the Durance basin the Würm retreat was marked by the dissection of the terrace formed at the maximum advance, but the Younger Dryas period caused a rounding of the terrace edges of solifluction and the deposition of a sheet of alluvial silt. Evidence for similar sequences is found in deposits in the rock shelters and caves of the Karst. These play an important part in the study of prehistory, but they are not always easy to fit into the general pattern.

Penck's chronology, which has just been quoted, has been questioned even with respect to the Alps. Some writers advocate five glaciations, the oldest, or Donau, preceding the Günz. This raises a matter of primary importance, the distinction between the younger and the older Quaternary, the latter being more weathered and found at much lower levels. In the younger Quaternary two successive systems of moraines can generally be recognized. The more distant of the two from the Alps is usually called the 'outer moraines', though these are for the most part quite close to the mountains. The main difference is the intense periglacial effects suffered by the outer moraines, whose original form has been completely modified.

In other regions, there is no evidence for five main glaciations. Four is the maximum. In the Germano–Polish plain only three have been identified: the Elster, Saale and Weichsel in order of decreasing age. A considerable interval separates the first two, for the Elster deposits generally consist wholly of erratic blocks. A temperate period (as indicated by the flora), with a sea level at times higher than at present, undoubtedly separates the Weichel and Saale Glaciations.

The differentiation of the several glaciations of North America raises the same problems. Some authors tend to increase the number of glaciations by promoting stadials to separate glaciations, while others group them into one. As in Europe, where the problem was first recognized, there is some divison of opinion between four or three glaciations, depending on whether the Alps or the Germano–Polish plain is taken as the model. Flint and many others accept four glaciations, in order, Nebraskan, Kansan, Illinoian and Wisconsin, the last, like Weichel, being subdivided into several stadials (Iowan, Tazewell, Cary and Mankato). Still others group the Illinoian and Wisconsin into a single glaciation.

In other parts of the globe fewer glaciations are usually recognized, probably because research has been less intensive, though more recent work is bringing greater precision. In Siberia, there is clear evidence for two glaciations with traces of a third and older. In China, four glaciations have recently been distinguished, and in Peru, three. This are still far from the eight climatic fluctuations deduced from marine deposits by Emiliani, using oxygen isotopes.

(c) **The Rhythm of Quaternary Climatic Change** The whole Quaternary is between 500 000 and 1 500 000 years long, or one-tenth of the length of the Pliocene, which is very short by geological standards. It must be borne in mind that during this brief period, at least 6 or 7 significant changes of climate occurred, completely changing the world's morphogenetic systems. Troll proposed a division of the Quaternary into three main parts whose duration does not seem too unequal. In the author's opinion, this division is the best from the geomorphological point of view.

(i) *The Older Quaternary* includes the oldest glaciations, older than the pre-Riss interglacial.

Generally, it seems that the extent of these early glaciations was rather different from that of later ones. Various lines of evidence suggest that, at least several hundred kilometres from the ice, a rather less severe climate prevailed than in a similar position during the later glacials.

The Günz–Mindel interglacial period seems to have been relatively short, downcutting by streams was limited and weathering of the deposits slight. It does not seem to have been very warm and this may explain the difficulty frequently encountered in separating these glaciations.

(ii) *The Middle Quaternary* consists mainly of an interglacial period, the Mindel–Riss or Elster–Saale, which seems to have lasted a very long time.

In the Germano–Polish plain, this period is characterized by the deposits of the Holstein Sea. Its long duration allowed tectonic activity to produce warping and even faulting in many areas. Furthermore, owing to its length, it played an important morphogenetic role. In the Paris Basin and in areas surrounding the Alps it was warmer than today, as is shown by reddish soils and in the Mediterranean region, fully developed red earths.

(iii) *The Younger Quaternary* includes the Riss and Würm Glaciations (Saale and Weichel, or Illinoian and Wisconsin of Flint), the interglacial which separates them, and the Postglacial. The penultimate glaciation (Riss or Saale) seems to have been generally more extensive than the final one. In regions bordering on the ice sheets, periglacial phenomena such as ice wedges also indicate that the cold was more intense. It was at this time that the climate reached its coldest in the Younger Quaternary.

The Riss or Saale Glaciation, it seems, should be divided into two main episodes by a temporary recession. In northern Germany, the second advance would be that of the Warthe.

The Riss–Würm Interglacial seems to have been short, like the Günz–Mindel, and marked by a renewed rise of sea level, the Eemian. The last glacial, Würm, Weichsel or Wisconsin, was generally marked by a slightly less extensive advance of the ice. The Würm recession is well authenticated by precise dating. It saw an improvement in climate during which the forest returned to south Scandinavia, followed by a very brief return of cold, the Younger Dryas period, contemporary with the Salpausselkä moraines. After that, glacial retreat was very rapid. This is the Late glacial. The accompanying rapid rise in sea level was the *Flandrian Transgression*, which produced a shoreline a little higher (about one metre) than the present, the *Dunkerquien*, dating to about 3000 B.P. Minor climatic fluctuations, by no means negligible, occurred on into the Holocene, and are fixed by the pollen zones.

(B) Area Affected by the Quaternary Cold Periods

Glaciation is the most fundamental feature of the Quaternary, but it was not limited to this era. Glacial deposits are known from other geological periods. Eocene morainic deposits have been identified in the Rocky Mountains, though this area had recently undergone strong folding so that the deposits might just be the work of local glaciers. This is certainly not the case in the Permo–Carboniferous and the Precambrian. Very widespread glaciations seem to have occurred at these periods. Evidence for the Permo–Carboniferous glaciation has been found in northeastern America, South America, central and southern Africa, India and southern Australia. The Precambrian ice extended over Greenland, Western Europe (perhaps the Cotentin Peninsula), the Far East, central Africa, Brazil and southern Australia. The areas covered by their deposits suggest that ice sheets occurred then, as in the Quaternary. Evidence for the Precambrian glaciation is particularly well known in the northern hemisphere, for the Permo–Carboniferous in the southern hemisphere. Both appear to have been more extensive than the Quaternary glaciation. Progress in research has led to the distinguishing of an increasing number of glaciations in the Palaeozoic and Precambrian, both in Africa and Brazil. Successive advances and retreats have taken place, with normal deposition in the intervening periods.

It is unusual for the Palaeozoic glaciation to have any morphogenetic influence today. In the case of the Quaternary it is essential to distinguish between the older and younger glaciations. The former have only an indirect influence on the present relief through the glacio-eustatic changes in sea level which they caused, and through the particular lines of development which they imposed on the regional landscapes of the areas they affected. Like more recent glaciations, they caused the damming of valleys, the formation of lakes, the burial of relief and the cutting of epigenetic valleys, it is therefore helpful to know their extent. To these indirect effects the more recent glaciations (Würm and Riss) add their more obvious influence in the form of fluvio-glacial sheets, little-altered moraines and characteristic pitted relief, which have been preserved intact. This applies even more to periglacial effects. Those belonging to the older Quaternary are usually no longer recognizable in the landscape except as fragments of terraces or rare deposits of much-weathered loess. These remnants are more useful in the reconstruction of palaeogeography, for which they are very valuable evidence, than for the direct interpretation of relief. By contrast, the Würm periglacial relief is almost completely preserved over extensive areas.

In studying the manifestations of cold climates in the Quaternary it is important to take periglacial effects into account. In addition to their great interest today, periglacial phenomena have considerable geological importance. During the Quaternary cold periods they have, as much as glaciers, moulded the surface of very large areas of the earth including those of densest population and greatest development.

The study of Quaternary periglacial phenomena is made difficult by two factors:

(*a*) the zonal pattern of the different types of periglacial environment has shifted with time in accordance with the varying rhythm of palaeoclimatic fluctuations. Thus, during the advance of the Würm (Weichsel) ice sheets, periglacial actions were very intense in northern Germany, while in the Riss (Saale), this was equally true of the Netherlands. The push moraines incorporate beds which were indurated by permafrost to a depth of several tens of metres. During the Würm retreat, however, it is possible to distinguish an initial period when the climate remained very cold, corresponding to the Brandenburg and Pomeranian stadials in north Germany. Afterwards the climate became rapidly warmer, being interrupted by one brief recurrence of intense cold.

Depending on the length of each periglacial episode, and the nature of those which followed it, the relief retains more or less distinct evidence of the effects of cold. When the ice later advanced over what was the periglacial zone of the early advance period, it usually swept away the frost shattered rocks and removed the cryoturbation features. Periglacial processes prepared the material for removal by ice. The reconstruction of the palaeogeography as accurately as possible to show the various morphogenetic phases which followed one another during the palaeoclimatic fluctuations of the Quaternary is of fundamental importance to geomorphology.

(*b*) The relationships of morphology and climate in the Quaternary are not simply those of the present day. The interpretation of Quaternary periglacial phenomena does, however, rely on a comparison with existing phenomena.

We shall study in turn the extent of Older and Younger Quaternary glaciations, and then the areas affected by periglacial action.

(1) The Extent of the Older Quaternary Glaciations

The status of the cold periods of the Older Quaternary is a controversial and complex problem. Faunas throughout the whole of this period consist of tropical or sub-tropical species. Yet evidence of relatively intense cold is found in regions whose climates have subsequently been more temperate. This is particularly true in the Rome area where quite marked periglacial effects occur. Perhaps the flow of very cold meltwater coming from ice lobes in Russia and Poland into the Black Sea cooled the Mediterranean in the Older Quaternary much more than in more recent periods when these glacial meltwaters drained more to the Atlantic. The work of Venzo in the Bergamo region shows a lowering of the vegetation zones by only 800–1200 m during the Donau, Günz and Mindel glaciations, that is about the same amount as in the Würm.

In the mountains and at their foot where valley glaciers descended well below the snowline, differences in extent are less marked; it is mainly at the foot of the Alps that they are appreciable. During one of the old glaciations, the Günz or the Mindel, the glaciers advanced as a piedmont lobe, as far as the south of the Saône lowlands which were temporarily covered by a lake. Ice, building up on the Swiss plateau also reached the Jura, where it advanced into the valleys as ice tongues which, added to by local glaciers, continued on as far as the Lons-le-Saulnier area.

The Scandinavian ice sheet on the other hand did not advance as far during the Elster as during the Saale. It did not go beyond the mouth of the Ems. In central and eastern Europe the opposite is true; the belt separating the two ice limits widens eastwards. The Elster ice encroached on the foothills of the Erz Gebirge, the Sudeten Mountains and the Carpathians in Poland.

Little is known of the extent of the older glaciations in Siberia. Nevertheless one thing is very probable: there could have been no extensive ice sheet at any period, though the contrary was believed for a long time. Novaya Zemlya and the northern Urals were covered by an ice sheet which joined the Scandinavian. It seems to have reached the coast of the glacial Arctic Ocean as far east as the Taimyr Peninsula. On the major mountains of central and eastern Siberia, the Sayansk, Stanovoi, Verkhoyansk, Kolima and Chukotsk Ranges, there were extensive ice caps. These fed piedmont glaciers which sometimes joined together to form a foreland glacis, especially around Verkhoyansk and Irkutsk.

In North America the continent was covered by a continuous ice sheet from west coast to east. The limits of the Nebraskan ice are admittedly vague; almost everywhere, the subsequent Kansan ice sheet advanced at least as far, and covered the Nebraskan deposits. It has been claimed that the upper stretches of the Ohio River and of the Missouri in the Dakotas, developed on the edge of the Nebraskan ice sheet as proglacial rivers. The Kansan glaciation is the better documented. In the east, between the Great Lakes and the Atlantic, its limit almost coincides with those of subsequent glaciations. It is clearly distinguishable mainly in the west, because of its greater extent there. The Missouri lobe has overriden the whole central part of the Missouri valley, but its deposits have been covered by more recent beds. Periglacial deposits of gravel and loess have been recorded in the Great Plains around the moraines but they have not been studied in detail.

In the southern hemisphere, too little is known for the extent of the older glaciations to be defined. They seem to have been on a large scale only in Patagonia and New Zealand, in regions where the later glaciations have had considerable morphogenetic effects. In Peru, the Mantaro glaciation, whose deposits have been subdued and converted into resistant conglomerates, seems to belong to the older Quaternary. It was of considerable size, producing a glacier 80 km long in the Mantaro valley compared with 30 to 40 km in the succeeding glaciations.

On the whole, the extent of the older glaciations was slightly greater than that of the younger, and more important, they did not develop along quite the same axis. They advanced further in continental regions, the Russian plains, Poland, Siberia and the central lowlands of the United States, but less far in maritime areas, such as Germany and the northeastern United States. The explanation of this difference probably lies in the atmospheric circulation of the time, but this has not yet received serious attention.

(2) The Extent of the Younger Glaciations

In general, the extent of the Saale or Riss is greater than that of the Weichsel or Würm glaciation. This is particularly clear at the foot of the great mountain chains, as in the Alps where the terms *outer moraines* and *inner moraines* are used. In the Riss, the ice formed a large piedmont lobe which spread around Lyons whereas in the Würm it reached no further than Rives (some 50 km to the east). In Bavaria the piedmont glaciers of the Würm reached only the foot of the Alps (e.g. the lobes of the Chiem See and Würm See) whilst in the Riss they extended much further out.

The North European ice sheet shows a similar pattern. In contrast with the Elster, the Saale and Weichsel ice spread in a southwesterly direction over the North Sea towards the British Isles. In the Saale, the Scandinavian ice reached the east coast of Great Britain and merged with the local ice cap, which it failed to reach during the Weichsel. During the Saale, the ice reached the lower valley of the Rhine, the Börde region and Upper Silesia, whereas at the time of the maximum Weichsel advance it reached no further than the southwest of Jutland, the eastern half of Schleswig-Holstein, the middle Elbe valley and the Poznan area. Further east, the two series of moraines become even further apart. In Russia, the ice front in the Moscow (Saale) glaciation skirted the area of the capital and then ran to the lower Pechora region. It has not yet been ascertained whether or not this ice made contact with the local ice cap of Novaya Zemlya. Siberia, as in the preceding periods, was covered only by local ice sheets. During the Weichsel glaciation there were no longer local ice sheets in Siberia but limited ice caps with piedmont glaciers.

In western Europe, periglacial effects of the Riss seem to have been the more intense. In France, it seems that features such as ice wedges, which characterize the most severe climates, largely date from this period. It was in this period above all that the vigorous cryoplanation of the chalk of Champagne took place and that the filling of the valleys by periglacial river deposits was most active.

In North America, the difference in area covered by the last two glaciations is less pronounced. Their limits very frequently coincide with those of the Kansan. In the west, in Minnesota and Iowa, the Illinoian ice sheet did not advance nearly as far south as the Kansan or even the Wisconsin. The latter is marked by a lobe lying midway between the limits of the two earlier glaciations. South of the Great Lakes, the pattern is the same as in Eurasia, and the Wisconsin terminal moraines are not as far forward as the Illinoian. The latter coincides roughly with the Kansan limit, forming two very distinctive lobes, the Illinois lobe and the Louisville-Cincinnati lobe. In the east the limits of the three glaciations are almost identical, with minor discrepancies.

In South America the extent of only the last glaciation is known, even approximately. In Chile, south of 42°S, the Andes glaciers discharged directly into the sea, excavating the fjords. It is possible that a small floating ice shelf bordered the continent near Tierra del Fuego. In Patagonia where it was drier, it is only south of 52°S that glaciers reached tidewater, no ice sheet ever developed. Valley glaciers coalesced in a piedmont glacis whose front was never more than 200 km from the foot of the Andes. Owing to the very great height of the summits as far as 26°S, the valleys were filled by a net of branching glaciers, In Ecuador two series of moraines occur, separated by loess lying on the weathered older series. As in the Alps, this moraine lies furthest out. In the Andes of Venezuela, I found evidence of two successive glaciations in the high Chama, the first definitely more extensive. Its deposits are fairly weathered, while those of the last glaciation are much fresher.

Important periglacial effects have recently been discovered in the Andes and at their foot, in Argentina, Chile and Bolivia. I have observed evidence of frost shattering on the summit of Italiya at about 2500 m, near Rio de Janiero. In the Andes in Venezuela, it is possible to fix at about 4000 m the lower limit of undoubted periglacial features, such as significant frost shattering and stratified screes. The recording of these phenomena is just beginning.

In Australasia, Quaternary glaciers appear only south of 40°S. In Australia only traces of a small local glacier are found on Mount Kosciusko, yet in Tasmania there was an ice cap whose thickness seems to have reached 500 m, and whose area covered about 25 000 sq km. New Zealand presents a similar arrangement, with a few small valley glaciers in North Island and a widespread intense glaciation in South Island where there were ice caps and branching valley glaciers in the mountains, piedmont glaciers at their eastern foot, and on the west outlet glaciers which reached the sea, forming fjords.

Würm periglacial effects assume great importance in the whole of the Wellington area: in particular, they remoulded the greywacke slopes, burying a complete system of gullies which had formerly dissected them. The same thing took place in the Riss (Cotton).

(3) Relationship of Periglacial and Glacial Phenomena in the Quaternary

Periglacial processes come into operation with little delay after the climatic changes which cause them, whereas glacial advances occur after a delay which is proportional to the size of the glacier.

Looking at the Quaternary as a whole, there is, however, a coincidence of glacial and periglacial periods. In eastern Morocco, Raynal has shown that moraines of several glaciers pass into piedmont fans which in turn are related to periglacial slope deposits, and sometimes affected by intraformational cryoturbation. He has identified five systems of these glacis, but evidence of the glaciations corresponding to them is preserved only in the case of the two most recent. During the Quaternary cold periods the relative distribution of glacial and periglacial zones was the same as at present. Some parts of the cold zone were transformed into centres of outward flowing ice and were occupied by ice sheets which today have disappeared, such as those of Labrador, Fennoscandia and the northern Urals. In between them, periglacial conditions existed which, beginning at the ice margin, reached far into temperate latitudes. Some regions, like a large part of eastern Siberia and perhaps also the coastal plain of northern Alaska, have been continuously subject to cold periglacial climates during the greater part of the Younger Quaternary, with only minor fluctuations corresponding to the Riss-Würm interglacial and to the postglacial period. Other more extensive areas have had alternating cold and temperate conditions, as for example the whole southern border zone of the Fennoscandian and Laurentian ice sheets.

In Europe, where the reconstruction of the palaeogeography is furthest advanced, the climatic difference between glacial and interglacial periods decreases from west to east, with a progressive change to the uninterruptedly cold climates in Siberia. In France, the periglacial zone reached the Mediterranean coast in the Crau and Costière on the lower Aude, under the effect of local cold winds. All the Mediterranean mountains show the effects of the Quaternary cold conditions, above 800–1000 m in the Rif, above 1200 m in eastern Morocco, 1400 m in the Aurès, and 600–700 m in the central Apennines.

The areas affected by the Quaternary cold thus show the same combination of glacier types as today: a predominance of ice sheets, piedmont glaciers in the many mountain chains which today contain important valley glaciers, and valley and cirque glaciers in mountains which today contain no glaciers. The extent and volume of Quaternary ice was made up essentially of the ice sheets, with, far behind, local ice caps and piedmont glaciers.

(C) Development of the Cold Periods

Basically, it is the development of the ice sheets which has to be explained.

(1) The Palaeogeography of the Würm: an Example

The most important work in this field has been done by the Germans (notably Büdel, Poser, Klute, Troll and Mortensen), and by the Russians, who have succeeded in drawing up a systemic inventory of the peat bogs of their country and producing vegetation maps for various periods of the Quaternary (Grichuk, Neustadt, Sukachev, etc.). These rely on a combination of geomorphological methods for determining the conditions of formation, and on pollen analysis for the climatic conditions: deduced from the fossil flora. Data from systematic meteorology form a final check on the reconstruction. Work of this nature forms quite a reliable base. Thanks to it, the climate of the Würm is the best known of all palaeoclimates.

Consideration of the two main factors provides a starting point.

(a) **The Snowline** This may be reconstructed from detailed geomorphological studies. It is easy to fix it for the glacial maximum, when dating errors are at a minimum. The chronology of retreat varies in different areas and does not allow accurate maps to be made for the later phases.

In Europe, the snowline at the Würm maximum lay at about 670–705 m in the Harz Mountains which were near the Scandinavian ice sheet, showing that this had advanced several hundred kilometres south of the area where the snowline lay at sea level. In the Vosges, it lay at about 700 m on the western slope and 900 m on the drier eastern slope, in the Black Forest at some 1000 m on the south and 900 m on the north. This pattern shows that snow fell predominantly with southwest or west winds, as is the case today. In the Bohemian Forest the snowline reached 1000–1100 m and in the Giant Mountains 1200–1259 m. In the Alps it oscillated around 1100 on the western slopes. It reached 1800 m in Corsica (east slopes), 1300 m in Istria, 1300–1400 m on the coastal slopes of Montenegro, 1900 m in the mountains of southeast Bosnia, and a maximum of 2300 m on the western slope of the lower Vardar valley and in the Pindus Mountains. It falls to 1900 m in the Djuradjura Mountains (Algiers), which are exceptionally wet.

(b) **The Treeline** This is deduced from pollen analysis. Wooded tundra did not extend northward beyond the foot of the Pyrenees, the Languedoc coast, the Riviera coast, the Florence basin, Croatian piedmont, Belgrade area and the foot of the Balkan Mountains. Further east, the situation is more complex: the Aralo–Caspian region was continuously steppe as today, so that the present forest zone to the north of this was then very much smaller. The forest represented by wooded steppe was limited to a narrow strip at the foot of the Carpathians, which continued on past Kiev, Tambov and Kazan. One thing is quite clear: at no point during the glacial maximum did the forest approach the ice either in the Alpine piedmont or on the limits of the Fennoscandian ice sheet. The latter was bounded by a zone of frost-debris tundra which was wider in the west where it reached the Boulonnais and covered the whole of southern England, but narrowed to 10–200 km in Russia. As far as the Ukraine, it was succeeded on the south by a belt of loess accumulation; beyond the Kiev area the frost-debris tundra was bounded by a tundra with dwarf birches. In Siberia, all these zones turned quickly northwards as the continental climate was much more favourable to vegetation than the maritime, as far as this cold zone was concerned.

From these data, German workers have made isotherm maps for the Würm maximum. This also makes use of such facts as the coincidence of the present northern limit of forest with the July isotherm of 10·5°C, the coincidence of the present snowline with the 1500 m contour in western Europe where the mean July temperature at sea level is 14°C, with 2000 m where it is between 17 and 18°C and with 2500 m where it is 21–22°C.

Moreover, the trace of the Würm snowline is in general parallel to that of the present time as is shown by the Vosges, Black Forest and Balkan Mountains. This shows that the atmospheric circulation was of the same type as the present. The theory of a strong anticyclone over the Fennoscandian ice sheet with out-blowing winds is supported by certain aeolian phenomena which were restricted to a marginal zone of limited width (in Germany, as far as the foot of the Hercynian Massifs).

It has proved possible to determine how much this cold period lowered the snowline compared with its present position. By comparing this with the isotherms deduced from the vegetation zones it is possible to get some idea, admittedly hypothetical and less precise than the preceding reconstructions, of the changes in precipitation during the cold periods. If the snowline is lower than the isotherms alone would suggest, this is because precipitation was more abundant, and vice versa. According to Klein, precipitation was generally lower, especially on the lowlands; the Paris Basin received only 50–60% of its present total, while Poland and western Russia received 20–30%. Only in the eastern and southwestern Alps did it reach 70–80%. On the whole, the difference in precipitation between lowlands and mountains was probably more marked than today, a circumstance which favoured the advance of mountain glaciers. These reconstructions are still hypothetical.

Without pursuing these absorbing speculations further, we have a number of reasonably firm conclusions about the climate at the maximum of the last glaciation, which will enable us to understand its mechanism better and hence its geomorphological effects:

(i) Atmospheric circulation was in general little changed by the glaciation. Apart from an impermanent anticyclone over the Fennoscandian ice sheet comparable to that over Greenland at present, it was dominated by low pressure systems. The glacial anticyclone had only a local influence.

(ii) The contrast between continental and maritime climates was maintained, as would be expected with this type of atmospheric circulation. This explains the distribution of glaciers in Siberia, where they were restricted to the mountains. In the lowlands, the summer was much warmer than in western Europe at the same latitude, as the flora proves, so that ice ablation was considerably increased. Precipitation was probably lower than at present, small as it is, and snow melted completely in summer, making glaciation impossible. This explains why, as Soviet writers maintain, general conditions changed little in Siberia during the Würm. The climate was merely colder than at present so that there was a slight retreat of the taiga limit southward, with the accompanying development of permafrost, which survives today in relict form. Siberia is one of the areas in middle latitudes whose geomorphological evolution shows least change from the Quaternary.

(iii) The distribution of mountain glaciers obeys very different laws. They are much more dependent on the accumulation of snow, than are ice sheets. Indeed the snowline is really a function of situation relative to cyclonic circulation. These glaciers seem to have benefited, at the Würm maximum, from a precipitation which increased more rapidly with altitude than at present.

(iv) Between and around the ice sheets was a vast periglacial zone of tundra and wooded tundra which at some points reached the northern coast of the Mediterranean. In western and central Europe the contrast with present-day morphoclimatic conditions was greatest. In eastern Europe and western Siberia, the wooded tundra passed directly into wooded steppe which stretched as far as the Black Sea and the semi-arid regions of lower central Asia. The forest belt was almost eliminated. In Siberia, a limited taiga survived from the foot of the Altai Mountains to the lower Lena.

(v) One basic fact stands out: the glaciations are associated with a temporary cooling of climate. The development of the glaciation enables two fundamental types of glacier to be distinguished which are similar to those of today: ice sheets, in whose formation cold plays the main part since their supply is very small, and local glaciers, in whose development cold is the principal factor, but is combined with snow supply. The latter, though acting in a secondary capacity, explains the difference in the extent of local glaciers with different orientations, though in the same climatic environment. Attention must also be given to the mountain relief surrounding each glacier, in a given climate. A large area above the snowline leading down to a steeply graded valley favours the growth of piedmont glaciers. As Vardaniantz has shown, stepped valleys cause jerky advances and retreats of the ice which may exaggerate the fluctuations in climate which initiated them.

(2) The Growth Mechanism of Ice Sheets

This problem does not only concern glaciology; it is also of fundamental importance to geomorphology. It has been shown that climatic fluctuations in the Quaternary were notable for their short duration; the question therefore arises as to the extent to which glaciers were able to remould the pre-existing relief. From this it is evident that the very conditions of the period of climatic change which were responsible for the formation of glaciers in a region, are extremely important from the morphogenetic point of view. It is probably during the transition from one morphoclimatic system to another that the most rapid changes in relief are effected.

The similarity between the Fennoscandian ice sheet (which might be taken as a type-example for the Quaternary) and the existing Greenland ice sheet, allows us to use the results obtained from a study of the latter in an approach to the problem of ice sheet growth.

From these, Cailleux developed his hypothesis, based on the principle of the autocatalysis of ice sheets as a function of altitude, an idea first formulated by Wegmann in 1941. When the climate began to cool at the end of the Pliocene, Greenland consisted of a basin surrounded by marginal mountains, and glaciers formed on them. Those which flowed outwards ended by reaching the sea where they were dissipated into icebergs. Those which flowed towards the interior spread out to form piedmont lobes. Assuming that glaciation increased progressively as the climate grew colder, the annual 0°C isotherm presumably descended until the whole interior basin of Greenland was below the snowline. The piedmont lobes spread out further until they coalesced and the interior basin became choked with ice whose surface rose gradually higher above the snowline which, at the time, was descending. Once the surface of the ice in the basin reached the same altitude as the snowline, there was both a decrease in ablation and an increase in supply. In addition to ice coming down from the margins, supply was increased by the formation of a surface snowfield covering the site of the basin. The result was a raising and progressive doming of the ice, until the altitude was reached at which it spilled over the peripheral mountain belt and acquired the convex profile of the ice sheet seen today. The decrease in temperature with depth shows that the lower ice is relict, having accumulated under a former, colder climate.

Research by the French Polar Expeditions to the Vatnajökull shows that the same pattern may have occurred there. The existing data on the topography of Antarctica supports the application of the same hypothesis. Three mountain chains rise through the ice on the margins of the continent, the Queen Maud Range (4600 m), the Executive Committee Range (6100 m), and Neu Schwabenland (3300 m). At their foot are three ice domes forming areas which are raised, relative to the rest of the ice sheet. These are the South Polar Plateau (3200 m), and the Marie-Byrd (2000 m), and Wegener Domes, the last being at a higher altitude than its bordering chain.

Results obtained by Quaternary research workers are also in favour of this hypothesis; the iceshed in Scandinavia lay 70 to 180 km east of the mountain crest line. In South America on the other hand, where glaciation was not intense enough to form an ice sheet, it was displaced outwards, to the west, at about latitude 41°S (Ljungner). The arcuate distribution of high ground around a semicircular depression from southern Norway to Karelia, then higher than at present (the postglacial uplift, which still continues, shows that isostatic equilibrium has not yet been restored), made the Fennoscandian ice sheet possible. The fact that this depression was open to the south led to the ice flowing in the direction of the Germano-Polish Plain and its encroachment on a region where the snowline was several hundred metres above sea level.

A similar relief pattern around Verkhoyansk led to the formation of an ice sheet during the Saale glaciation under a more severe climate than the Würm, when only piedmont glaciers developed. These failed to unite in a single mass for, owing to the higher temperatures, the snowline did not descend low enough to embrace the surface of the piedmont ice.

In North America, Flint has advanced the theory that the ice sheet grew steadily in the form of a piedmont mass at the southern edge of the high island ranges in the North Canadian Archipelago, Ellesmere and Baffin, and then the high mountains of northern Labrador which completed the semicircle. Its more northerly position than that of the Fennoscandian ice sheet (Ellesmere Land is at 80°N, while northern Norway is only at 70°N), allowed it to spread further from its original amphitheatre, over the wide central lowlands. In the interior basin of Alaska, on the other hand, as in that of Verkhoyansk, autocatalysis did not operate and the Würm ice failed to develop beyond the piedmont stage.

The application, to the various ice sheets, of the theory of autocatalysis as a function of altitude, gives satisfactory results if proper allowance is made for local relief. It explains the location of the principal continental ice sheets being not on the highest and most extensive mountain chains, but at their foot. This is shown clearly in North America: it was within the highland arc, in the northeast of the continent, that the ice sheet began its development, not on the highest mountain chains but in a long narrow strip on the shores of the Pacific. A corridor more than 1000 km wide seems to have persisted on the site of the Mackenzie depression and the Canadian Prairie, between the two great glaciated areas, throughout all the cold periods of the Quaternary. A comparison of the Alpine and Fennoscandian glaciations invites the same conclusions, though the difference in latitude between them makes it a less convincing example.

One final point should be noted, the close relationship between continental ice sheets and ancient shields, which is probably not just fortuitous. These ancient massifs are in fact more continuous than the recent fold mountain chains and form more effective barriers of the type required by the theory of autocatalysis of ice sheets as a function of altitude, especially when they have a raised rim, or *Randstufe*. They are not bordered by subsidence troughs and their block structure frequently results in broad sloping margins which favour the union of piedmont lobes. Certain facts suggest that this theory might be applied to pre-Quaternary glaciations. In Bahia, Brazil, I found a tillite containing fragments of crystalline rocks resting on Precambrian gravel. This indicates that the glacier came from a metamorphic ridge and spread across the overlying beds which formerly had been deposited at its foot.

(3) Origin of the Cold Periods

The hypothesis of the autocatalysis of ice sheets in relation to altitude involves a threshold of a climato-topographical nature; the coincidence between the surface of the accumulated ice of the piedmont and that of the snowline. On either side of this threshold, a slight modification of conditions may help or hinder the formation of an ice sheet. This helps to explain their small number, two at present, five or six in the Quaternary, and their lack of continuity in time; Precambrian, Permo-Carboniferous and Quaternary. It is enough, at these periods, for a certain threshold to be crossed in certain regions, in the course of numerous climatic fluctuations, for the mechanism responsible for ice sheet development to be set in motion.

Some authors have, even recently, sought an explanation of glaciation in the uplift of land masses in the Pliocene. This is difficult to accept in view of the location of some, including the larger ice sheets, on ancient massifs. The alternating glacial and interglacial periods cannot be correlated with successive uplift and depression. Other orogenic periods have not led to widespread glaciations. This explanation may possibly hold in a few special cases of recent glaciers in mountain chains where no trace of earlier glaciations is found, as for example, in the Venezuela Andes. But it should be employed with caution, since it is extremely difficult to say with certainty that no earlier glaciation took place. It has been used in the Andes of Peru, but the discovery of the important Mantaro glaciation means the exploration must be referred to a more distant past or rejected altogether.

Other authors have regarded the Quaternary glaciations as being the result of direct autocatalysis. According to this, a slight cooling of the climate allows a glacier to form. This in turn further cools the climate, increasing the nourishment of the glacier and enabling it to grow still more. Certain observations make it difficult to support this theory. Why for instance, have some glaciers developed into ice sheets while others such as those in the Alps and the Rockies, have not? It appears not to be a case of climatic change resulting from a change in the extent of the ice, but the exact opposite. Thus, during the Würm retreat, though the ice sheets still covered northern Sweden, meltwater was very abundant. In Russia, a temperate flora and avifauna gradually occupied the area abandoned by the ice; this ice mass, though large, was not sufficient to cool the atmosphere enough to offset the general change in climate. Conversely, the slight but gradual contemporary amelioration of climate has been enough to cause a spectacular retreat of local glaciers and to upset the temperature distribution of the Greenland ice sheet.

Again, there is evidence of an important cooling of climate prior to the advance of the ice sheets. In north Germany, Denmark and Holland, the advancing Fennoscandian ice disturbed gravel spreads of an earlier date. This unconsolidated material was moved in sheets, 30 to 100 m long, which were thrust over one another on low angle faults. Their form is, on a smaller scale, exactly that of the so-called 'hard rock tectonics', Only one explanation is possible: they must have moved in a frozen state and therefore in a climate producing permafrost. Cooling of the climate thus preceded the ice advance. But the slow build-up of the ice sheet introduces a time lag between the climatic change and the response in glacier variation, a time lag which is much greater during the advance than during retreat. The beginning of the Würm between 70 000–80 000 and 55 000 years B.P. (before present), was marked by a slow gradual cooling which led to the replacement of deciduous trees by conifers in the centre of western Europe, and the latter by the arctic forest and finally by tundra. At the same time the soil remained fairly moist, probably in most areas because of reduced evaporation. These conditions would favour a positive glacier balance-sheet, the gradual development of mountain glaciers, then piedmont glaciers and finally an ice sheet. Thus, the considerable time lag which indirect autocatalysis demands, does in fact exist, and lends support to this theory.

The whole problem is thus reduced to determining the causes of climatic variations in geological time since the most pronounced of these are sufficient to explain glaciations within the autocatalysis theory. It is a complex problem which concerns us only indirectly: very short summaries of the theories are adequate here.

(a) **Geophysical Theories** These are concerned with the physical character of the planet, changes in which might have caused climatic fluctuations responsible for the glaciations. The geologically short duration of the glaciations makes such explanations *a priori* unlikely. Indeed they encounter great difficulties, the chief of which are as follows:

(i) Continental drift (Wegener's hypothesis): the older glaciations such as the Precambrian and Permo–Carboniferous, should be related to the disruption of Gondwana. Yet their distribution in the Precambrian does not coincide with Wegener's reconstructions, nor is his hypothesis tenable with regard to the Quaternary.

(ii) Displacement of the polar axis, recently revived by Blanchard: the distribution of climatic zones during the Würm shows a displacement related to their present position, and not a lateral movement. This theory must therefore be rejected.

(iii) Variations in heat from the earth's interior: it is agreed that during cold periods, the mean temperature on the earth's surface must have fallen by some 10°C. Since today (in an interglacial period), heat from the earth's interior represents only 0·33% of that of the sun, its contribution is so slight that it seems unlikely that it could account for the actual variations.

(b) **Oceanographical and Meteorological Theories** These invoke modifications in the dynamics or properties of the atmosphere. The great similarity between the dynamics of Würm and present climates argues little in favour of these theories. Nevertheless, such modifications cannot be entirely excluded.

(i) Variations in the atmosphere's power of absorption due to volcanic activity, either by putting dust into suspension in the atmosphere or by increasing the amount of CO_2. In this case, cold periods should have coincided with phases of large-scale volcanic activity. Such a case might be made for the Permo–Carboniferous, but the enormous outpouring of lava in the Miocene failed to produce a glaciation. Moreover, the emission of large amounts of CO_2 would have had serious repercussions on life for which there is no evidence in the Quaternary.

(ii) Modifications in sea currents and in general atmospheric circulation. There is no doubt, as Behrmann has emphasized, that the glacio-eustatic lowering of sea level greatly disturbed the oceanic circulation during the cold periods. In the Atlantic, he claims, the Faroes–Icelandic ridge must have emerged for half its length and the Gulf Stream must have failed to reach the Arctic basin, a situation which would have helped to cool this area. Actually, the depth of this ridge, which is at present between 160 and 700 m, must have been between 100 and 600 m during the glacial maxima. What is more, the mechanism invoked by Behrmann presupposes the cooling of the climate as the cause of glaciation. Changes in sea level might have played an auxiliary part but were not the initial cause. As for modifications in atmospheric circulation, these contradict what is known today about Würm climates and the meteorology of Greenland.

This line of approach has been taken up and modified by Ewing and Donn who see in the Arctic Ocean a reason for fluctuations. Amelioration of climate causes the melting of the pack ice, higher sea temperatures and an increase in precipitation which leads to the development of mountain glaciers. The cooling of climate transforms these into piedmont glaciers. The process invoked by Behrmann may then play an auxiliary role.

(c) **Astronomical Theories** These rely on changes in the amount of heat received on the earth's surface, and bearing in mind the important part this plays in climate (Maurain), they have an inherent probability.

(i) Changes in the radiation received by the earth (Croll's hypothesis): the moon, sun and some of the planets cause periodic changes. Taking into account only the moon and the sun, the period is 21 000 years. To this may be added variations due to changes in the eccentricity of the earth's orbit (periodicity 91 800 years) and those due to changes in the angle of the axis of the poles to the plane of the ecliptic (periodicity 40 000 years). The combination of the three variables gives a very complex curve. Mathematical calculations indicate changes in the relative length of summers and winters without any change in the amount of heat received by the earth. Croll's theory as recast by Milankovitch, produces results which agree with some of the known facts. In the course of the last 600 000 years, there should have been four cold periods, each of which was divided into two, except the last, which had three secondary phases. The time interval between the second and third cold period should be much longer than the others (three to four times). The theory implies, however, that the equatorial zone was not affected by the cold periods. Yet at high altitudes Quaternary glaciation has been identified there and formaninifera found in submarine cores demonstrate a cooling of surface waters at the Equator. Moreover, Simpson considers the resulting changes in temperature would be too small compared with the known facts.

(ii) Changes in the intensity of solar radiation: these are due to two causes; internal, occurring within the sun (variations in sunspot activity), or external (the effects of clouds of cosmic dust). Some believe that these cosmic clouds, by absorbing radiation, reduce the amount received by the earth. Others, including Hoyle and Lyttleton, maintain the opposite: that these clouds falling on the sun release energy, causing an increase in solar radiation. Huntington claimed that variations in the intensity of solar radiation modify the cyclonic circulation and consequently climate. During periods of greater sunspot activity, the cyclonic circulation becomes more pronounced in polar regions and leads to increased snowfall and consequent glaciation. It has, however, already been shown that glaciation depends primarily on the advent of cold. Simpson argues in the opposite direction: an increase in solar radiation causes a greater increase in temperature at the Equator than at the Poles, increased evaporation and a high rate of atmospheric circulation, whence greater cloudiness and heavier snowfall. According to this hypothesis, however, glaciations should coincide in general with a warming of climate. In fact the opposite takes place. The large southward extension of periglacial phenomena to Portugal, Corsica and Languedoc, provides evidence of this. The view that a decrease in solar radiation at the earth's surface leads to a worldwide cooling of climate seems much more in agreement with the facts cited above. This does not exclude other effects but there is not enough data available to attempt to define them.

In short, there is a great need for further observations on ice sheets and palaeoclimates.

The following conclusions may be drawn from this study on the former distribution of glaciers.

(i) Ice sheets greatly predominate: they have been by far the most extensive glacier type in former glaciations, as they are today.

(ii) It is possible to distinguish, as at present, between ice sheets and local glaciers, whose relationships with successive climatic changes and the glacier regime are not always the same.

(iii) Glacial periods and cold climatic phases are closely linked; cold preceded glaciation and was essentially the cause of it. In mountainous regions, however, humidity is a secondary causal factor, the precipitation gradient showing a greater increase with altitude than at present, although precipitation was smaller than at present in the whole of the temperate and subarctic zone.

(iv) There was a considerable time lag between the advance of the ice sheets and the climatic changes which led to their development. The formation of ice sheets was thus preceded by a period of periglacial climate which lasted long enough to leave its mark on relief.

All these conclusions are necessary to an understanding of the morphogenetic action of glaciers: the role of periglacial phenomena will therefore be analysed before that of glaciers.

PART TWO

Periglacial Processes and Landforms

THE extent of the Quaternary glaciation was due to a lowering of temperature. Important periglacial effects were produced at times of glacier advance, over a period whose length depended on that of the glaciation. In recent years a significant part in glacial sculpture has been attributed to these periglacial effects of the advance stage. Frost shattering produced a large volume of debris which the glaciers later picked up and incorporated in their moraines.

The sequence of a periglacial phase at the onset of a cold period, followed by a glacial phase, demands a study of periglacial processes; a knowledge of them is indispensible to a correct appreciation of the work of the glaciers which succeeded them.

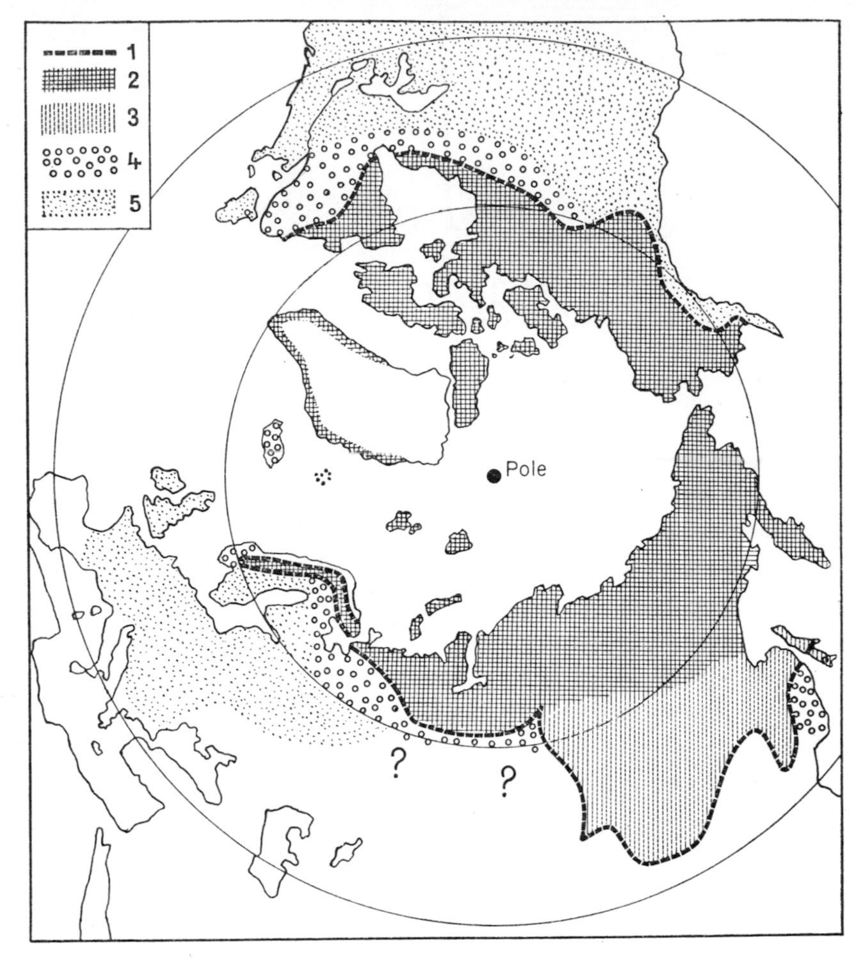

FIG. 7 The periglacial zone of the northern hemisphere

1. S. limit of permafrost 2. Existing areas of permafrost 3. Areas of fossil permafrost 4. Area of minor periglacial phenomena, thufur, string bogs, etc. 5. Area of Würm periglacial phenomena.

After the Great Soviet World Atlas for the U.S.S.R. and many sources cited in the references, for N.W. Europe and N. America. The present permafrost limit, known precisely in Siberia, is very approximate in N. America where no detailed study has been published.

CHAPTER 1

Characteristics of Soil Formation in Periglacial Areas

THE general changes in the surface of the lithosphere at its contact with the atmosphere, which result in the formation of soils, take on a characteristic form in cold environments. The vegetation cover is usually sparse and often discontinuous. Frost hinders its growth for long spells. Like that of hot deserts it has adapted itself to difficult conditions by limiting its requirements, it can exist with a low intake of calories, mineral salts and water and it therefore has very little influence on the surface of the lithosphere. Biotic factors do not play the large part in soil formation that they play in the humid tropics or even in the temperate zone. The factors are purely physical, subjecting the rocks to intense mechanical pressures. The most important and characteristic of these is frost, hence the term cryopedology, given to the study of soil formation in cold environments.

We shall examine in turn, the distribution of frost in the ground, its action on the soil, and the role of other soil-forming factors, especially those of a biochemical nature.

(A) THE OCCURRENCE OF GROUND ICE

The occurrence of frost in the ground is little understood because of the backwardness of the study of soil climate. As a result, a satisfactory and complete picture cannot be given. One is compelled to deal with mechanisms rather than quantitative data as these are few.

(1) The Factors

There are two basic concepts: the heat budget of the soil and its thermal regime.

(a) The Heat Budget of the Soil This is broadly determined by climatic influence which, among the many factors which control ground temperature, is markedly dominant. The flow of internal heat, arising from depth, is only of the order of 47 gramme-calories per square centimetre: enough in a year to melt ice one centimetre thick. The flow of external heat, derived from the sun, is on average 5000 times greater. It is therefore mainly changes in the temperature of the ground surface which control the heat budget. Residual or fossil permafrost or dead ice survives for a very long time when protected from the flow of external heat, melting only very slowly from its base. Hence the large amount of fossil ice and residual permafrost which survives in Siberia, Alaska, Canada and Manchuria.

The heat budget of the soil therefore depends essentially on the amount of heat received from and emitted to the atmosphere.

(i) The intake of heat is the result of direct solar radiation, which is the most important source; also of indirect solar radiation (e.g. heat given off by clouds which are themselves heated by the sun), which increases the humidity of the air; of conduction (i.e. contact between the air mass and the ground), and of certain exothermic physical phenomena whose overall importance is slight, such as the release of heat from the crystallization of ice or by the condensation of water vapour.

(ii) Heat loss is due to convection, the heating of the air in contact with the ground, or radiation, which takes place only at night, particularly when the sky is clear, for during the day it is more than counterbalanced by the intake of heat from solar radiation, or by various endothermic phenomena such as evaporation of water and melting of ice. With temperatures near freezing-point, a film of ice may form as a result of strong evaporation from a very humid soil in a dry climate, for example during strong winds. Heat loss due to radiation is very important in climates characterized by clear skies and a long winter night (as in Canada and Siberia).

Below the surface of the soil, another factor must be taken into account: the thermal conductivity of the soil, which regulates the diffusion into it of the temperature occurring at the surface. Farmers have realized the importance of this in speaking of 'warm soils' and 'cold soils'. A warm soil is one which heats up quickly (but also cools quickly); it is characterized by a wide temperature range and good conductivity.

Colour plays an important part, especially when the vegetation cover is incomplete, for dark soils absorb heat better. Porosity is equally important: loose, porous, well aerated soils are better conductors; thawing takes place more rapidly in a sand than in a clay. A slab of compact rock is a good insulator. By breaking up the surface of the soil, periglacial processes facilitate frost penetration and therefore their own continued action (an example of autocatalysis). Water-holding capacity is important, since this causes poor conductivity: very wet soils are 'cold soils'. A sandy soil with a thermal capacity of 0·3 when dry, has this increased to 0·7 by saturation with water.

For all these reasons variations in soil temperatures differ from those of the atmosphere. They obey their own laws and cannot be deduced from the shade temperatures of meteorological observations.

(b) **Variations in Soil Temperature (Thermal Regime)** As a rule the range of temperature in the surface layer of the soil is greater than that of the air above, especially in dry sunny weather. It is, however, smaller at greater depth, or in cloudy weather. Nevertheless, in most cases, the number of freeze–thaw cycles in the upper part of the soil is greater than the number of oscillations in air temperature on either side of 0°C (in the Kerguelen Islands, 238 against 120 according to Meinardus). In dry climates with clear skies, this difference is still greater, hence the intensity of periglacial processes in high arid mountains and continental Arctic climates.

Where the soil is protected by vegetation or a snow cover, this difference is reduced and may even be inverted. Underneath snow, the ground is to a large extent protected from oscillations in air temperature around 0°C. Indeed fresh snow reflects 80% of the heat it receives. The vegetation cover is to a high degree thermically inert, slowing down the transference of heat to the soil. Under forest, the ground freezes later and also thaws later than in the open areas nearby. Undecomposed forest litter and, more especially, peaty mould are excellent insulators. In the tundra, peat retards the thaw by hindering the penetration of positive thermic waves during the short summer. In Alaska, it is enough to clear the vegetation in an area of permafrost to cause a thickening of the active layer or mollisol, as well as serious subsidence.

Wetness of soil favours surface frost; during the day the heat does not penetrate, while at night radiation causes a large loss of heat which is not replaced by heat from below. This causes the surface to freeze, but only to a shallow depth. In very severe climates, where summer heating is weak, the soil of the flood plains is abnormally cold. Ice does not prevent

the penetration of negative thermal waves in winter as this is of such duration and intensity that the lower thermal conductivity of the ice hardly affects the issue. In summer, flooding by cold waters from melting snow provides excellent insulation and the thawing of the underlying soil is impeded. Near the limit of permafrost in Alaska, it is better developed under flood plains than on the hill slopes. In the case of lakes, the water in winter forms a sheet of ice several metres thick. This acts as an efficient insulator so that frost penetrates less rapidly into the underlying ground than under the flood plains which dry out in autumn. The permafrost is locally at greater depth, and may even be absent.

The soil therefore has a thermal regime of its own controlling the way frost operates in it.

(2) The Operation of Frost in the Ground

Changes in the temperature of the soil to a given depth, and the cycle of freezing and thawing, are controlled by the penetration of thermal waves from the surface. It is these changes which decide the type of ground ice, the morphogenetic importance of which is fundamental.

(a) **The Penetration of the Soil by Thermal Waves** When thermal waves enter the ground, they are both weakened and slowed down. In Paris, where the daily and annual ranges of temperatures are approximately equal, the daily frost penetrates to about one metre, the annual to 20 metres. The rate of penetration decreases with depth, reaching 0·5 m in 12 hours, 1 m in 24 hours and 15 m in a year. The cycle of temperature changes at depth follows its own course, out of step with atmospheric changes.

The influence of snow cover works in the same direction, it decreases the rate of change by 1·1–2·5 times and reduces up to 2·5 times the depth to which it is felt.

The penetration of frost waves differs from that of thaw waves, for the melting of ice requires a large amount of heat. Therefore a much stronger thermal wave is needed to thaw a given depth of ground than is necessary to freeze it.

When the freezing of the ground is seasonal, it takes place entirely from the surface downwards. In areas of permafrost, however, the winter freeze-up is effected simultaneously from above and below, so that the last layer to freeze is in the middle, a few decimetres below the surface, a fact which has great significance in the resulting forms. Thaw in permafrost regions on the other hand, takes place downwards from the surface

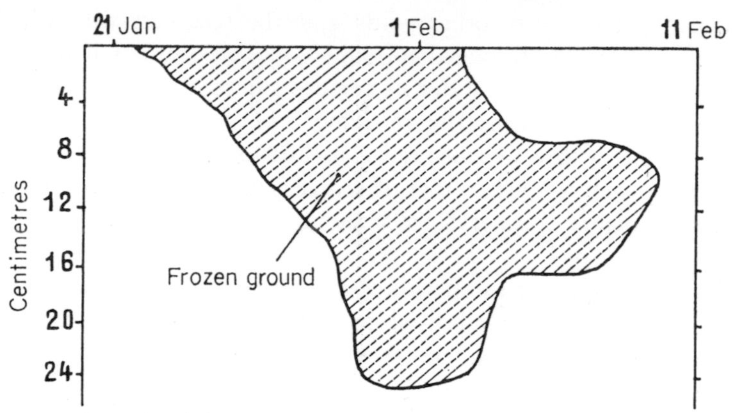

FIG. 8 Advance of frost and thaw into the ground

Period from 21st January to 11th February 1947, observations made at Saint-Maur.

There are two clear periods, up to 1st February when the frost penetrates into the ground so that the frozen layer thickens steadily; after 1st February the thaw begins, taking place in two directions, upwards from the base of the frozen ground and downwards from the surface of the soil.

Once the thaw is far enough advanced, there is a frozen layer at depth, between two thawed layers.

only, while in areas of seasonal frost, thaw occurs from below due to heat liberated from unfrozen layers at depth. In the case of permafrost a surface layer is thawed and steadily increases in thickness; with seasonal frost, a bed remains still frozen at depth for some time, between thawed materials.

(b) **Ground Ice** This is responsible for the form of the various microstructures which reflect the arrangement of ice crystals. It is especially well documented for unconsolidated rocks: clay, silt, sand and gravels. According to Kokkonen, Beskow and Taber, the following may be distinguished.

(i) *Ground frozen massive* This is the simplest type; ice crystals are distributed evenly throughout the bed. They form in the pore spaces binding the mineral constituents together. There are two subdivisions. In the first, the soil is frozen massive and all the pores are filled with ice, so that it is hard and impermeable. In the second, the frozen soil remains porous as the voids are incompletely filled with ice, it is less cohesive and air may pass through it.

The nature of the soil plays an important part here, directly through the density of pores, or other voids and the readiness with which its constituents may be dislodged to allow complete saturation by ice; indirectly by the volume of water its texture allows it to absorb and by its capillarity which controls the movement of water through it during freezing. Soils with well-cemented constituents assume a massive structure when frozen, similar to that of coarse sand; the particles are welded together by scattered ice crystals, without ice segregations.

(ii) *Surface ice segregations* In this case the ice forms a crust on the surface of the mineral soil. Two subdivisions may be distinguished: glazed frost and needle ice. Glazed frost, common in temperate climates, is formed by rain falling on frozen ground. Little is known of its geomorphological effects but they probably are by no means negligible. The surface of the ice is extremely slippery and may aid the transport of particles as long as they do not get frozen to the surface of the ice itself.

Pipkrakes (needle ice) consist of fibrous ice formed by exudation. Water concentrates on the surface of the soil and freezes, forming ice needles standing side by side. They sometimes form beneath the surface skin of the soil if it is friable, or beneath leaves or stones which they heave up. They can assume several forms:

massive: entirely of minute columns of ice, standing side by side, with no air spaces between them;
porous: the minute columns form groups separated by air spaces;
discontinuous: the pipkrakes form groups in favoured spots.

As with all crystals formed by exudation, they develop perpendicular to the cooling surface, generally that of the soil. They may also form on the under side of stones though this is not necessarily parallel to the ground surface.

Climate is very important in their formation. Pipkrakes require a sudden severe frost on moist ground. Often they form in a single night and may continue to grow during several successive nights, but their development never spans a lengthy period. They belong to climates with a large daily range of temperature.

The development of needle ice also depends on the nature of the soil. It is favoured by a soil with a high water content and by the proximity of a water-bearing bed. For the crystals to grow rapidly to a large size, an abundant supply of water is necessary. Granitic sands, and clay soils containing pebbles (weathered alluvium for example), which permit easy movement of water, are the most favourable in our type of climate.

(iii) *Ground ice segregations* Here the ice forms discrete masses such as

1a Alpine surface

Frost shattering of impure Triassic Limestone, on the edge of the Brandnerferner, Vorarlberg, Austria, at 2800 m. Rock reduced to flat platey fragments.

b Alps: stony solifluction, Chambeyron, at 2840 m.

Solifluction by needle ice (contemporary Periglacial); plates or rods of schist debris moving over the turf, which is still present below the stones. Lobate arrangement.

2a Merry-sur-Yonne Le Saussois
Differential frost sculpture in reef limestone, partly dolomitized, Yonne, France.

b Stone stripes in th Ticlio Pass in Peru, at almost 4800 m.

c Periglacial terracettes on the side of the Alvierbach Gorge at Brand, Vorarlberg, Austr.
Steep slope (40°) in moraines at 1500 m. This is only a type of creep, not specifically Periglacial.

lenses or beds, within the body of the soil. In the middle of homogeneously frozen ground, usually frozen massive, bodies of pure ice are found. Their dimensions vary widely, ranging from several centimetres or even millimetres, to 3–4 metres in thickness. They usually have a sheet form, generally lenticular, sometimes contorted where the pressure of the ice has deformed the beds. They may also form wedges, with a tapering cross-section penetrating vertically into the ground. This development is guided by discontinuities within the strata.

It is, therefore, possible to distinguish three types of large scale ice segregations of different origin.

(i) Horizontal, lenticular segregations formed at the frost limit. As frost penetrates the ground, it attracts water by the process of crystallization, and capillary movement of water enables the segregation to grow. For this movement the material must be of a certain grain size. In certain conditions, the ice may form at a depth of a few millimetres or centimetres, causing some desiccation of the surface layer of the soil. Where the frost lasts long enough, sublimation may almost completely remove the ice crystals and the surface soil becomes loose and liable to aeolian ablation. It is this which leads to dust storms on intensely frozen ground.

(ii) Lenses of clear ice, reaching several decimetres in thickness and several metres in width. These do not form as a rule by simple segregation. In Siberia, it has been shown that they have been formed from water lying in small lakes and, cut-off channels on flood plains in late autumn, frozen by the winter frost and buried by alluvial deposits during the floods of the general thaw. The alluvium prevents them melting in the following summer and they are incorporated in the permafrost.

(iii) Ice wedges, which according to Russian research workers, especially Popov, result from the introduction of allogenous water by rivers in flood. They form only in alluvial plains; moreover, they have been recorded only in more or less washed gravels. Water penetrating the frozen ground along contraction fissures solidifies there as a narrow vein which widens in subsequent years, since the discontinuity produced causes the fissures to reopen at the same place. Proof of this mode of formation *per decensum* is the vertical foliation of existing ice wedges, caused by thin films of alluvial silt introduced with the water.

Ice wedges form slowly over many winters. They are joined to produce polygonal patterns, which are related to changes in the volume of the soil caused by freezing. They require a climate with very severe frost and occur mainly in those parts of the subpolar region with cold dry winters (Siberia, Alaska and northern Canada). When ground conditions are favourable, ice segregations are better developed when frost penetrates steadily, allowing time for capillary movement to supply moisture. In our climate, they never appear at the surface but at 10 or 20 centimetres depth, where the thermal wave is somewhat weakened. Below 20 metres, which seems to be the maximum depth reached by winter frost in polar areas, none is formed. In permafrost regions, these segregations grow only to a few millimetres in thickness and do not show vertical variations. The thick lenses consist of fossil ice. The permafrost impedes the movement necessary to concentrate ground water.

Segregated ice in the form of thin lenses requires a soil saturated with water at the beginning of the freeze-up (or supersaturated in the case of plastic clays), and a fine soil (clay or silt). Sands and gravels always freeze massive, either solid or porous according to their water content at the beginning of the freeze. Solid freezing of coarse sands and gravels is exceptional except on alluvial plains where the water table reaches the surface. Frequently, very porous material is dry enough at the time of freezing for the water to form small segregations of ice which are quite lost in the mass, leaving the greater part of the bed loose, favouring wind action. In silts and clays the freezing of the ground is progressive, beginning in the largest interstices, where water is present in larger amounts and it therefore freezes more readily; the film of water, surrounding the soil particles, which moves to this by adsorption, freezes only at a lower temperature. Ice segregation in this case requires a slow penetration of the ground by frost. If penetration is rapid, the ground freezes massive, even in the case of the densest clays. The finer the material, the more rapid the freezing must be, for it to freeze massive. For some clays, the speed required is such that it is rarely achieved in nature. The materials suitable for the formation of this segregation include all clays and marls, silts and the finest sands. Of these, the most suitable are the silts.

(3) The Geographical Distribution of Ground Ice

This distribution, with its seasonal variations, is at once a function of:

(i) Meteorological conditions, summarized in one of Grigoriev's formulas quoted by Sumgin, that the depth reached by frost in the soil is proportional to a coefficient:

$$K = \frac{\text{Sum of the mean monthly negative temperatures}}{\left(\begin{array}{c}\text{Mean monthly}\\ \text{thickness of snow in}\\ \text{centimetres}\end{array}\right) \times \left(\begin{array}{c}\text{Sum of the mean}\\ \text{monthly positive}\\ \text{temperatures}\\ \text{in °C}\end{array}\right) \times \left(\begin{array}{c}\text{Total rainfall for}\\ \text{months of positive}\\ \text{temperatures, in}\\ \text{millimetres}\end{array}\right)}$$

(ii) the time taken by differences in temperature to penetrate the soil.

(a) **Diurnal Frost** If there is air frost, but no ground frost, pipkrakes are formed. These form only with very rapid alternations of freeze and thaw, lasting only hours, usually with night frost. They cause a particular type of cryoturbation, pipkrake cryoturbation (*Kammeissolifluktion*, in German). It takes place in various climates, but is particularly common in intertropical mountains, where there is a large daily range of temperature and a small annual range, so that other types of frost are precluded. In France it is frequent in the southern Alps, with their sunny climate and large diurnal range of temperature. It is also common in fine spring weather in continental-type climates (e.g. Cevennes and Rhône valley).

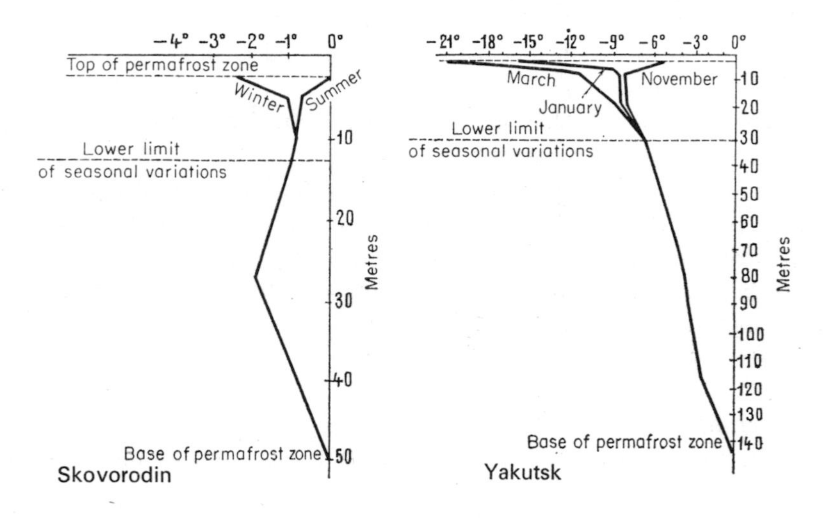

FIG. 9 Temperature profile of the ground in areas of normal and relict permafrost (*after Cressy*)

(a) Skovorodin, Soviet Far East. Seasonal changes are felt down to 13 m. Normally the temperature of the ground should rise, as at Yakutsk, down to the permafrost base. Here, however, it falls as far as 27 m, after which it rises down to 50 m. This anomaly is due to the fossil cold wave which penetrated the ground during a former period when temperatures were lower. This bulge will be found at increasing depth as it dies out. Then its effect will be that the base of the permafrost is at a lower level than it should be under the existing climate.
(b) Yakutsk, Central Siberia. Seasonal changes occur down to 30 m. In March, the temperature falls steadily from the surface down to this level. In November, on the other hand, the cold wave has not penetrated deeply, though the surface may be frozen; the temperature falls with depth before increasing.

This is the normal permafrost pattern, with a continuous rise in temperature from the lower limit of seasonal variations to the base of the permafrost.

Mountains in dry areas, with strong insolation and a large diurnal temperature range, are especially affected. This may occur in winter if there is not continuous frost, or else in spring and autumn (e.g. in central Asia and the western United States). Night frost is important in the arid Andes where Troll recorded it in the Puna de Atacama and in Venezuela at about 4000 metres, in an equatorial climate, in windswept areas where the vegetation is open and frosts particularly sharp.

(b) **Seasonal Frost** This occurs more or less with diurnal frost, according to climate. The latter becomes seasonal when the temperature remains continuously below 0°C for more than 24 hours.

With oceanic climates, winter temperatures are variable but rarely very low and the penetration of frost into the ground is slight. But when it reaches a certain depth, the subsequent thaw may take a fairly long time: 8–15days in Alsace for depths of 0·3–0·4 metres. In these conditions, night frost may play an important part.

In continental climates, however, frost lasts for longer periods, decreasing the number of freeze–thaw cycles but increasing the depth to which frost is effective. Thawing is retarded by this very depth, and alternations of freeze and thaw occur mainly in spring. Finally, in some areas, frost has a daily rhythm, with frost by night and thaw by day. Seasonal variations are too small to cause a seasonal frost.

(c) **Permafrost** When the positive thermal wave penetrates less deeply than the frost, the latter affects layers where the effects of summer heating are not felt. A stratification of the ground is then produced:

(i) at depth, a permanently frozen layer, the permafrost or pergelisol. It is sometimes called *merzlota* (Russian) or *tjäle* (Swedish) which means no more than 'frozen ground', without any indication of permanency.

(ii) at the surface, a layer which thaws in summer but freezes again in winter. For this (the 'active layer' of English authors) the term *mollisol*, proposed by Bryan, has been adopted by Cailleux. This schematic stratification is far from being regularly developed in nature. In the limestone areas of Spitzbergen, for instance, Corbel has observed a mollisol one metre thick with blocks of frozen soil in places at the surface, and in the upper 20 metres of the permafrost thawed fissures allowing water to circulate and carry down sand. Below this, the permafrost was frozen solid, all the voids being full of ice which, in the largest voids, drained slowly downward. At the coastline where the temperature is slightly above 0°C under the pack ice, the permafrost ends abruptly. It is also missing below large rivers which are never frozen solid.

Under present-day conditions, a mean annual temperature of at least −2°C, is believed to be necessary for the continuance of permafrost, and not 0°C as was formerly believed. This is largely because of the thermal protection provided by snow. The incidence of snowfall is also quite important, autumn snows hinder the development of permafrost. Stormy climates where the snow is blown away in winter favour it (e.g. the Barren Grounds of north Canada, and the Siberian coastlands).

In Alaska, Péwé has established by mapping that the limit of the permafrost on the west coast occurs where the total sum of mean daily negative temperatures reaches 3000, and in the interior where this exceeds 4000. The cooler summers on the coast help to explain this difference.

In some cases a local permafrost may develop, associated with karst phenomena such as ice caves and blow holes (e.g. in the Urals).

If former fluctuations in temperature have affected deeper levels than present-day frost, the sequence becomes more complex. Where a climatic amelioration extends over several years, the winter frost may not reach the top of the permafrost, as is frequently the case at the geographical limit of permafrost. There is then:

1. an annual mollisol, which corresponds to the depth reached by last winter's frost;
2. a mollisol several years old, corresponding to the layer thawed during a summer but not frozen again last winter;
3. the permafrost below the depth reached by thaw.

(d) **Relict Permafrost** This results from a long-period change, so that former fluctuations of temperature affected greater depths than frost does today. The minimum ground temperature occurs below the depth reached by annual temperature fluctuations. This is very common, occurring in Alaska, for example. It results from a general amelioration of temperatures over the last few centuries, a tendency which has recently accelerated. It may be compared with the temperature distribution in the Greenland ice-cap, which is colder at 50–1000 metres than at the surface. This lower figure would correspond to the former annual average. Usc of this data makes possible the reconstruction of temperature curves for a period of several centuries.

In areas of relict permafrost there may be several alternations of frozen and unfrozen layers, the latter being the *taliks* of the Russians. The lateral extension of these layers may form a complex pattern as they bifurcate and reunite. Masses of fossil ice may be found at depth, as often occurs in Siberia, formed from frozen rivers or lakes buried beneath alluvial deposits. It may also occur beneath the sea. These bodies of fossil ice are very important from the geomorphic viewpoint: they play an essential part in the production of *thermokarst*. These phenomena are of particular importance at the limit of present-day permafrost. The existence of fossil permafrost means a very complex distribution of ground ice both horizontally and vertically.

The thawing of permafrost is accelerated by the existence of lakes which do not freeze solid in winter. Beneath them the mollisol may extend 20 or 30 m deeper than in the surrounding area. Thawing is also promoted by the removal of the natural vegetation, as this helps in the warming of the ground. The clearing of a field may cause a fall in the upper limit of the permafrost of 2–4·5 m in a few years. *Thermokarst* features are produced. Preservation of permafrost is aided by certain materials, such as silts and certain clays in which thick masses of ice have been observed, and by peat bogs. The latter, as Russian research has shown, are good conductors when frozen but poor when not (hence the use of peat as an insulator). This means, however, that frost penetrates easily beneath peat bogs but thaw is hindered. The mollisol under them is very shallow, being 0·25–0·50 m in Siberia compared with 2–5 m in the nearby forest.

In Siberia, according to Popov (1956), the present-day retreat of the permafrost limit may be caused not so much by a milder climate as by increasing continentality, which, because of warmer summers, leads to a thickening of the mollisol. Palaeoclimatic research has established that during the Quaternary the Siberian climate changed little but merely alternated between a more and a less continental regime. Local effects are superimposed on this general trend. Among the most important, in addition to the clearing of land for cultivation, are forest fires, which may increase the thickness of the mollisol by several metres at a time.

The distribution of relict permafrost is related to that of the ice of the last glaciation. Ice sheets occurred in western Siberia, as it was relatively humid, but in central and eastern Siberia, which was more arid, there was a very severe climate under which permafrost developed. Where this relict permafrost occurs in conditions which would produce permafrost today, it continues unaltered; where present-day conditions do not induce permafrost, it shrinks and disappears. In the Amur region, it is still 400 metres thick.

Ground ice is indeed a complex phenomenon, as yet little understood. It results from climatic features, though its development does not follow them exactly but becomes to some extent independent of them, because of the special laws which control the surface temperature of the soil and because the penetration of frost into the ground follows its own pattern and is slow to respond to atmospheric changes. Ground ice may therefore acquire a certain degree of independence of present-day climate and may be controlled in part by geological factors.

(B) The Action of Frost in the Ground

Repeated freeze and thaw of the soil leads to powerful mechanical processes which give it a special texture (the shape and size of the particles of which it is composed). We shall study in turn surface sorting by frost, the effects of cyclical changes in volume, and solifluction phenomena.

(1) Surface Sorting by Ice

Surface segregations of materials result from a special process: the effects of sorting, dependent on the differential movement of the elements which make up the soil. This may operate in two ways depending on the form of the surface.

(a) **Taber's 'Frost Heaving'** (differential uplift by frost) In fine materials the size of silt (about 0·03 mm), segregations of ice are formed by the drawing up of water from the underlying mollisol, a process depending on a balance between porosity and capillarity. The resulting increase in volume may be very great: 50% in laboratory experiments, 40% by weight of ice in a frozen silt near Nome in Alaska and in a loess-loam in Alsace; 80% in silts in central Alaska. In coarser materials, this upward movement of water and the resulting ice segregations do not occur. In a fine soil, according to Taber, there would be a progressive swelling of the fines, which might reach 20, 40, 60% or more. This increase is greatest near the surface, because, at the onset of frost, there is a higher degree of saturation produced by the uplift of water, by condensation from the atmosphere and by evaporation. As a result, a thrust is developed, due to the swelling of the underlying part of the soil as the process continues. The uplift of the surface carries with it stones held in the soil by the frost but whose base may be in the still unfrozen mollisol. The latter fills the available space so that no void is formed, this space being more readily filled because the frozen surface layer exerts a pressure on the mollisol. The stone is winched upwards. During the thaw, the fine fraction of the soil will begin to sink, but at first the soil under the stone is still frozen so that the stone cannot sink. With every freeze–thaw cycle, the stone rises a little higher. This explanation of Taber's implies that the stone is not a good conductor of heat during the thaw or of cold during the freeze, and that it does not subsequently sink by gravity into the mollisol. These two conditions are not necessarily true. They are most likely to occur when the stones are poorer conductors than the soil and when they are elongated and stand more or less vertically.

Schmid, who worked in the Mainz area, proposes a different explanation of the uplift of stones by frost. Where the stone is a better conductor than the soil, freezing occurs more rapidly on its lower face, causing a segregation of ice there, which lifts it. This, however, does not explain why the stone does not sink back during the thaw, because of the more rapid melting of the ice on which it rests. Differences in the weather at freezing and thawing may be significant; frost in clear weather is accompanied by heat loss due to radiation, and thaw in humid overcast weather by warming due to conduction. In some cases at least, *pipkrakes* also play a part.

(b) **Cryoturbation by Pipkrakes** Depending on the site, this causes either vertical movements leading to sorting, or lateral movements, a form of solifluction.

On flat ground it results in differential uplift. During freezing, a stone, being a better conductor than the fines, cools rapidly to freezing point. Ice crystals of the *pipkrake* type grow vertically downward from its lower face, uplifting the stone. During the thaw, the *pipkrakes* melt and the stone subsides. This hypothesis assumes that stones are better conductors than the soil and that they lie close enough to the surface to be affected by rapid changes of temperature. The movement is more likely in the case of elongated stones in a vertical position, as there is then more chance that frost will occur beneath the stone but not in soil at the same depth.

On sloping ground, freezing causes the uplift of blocks or even crumbs of soil on the surface, along the axis of growth of the ice crystals, that is perpendicularly to the cooling surface formed by the lower face of the stone (which is generally parallel to the surface of the ground). During the thaw the needle ice melts and the stone sinks, under the effect of gravity, obliquely to the surface of the ground. The displacement, in mathematical terms, of a stone lying exactly flat on a uniformly sloping surface, is proportionate to the amount of uplift and the slope of the surface.

This movement is most likely where the stones lie flat on the surface of a moist humous soil. The humus prevents the frost from penetrating the soil, while ice segregation occurs underneath the stones because of their good conductivity. In such conditions, Schmid recorded, on a 26°

slope near Mainz, displacements of 2–32 cm in a single winter. But the displacement of blocks under the effects of uplift by frost today takes place only in special conditions, notably when the blocks have advanced over a humous soil and thus have the advantage of significant ice segregation on their lower face. When the blocks are heaped up without a matrix or when they rest directly on solid rock, no segregation of ice can occur and there is no movement of individual blocks.

In a temperate forest region without oceanic influences, *pipkrakes* may have great geomorphological importance, as quantitative data collected by Schmid shows. Their maximum length reaches 10–15 cm in the mountains of central Germany, and some have lifted debris to a height of 12 cm. The weight of uplifted fragments varied between 650 and 7200 grammes per square metre in the Black Forest and in the Taunus. Under the forest cover, the uplifted material consisted of dead leaves, twigs, pine needles and aggregates of soil bound by humus. The underlying soil, formed from various metaphoric rocks (gneiss, quartzites, sericitic and micaceous schists), always contained more than 5% of fines, and usually 15–20%.

Pipkrakes, or needle ice, are one of the main causes of soil creep in a temperate climate, for they are active even in forest areas. They have even been assigned a role in the origin of polygonal soils. In a heterogeneous soil, frost-heave is never uniform, being greatest where the supply of water or the grain size promotes over-saturation. In such places blocks move faster upward and the ground surface is raised above the surrounding area. After the blocks have reached the surface in summer, they are moved to the edge of the low dome by *pipkrake* cryoturbation and accumulate there. Their weight displaces the mollisol towards the raised centre, and further increases the contrast in grain size between the two parts of the soil. This hypothesis provides a possible explanation of polygonal soils.

(2) The Effects of Cyclical Changes in Volume

These depend on the nature of the bed rocks or of the deposit.

(a) Consolidated Rocks The basic factor is the increase in the volume of water when it is changed to ice. This subjects the rock to pressures which break it. In natural conditions, the average pressures affecting rocks from this cause are of the order of 14 kg per square centimetre, enough to shatter many types of rock. This frost shattering (Fr. *gélivation*) depends upon the distribution of water in the rock and the strength of the rock.

(i) *Water content* If all the pores in the rock are not filled with water, the expansion of the water may be unhindered and little or no pressure exerted. There is then no frost shattering. A rock with discontinuous cavities into which water cannot penetrate, such as pumice, is not very liable to frost shattering. The same implies where joints are too large, open and dry. The process is at a maximum where the rock is traversed by regular fissures, a few tenths of a millimetre to a few millimetres wide. It is probable that the effect of compressed air is of great importance in micro-shattering, for water has difficulty in reaching the bottom of sealed-off voids and usually just manages to close the opening. On freezing, if its expansion in other directions is prevented, the water compresses the air in the pores and close joints, thus subjecting the rock to considerable air pressure. Repeated many times it causes fatigue, a well known phenomenon in rock mechanics. Microscopic cracks, of the order of capillaries, are gradually enlarged until fragments are broken off.

(ii) *Rock strength* This depends on the microscopic texture of the rock, though its relation to the mechanics of frost shattering has never been worked out. The same applies to mechanical tests of pressure, such as the Brinnell ball test.

My own work on frost shattering, based on a combination of laboratory experiments and field observations, has yielded the following conclusions.

Frost is effective only in damp conditions. Dry rock is not shattered by frost. Fragmentation may occur in dry conditions but it is solely on account of tension developed by alternate expansion and contraction due to temperature changes (thermal shattering). An abundant supply of water to fill the pores and fissures of the rock is essential. Fragments of frost-susceptible rock buried in damp loess reacted differently from samples of the same rock subjected to identical temperature changes but half immersed in water. In loess, the fragments detached are smaller, consisting of silt and splinters a few millimetres long, and about five times less abundant. This shows how the same rock, subjected in nature to frost shattering beneath the soil, behaves differently when subjected to it in the open air (e.g. a rock cornice). Frost shattering of rock cliffs produces stones with little silt, mainly forming gravity screes, occasionally stratified screes (Fr. *éboulis ordonnés*) but rarely solifluction flows. Beneath a debris cover, frost shattering operates more slowly, yielding finer debris, which is often liable to solifluction. This debris added to the waste mantle, may give rise to solifluction flows by autocatalysis. These processes determine the evolution of periglacial slopes.

With a uniform lithology, it is differences in the supply of water to the rock that cause differential frost shattering. For example, the foot of slopes, being wetter, suffer more intense shattering. In the case of rocks covered by soil, the soil moisture is of primary importance in the effectiveness of freeze–thaw. A permafrost horizon, by preventing soil drainage, accentuates it. The concentration of moisture in minor valleys (Fr. *vallon*) acts similarly. In this way a *vallon*, once formed, becomes the site of accentuated frost shattering and may extend by what is headward erosion due to frost shattering alone. These are the *vallons de gélivation* of French authors.

Conversely, a pavement of massive rock or even a cornice with widely spaced joints, without a permafrost horizon so that water is not retained, is not likely to suffer frost shattering. In a periglacial environment steep and dry slopes are to some extent immune. This is all relative, however, since these slopes are attacked at the foot where moisture is concentrated.

Climatic conditions also exercise a close control over frost shattering. My own experiments have shown that, generally speaking, a given number of frost cycles with a wide temperature range (conditions similar to those on the west coast of Greenland or western Siberia) would produce more debris than twice as many frost cycles of smaller range, such as occur in south Iceland. This does not mean that the evolution of relief in Greenland is more rapid than that of Iceland, for other factors intervene, especially the number of freeze–thaw cycles, which is very much greater in maritime climates with moderate frosts than in continental climates with very low temperatures. Further measurements are necessary to answer this question raised in the laboratory.

The type of debris produced experimentally by a moderate degree of frost differs markedly from that produced by a severe frost. The former produced a much smaller amount of coarse debris (and this was mainly chips a few centimetres long): 2·1% compared with 21·5% from severe frost on fragments of Muschelkalk from Alsace. On the other hand, the amount of granules and silt produced was about the same. From these results the following conclusions may be drawn. With freeze–thaw cycles of small amplitude, the thermal wave penetrates but superficially and, thus, can only detach small fragments. With severe frost, however, the whole mass of a block is penetrated so that it is split across. Spalling of the surface also occurs as in the first case.

Lithological influences play a very important part, resulting in the two types of shattering which I have distinguished. *Macrogélivation*, which exploits the structure of the rock, operates along joints, cleavage planes and bedding planes. Except in finely stratified rocks, or sandstones and glomerates whose constituent elements are detached, it usually breaks off large pieces, usually joint blocks. *Microgélivation*, on the other hand, cuts across the structure of the rock and shatters its constituents. In a sandstone or a sand it splits the grains. It has so little relation to structure that, for example in a stratified rock, it breaks off splinters oblique to the bedding.

Macrogélivation exploits existing weaknesses in the rock; *microgélivation* cuts into solid rock. The latter varies greatly in intensity, in the proportion of 1 to 1000 for common rocks alone. It affects mainly very porous rocks and rocks of little mechanical strength. The majority of rocks under natural conditions, however, suffer the effects of both *macro-* and *microgélivation*, in varying proportions. In a general way, sedimentary rocks are more subject to *microgélivation*, the less they are compacted. Metamorphic rocks are little affected when they are fresh; they become susceptible when they have undergonc an initial weathering whose effects may be invisible to the naked eye. Weathered crystals are at once less resistant to pressure and more permeable; it is these that *microgélivation* exploits. This fact is of great geomorphological significance. It explains the rapid degradation, under periglacial condition, of the surface of ancient massifs which have undergone Tertiary weathering.

The variety of factors promoting frost shattering (supply of water, climate and lithology) explains the very large range in the size of debris it produces. The debris size controls periglacial slope evolution.

Unweathered igneous rocks produce blocks, especially joint blocks whose size is controlled by the spacing of the joints, and in volcanic rocks, of contraction cracks (Bout). Columns in volcanic rocks are forced apart and broken. The rate of *macrogélivation* is a function of the relationship between the spacing of lines of structural weakness and the depth reached by frost. In general, it is much faster in severe climates where intense frost goes deep enough to exploit the joints fully and spring the blocks they enclose. In oceanic climates it is *microgélivation* which is dominant. This produces much silt, which promotes solifluction and produces a different type of slope.

Generally speaking, frost shattering is a form of particularly intense fragmentation. Indeed it is the most efficient form on the earth's surface. Where it is active, it causes a rapid retreat of rock faces, and a ready disintegration of the bed rock where it is overlain by a debris cover too thin to protect it from alternations of freeze and thaw. It also gives rise to most of the scree slopes which characterize the foot of rocky cornices in temperate and frigid zones. Because of its importance, the cold phases of the Quaternary, even those of short duration, have left a distinctive mark on the landscapes of a large part of the earth.

(b) **Unconsolidated Deposits** Unconsolidated materials which are more or less homogeneous suffer two effects from frost: first the fragmentation of their constituents producing a steadily decreasing grain size, and secondly their rearrangement. This gives rise to structural soils where fines are present. Four major types of frost disturbance may be distinguished.

(i) *Frost heaving* This results from the increase in volume of water as it changes to ice, especially when segregated ice is formed.

Even in soils which heave very little during freezing, there is a slight increase in volume owing to the disruption of the surface layer by the growth of ice crystals. Measurements by Schmid have shown that the surface level of such soils has risen 1–2 mm after a period of frost. This destruction of surface cohesion favours ablation, hence the destructive character of meltwater and the ease with which the wind works on dry soils broken up by frost.

On the whole, however, frost heaving is a result of the increase in the volume of water exceeding that of the voids in which the ice crystals may develop. The higher the degree of supersaturation, the greater this is, though in our climate supersaturation is rarely reached. In loess near Mainz, Schmid (1955) records a heave of 13 mm due to a frost penetrating 32 cm on an artificial slope of 45°. His experiments and measurements in the field appear to indicate a greater frost heave with higher minimum temperatures but continuous frost, than with lower minima interrupted by slight thaws. Measurements of capillary porosity before freezing and of the volume of water forming the ice segregations, substantiate the theory of supersaturation by suction, towards the lower limit of freezing. In a loess near Strasbourg for example, where frost had penetrated horizontally from the side of a pit, 60% of water was found, against a capillary porosity of about 45%. Ice segregation in such cases is accompanied by a heave corresponding to the excess water plus the difference in volume between the water and the ice.

Very often, especially in cold climates, frost heave produces an uneven surface, giving a hummocky microrelief. This is due to ice segregations related to local differences in water supply during freezing. There are two main factors involved. Tufts of vegetation decrease the depth reached by thaw, so that the soil underneath absorbs a smaller quantity of water and expands less on freezing than the surrounding bare ground, so that the vegetation ends by occupying the hollows. Secondly, water may come up through the permafrost by forcing its way along fissures or unfrozen zones. This is especially true in areas of residual permafrost where lenses of ice several metres across, or even several tens of metres in thickness, and from several metres to more than 100 m in diameter, form by the freezing of water which has such an underground supply. These ice masses and the hills which they raise are called *hydrolaccoliths*.

(ii) *Irregular subsidence of the ground* This results from the melting of underground ice. It is part of the normal evolution of hydrolaccoliths. Subsidences may also be caused by the melting of masses of fossil ice in regions of relict permafrost, giving rise to what is often called *thermokarst*, though the name is not a good one. The present-day long term-amelioration of climate is increasing their number in Siberia and Alaska. Clearing of vegetation, cultivation and above all building construction, by facilitating the penetration of positive thermal waves, is giving rise to a man-made thermokarst which is causing serious problems.

(iii) *Development of ground fissures* The cause in this case is the lowering of the temperature below 0°C, causing contraction. The coefficient of expansion of ice is relatively high, 50×10^{-6}, almost five times more than that of steel, so that cracks appear even with a slight frost. With temperatures of −30° or −40°C, a network of contraction cracks is formed similar to those shown by clays or muds on desiccation.

If a crack remains open after thawing sets in, it is filled with materials which have already thawed out at the surface. These run down its sides in a soliflual state. More often, in sufficiently cold climates, it is water which flows in during the thaw and freezes again on the walls which are in the permafrost. The crack, empty in winter, is filled in summer. The volume of ice grows and so increases the contraction of the following winter. The ice wedge gradually grows thicker. Péwé's work in Alaska has shown that ice wedges are built up by successive films of ice deposited parallel to this axis. They may reach several decimetres in width. They can, of course, form only in the permafrost, for cracks formed in the mollisol in winter disappear during the following summer. Ice wedges extend only a certain distance below the surface. In very severe climates such as that at McMurdo Sound in Antarctica, there is not enough water to fill the cracks. They therefore remain empty or trap blown sand. The gradual thickening of ice wedges develops an outward pressure which usually folds the material on their edges back and upwards. These structures are still recognizable in deposits after the climate has improved enough to melt the ice. They are known as *ice wedge structures* (Fr. *fentes en coin*). The ice wedge structure consists of the shell of the ice wedge with its disturbed bedding, and its filling of debris which has slipped in from above as the ice melted. During the climatic amelioration, the ice of the wedge melts less quickly than the surrounding ground thaws. As it thaws, this ground subsides so that the sites of ice wedges form small ditches in the midst of the marshy tundra, as may be observed today in some parts of Canada.

(iv) *The effects of compression* These occur only in the presence of permafrost and a seasonal thaw to at least one metre. During the autumn frosts the following threefold stratigraphic sequence is formed. At the top is the refrozen layer which is solid and increasing in volume as the water expands during its conversion to ice. Below is the remaining unfrozen mollisol which remains fluid as long as the freezing layer alone has not drawn up too much of the water it contained. At the base is the permafrost, solid and impermeable.

The freezing of the surface layer is accompanied by an increase in volume which exerts pressure on the still unfrozen mollisol. This causes deformations exactly similar to those produced by experimental tectonics. It is responsible for some types of folding and injections.

(3) Solifluction Phenomena

These result from the fluid state of soils containing fine material. They cannot occur with coarse debris, such as block fields which lack fines.

The transformation of water from the solid to the liquid state, and vice versa, modifies the electrical state of the ground, causing considerable changes in the colloidal minerals. This is a complex process which is not fully understood. However, recent research has shown that the migration of water in fine soils during freezing is due to osmotic phenomena and an increase in adsorption under the influence of changes in electrical potential. Since that of ice, $e/2r$, is higher than that of water, $e/81r$, there is an attraction of water to ice during freezing which leads to the formation of ice segregations. During thaw, part of the colloids in the soil are flocculated, losing their cohesion. The water released by the melting of the ice segregations gives a semi-liquid consistency to the surface layer. The mechanical properties are then totally different from those existing before freezing. In soils with a low index of plasticity, the limit may then be easily reached. Thixotrophy may appear when a weak mechanical effect is enough for this threshold of liquidity to be crossed. This particular pasty state of the soil is described as soliflual. Broadly, one may say that under frost conditions, silt and colloidal material play the role of lubricant to the soil.

Two factors influence the attainment of the soliflual state. One is the grain size and the other the nature of the clay minerals. Two phenomena accompany the change: modifications in the colloidal structure by frost and variations in the water content of the soil owing to frost.

(a) **Modifications in Colloidal Structure** According to Steche (1933), coagulation of the colloids is controlled by the presence of free ions. If they are numerous, they coagulate the colloidal particles into larger groups, decreasing the contact strength which is responsible for the cohesion of the colloid. The progressive freezing of the soil concentrates water carrying free ions in a thin layer of soil which is in the act of freezing. Suction due to freezing thus concentrates the free ions in the zones of supersaturation in ice, which are near the surface. Condensation and vaporization, which take place in air (here contained in the voids in the soil), help the process.

Thaw affects the surface first, and the concentrated free ions there coagulate the colloids which lose their cohesion. Kaolinite is little affected. The presence of limestone on the other hand increases the process. Hence the marked susceptibility of fine limestone debris to solifluction, and the very gentle slopes on limestones producing abundant silt under the effects of freeze–thaw (chalk for example).

The concentration of water by suction in the surface zone of the soil indirectly destroys colloidal cohesion and so produces a crumbly soil with a considerable water-holding capacity. This lubricates the soil, making it more liable to flow. Once the colloids are flocculated, the liquidity limit is much more rapidly reached, and the soil reaches a soliflual state.

This process enables the surface soil to flow even where permafrost is absent. Clay soils, having thus partly lost their cohesion, are eroded more rapidly by water when deprived of a vegetation cover. In our climate, this explains the considerable suspended load of streams during a thaw.

(b) **Changes in Water Content** The changes in water content brought about by frost result from its concentration by suction during the formation of ice segregations. The water content of fine material during thaw often exceeds the liquidity limit for the majority of soils. Only coarse sands, gravels, boulder beds and clays indurated by iron oxide are not affected. As the research of Atterberg has shown, a soil which has passed the liquidity limit behaves as a fluid. It is subject not only to the law of gravity but also, according to some authors, to convection.

The convection hypothesis. Though convection is normally associated with a liquid or gas, it has been applied to material in a soliflual state, on two counts.

(i) The difference in temperature between the material at the surface

3 *Juxtaposition of ice streams in a large Alaskan valley glacier, St Elias Range*

4 *Relief of an ice sheet bed: modelling of drumlins in gneiss. Northern Canada*

and at depth. The surface is warmed by solar radiation, while below, in contact with the permafrost, the temperature remains at 0°C. This situation occurs essentially in a thaw; during freezing, it is less efficient because the surface freezes solid. The maximum density of water is at 4°C, so that convection currents are set up between the surface and the base of the mollisol.

(ii) The difference in the density of mud because of its content of granules, gravel, etc., or of air bubbles, may set up convection.

It seems possible that such convection plays a part in the formation of polygonal soils. Indeed, the results of convection may be seen in fossil periglacial soils whose grain size it too uniform and too small to allow differential uplift by frost. Nevertheless, the convection hypothesis is strongly challenged by the majority of recent studies. It seems able to account for certain pockets and involutions in beds of uniformly fine grain size, but not for polygonal soils.

The role of gravity. Gravity causes movements down slopes. These take the form of a slow muddy flow, of the order of several centimetres per day or per week. This speed varies. At the base, there is a transition to the substratum, which is also somewhat muddy and marked by a slight deformation of the bedding. The deeper the thaw, the thicker the beds set in movement. There is never a clean break with the underlying rock, comparable with that occurring between a stream deposit and its bed. In the moving mass, the speeds of the components vary with their internal friction coefficient. The result is a lenticular movement, with pockets of several large boulders enclosed in finer material, or sheets of sand or gravel in the middle of clays or silts. Debris size is very variable and changes very rapidly within a flow, causing variable rates of movement within it, and a complex bedding, with pockets, whorls, etc.

Soliflual movement under the effect of gravity takes place even under a vegetation cover in the temperate zone. But unlike the process in cold climates, it occurs only in materials very rich in fines so that they cross the liquidity limit easily.

There is therefore an intense mechanical action in periglacial soils, due essentially to frost weathering, which shatters the rock, causing it to produce abundant debris, and to the mobile state of the material so that it is sorted under the influence of gravity and possibly convection. This accounts for the frequency in periglacial soils, of geometric and other systematic patterns.

(C) Biochemical Soil Processes

Biochemical processes which play an important part in the soils of other latitudes, are very weakly developed in periglacial soils, in spite of the abundance of surface water, and the fine state of the mineral soil which is often reduced to silt by frost. In other climatic regions these conditions would be extremely favourable to the chemical and biochemical weathering of the rock.

(1) Vegetation Types

The biogeography of cold environments has geomorphological significance, not so much because of its direct influence (owing to the weakness of biochemical action), as of its indirect effects. The vegetation cover hinders mechanical processes and affects the penetration of thermal waves into the ground. Depending on the type of vegetation, this indirect influence varies considerably.

(a) **The Tundra** This is the predominant type. Of low growth, it resembles a barren moor composed of perennial species, for the short duration of the growing season excludes annuals. Even the perennials have often insufficient time to reproduce themselves.

The species consist of mosses and lichens which form a close mat, and plants which spread underground by rhizomes and grow from bulbs, and woody, dwarf species growing in cushions. The kinds of tundra, which are numerous, have been defined mainly by the Russians. First of all there are the discontinuous growths on the glacial limits, found for example in the borders of polygons. This type is characteristic of the Barren Grounds of North America; the plants form small patches amid bare soils. Their distribution is a function of two factors. The first is summer temperature which provides the calories necessary to growth: where the temperature of the warmest month falls below 6°C, there is no continuous plant cover. The second is the strength of the winter winds, which may sweep the snow away and hinder the growth of vegetation. This is true of the whole Arctic area of North America.

Further south, between the Barren Grounds and the forest, there are two other types of tundra. The tundra proper forms a poor heath, a vegetation which is continuous but not dense, whose composition varies with ecological conditions, being xerophilous on the rises, in the hollows forming peat bogs. The wooded tundra makes the transition to the forest;

woody species increase and become taller. In sheltered areas they may form thickets.

(b) **The Taiga** This extends into the periglacial zone, but the features which occur there are peculiar to this zone because they are essentially linked to relict permafrost. Such are the ropy bogs whose distribution extends beyond that of typical periglacial phenomena. The taiga offers particularly suitable conditions for the survival of relict permafrost, on account of its peaty soil consisting of a thick cover of acid humus which decomposes slowly. This forms an excellent insulator, which is often reinforced by a dense ground cover of mosses and lichens. The podzolic nature of the soils favours ice segregation and cryoturbation.

(2) Characteristics of Periglacial Soil Formation

The weakness of biochemical activity in periglacial areas is due to the state of the soil water, what one might call the 'structure' of the soil water.

For a large part of the year it is solid; it is not in a suitable state to combine with minerals in the soil nor to dissolve them. The rest of the year, in most cases, it is at a very low temperature. Conditions are not favourable to some processes, the migration of silica does not occur, nor does the kaolinization of felspars.

The solution of limestone can take place more readily, however, because of its increased solubility in carbon dioxide. Corbel has shown the importance of this in karst development. This is offset by the existence of permafrost and by the long duration of frost. There is, none the less, in cold environments and especially in high latitudes, a particular type of karst. In most cases, however, the total amount of limestone passing into solution is small and large amounts of fine particles of it remain in the soil where they play an important part in promoting solifluction. The evolution of periglacial limestone areas takes place by mechanical rather than chemical processes. The physical state of the water is all-important: though abundant, it is not a free agent, acting on the soil minerals. Its potency is greatly reduced. A large part is adsorbed to silt particles and does not circulate freely, so that it cannot carry away minerals in solution.

The weakness of biochemical processes is also shown by an analysis of the water itself. The content of dissolved minerals is very small, that of organic acids is considerable. This weakness is confirmed by the character of existing periglacial soils. Where they are covered by vegetation, the profile shows a surface layer of very acid humus, but very often there is no zone of leaching, and in most cases no zone of concretion. Where there is no vegetation, there is no chemical difference between the mineral soil at the surface and that at lower levels. Fossil periglacial formations show the same feature where they have been protected from subsequent weathering. Their surface horizon is never decalcified nor are there iron or calcareous concretions at depth. The only widespread feature is a thin bed of limonite or of loose manganese dioxide. The presence of acid organic matter renders soluble, organic compounds of iron and manganese. During freezing these solutions separate out, pure water freezing first and leading to a concentration of the metallic oxides in the residual water and eventually to their precipitation. This accounts for the frequent deposits of iron and manganese in gravels and the brown veins which, in homogenous deposits, especially sands, form rectangular nets apparently following the pattern of fissures.

(3) Some Periglacial Organic Soils

Periglacial soils have a character which suggests a degradation from those of the temperate zone. They do not fall so clearly into categories and they develop much more slowly. They are found only on the limits of the periglacial zone, in the transition belt where there is a considerable vegetation cover, either tundra or mountain grasslands.

In the tundra of northern Russia, soils occur only with unusually good drainage, where a lateral escape of ground water allows a downward movement leading to leaching. Such are the conditions under which podzols are developing, according to Tsyplenkin. But leaching is much reduced and does not affect the colloids, which are flocculated by frost. The podzols remain in the embryonic stage and develop very slowly. They are characteristic of only parts of the Arctic, such as Greenland (Cailleux) and the west of the Soviet Arctic. They are found on the Kola Peninsula where there is no permafrost. Associated sometimes with gleys, they may reach a total thickness of 30–40 cm, of which 7 cm represents the leached horizon. Towards the east, podzols become more rare and are met with only on sands with very good drainage conditions. Their thickness decreases below 0·3 m. They disappear completely to the east of the Taimyr Peninsula.

Tsyplenkin also records embryonic gley soils, characterized by slight iron mottling and without clear profiles. The gleyed horizon begins remarkably close to the surface, at only 3–9 cm according to site. This reflects the very poor drainage of these regions. Again, these soils are best developed in the west.

Everywhere else, the tundra grows on a soil characterized by a sharp junction between the overlapping organic layer and the mineral soil. This organic layer plays a very important geomorphological role as a frost insulator when it has a large water content. It reduces the thickness of the mollisol. As Tsyplenkin points out, the attack on humus is carried out by fungi, not by bacteria, which are not very active because of the low temperatures. A high proportion of fulvic acid is liberated (69% compared with 13·9% of humic acid) and this assures a high degree of mobility of organic matter in solution, though it hinders the attack on the mineral soil. The organic cycle is also strongly influenced by the nature of the vegetation and Perelman has shown that lichens and mosses, which form the greater part, are very different from the higher plants. Their growth is very slow, 1–10 mm a year in the case of lichens, and they contain less albumin and very little mineral salts in response to their environment. Even when they form a dense cover they cause only a very weak biochemical action. They act mainly as a brake on the movement of soil particles (*bound solifluction*).

CHAPTER 2

Microrelief and Soils due to Frost (Cryopedology)

BIOCHEMICAL action is of little importance in the development of the land surface in cold environments. Very often the vegetation takes refuge in areas where mechanical processes are least intense, plants in the tundra often occupying the more stable stony borders of polygons rather than the fine centre. Troll has shown that, in the Andes of northern Argentina, vegetation is non-existent on silt and clay soils because of the intense development of needle ice.

These regions are characterized by the exceptional importance of mechanical morphogenetic processes operating on the surface of the soil, subjecting it to repetitions of freeze and thaw which impress deformations on it and cause frequently repeated movements. This occurs on such a scale in no other morphoclimatic zone. In arid regions, it is true, wind produces on the surface of sands a microrelief of ripples which are constantly in movement, affecting the whole surface. But it involves only the sands, whereas in periglacial conditions, the freeze–thaw cycle affects all rocks. The widespread occurrence of these powerful rhythmic processes forms a whole series of characteristic features on the soil surface of the periglacial zone, making it the richest in distinctive microforms. A knowledge of them is indispensable to the geomorphologist, not only because they form part of the relief but, more important, because of the light they throw on the processes in operation. The evolution of these microforms mirrors on a smaller scale that of the whole relief. It is therefore with them that a study of landforms must begin.

The study of periglacial microforms is usually called 'cryopedology'. This is not entirely satisfactory, for a considerable part of these microforms does not concern soils. One may, ignoring the scientific meaning of the term, talk of polygonal soils, but few would go so far as to include in cryopedology the study of slip lenses or stratified screes (which are zonal varieties of slope deposits), or an Alpine gravity scree, in a classification of mountain soils.

(A) A Tentative Classification

The present state of knowledge puts a genetic classification out of the question; the conditions under which some forms develop are poorly documented and remain in dispute. An attempt at a genetic classification would mean taking sides and would hinder the presentation of matters still in dispute. Furthermore, it is very probable that a combination of several factors operates in many cases. It seems preferable to base a classification on the form of the patterns as these are well described in several areas.

The plan followed will be, first a study of patterned ground (both open and closed patterns), secondly unsorted soils whose constituents show no arrangement (hummocky ground and terraced slopes), then soils of flat areas and slope deposits as a whole.

(I) Soils with Geometrical Patterns

These are often called 'structural soils'. But this term does not indicate whether one is dealing with the arrangement of the different elements within the soil or the overall pattern of the microrelief of the area. To a pedologist, nearly all soils have a 'structure'. Therefore the term 'soils with geometrical patterns' is preferable. The patterns fall into two broad groups: the closed pattern found on flat surfaces, and the open pattern always on appreciable slopes.

(1) Closed Patterns

These consist essentially of the broad group of polygonal soils, which may be subdivided according to the nature of the material, the dimensions and the form of the patterns.

(a) Classification of Closed Patterns

(i) *Simple sorted patterns* These are formed by the arrangement of the material in geometric figures, without which the soil would be very poorly sorted. Stone circles, like stone roses, are composed of coarse debris such as that of block fields formed by freeze–thaw. In the *stone roses* (or *stone packings*), a large block is surrounded by smaller stones which are usually flat and standing on end. They are found entirely on Arctic coasts near sea level. In *stone circles* this pattern is turned inside out, the larger debris forming the periphery. Stone circles occur on the flat areas of block fields, where ground water is relatively abundant. Debris of different dimensions is size-sorted as in typical stone polygons. The latter consist of small areas of fine material, clays or silts, with some sand and occasionally some gravel, surrounded by a border of stones. These stones often increase in size away from the fine centre, they lack a packing of fine material and they often stand vertically. The diameter of the polygons varies from 10 cm to 2 m. The sorting is confined to the surface; underneath is an unsorted mass of coarse and fine debris from which the polygon has been formed. There are two types of stone polygon, *rooted polygons*, whose coarse borders extend down to the unsorted substream, and *floating polygons*, where fine material intervenes between the base of the stone border and the substream.

As in the case of stone roses and stone circles, polygons are always found in flat areas where a good supply of ground water and, even more important, a certain amount of clay is present. They often occur on the floors of dried-up lakes. Transitional forms between circles and polygons are probably related, corresponding to successive stages in an evolutionary sequence, which is a function of the progressive frost shattering of blocks and contraction of the spaces between the patterns.

(ii) *Simple unsorted patterns* These occur only on clay or silt soils with little coarse debris. Differences which occur are mainly in size. *Mud polygons* tend to be relatively small, of the order of a decimetre, rarely reaching a metre. Their form resembles that of stone polygons except that they lack the stone border. The whole surface consists of fine material, with sometimes a few plants marking the margins. *Tundra polygons* are similar but are much larger, forming a giant polygonal net with sides 50–200 m long. Their borders are slightly raised so that they are drier and more favourable to vegetation growth, for they occur on very flat country.

(iii) *Complex patterns* These are subdivided polygons, or polygons within polygons. When, in the middle of a polygon, there is a 'stone bridge' joining two opposite sides and tending to subdivide it, the result is a segmented polygon. This seems to be an evolutionary stage. Segmented polygons have frequently been observed; Ahlmann describes segmentation at two levels: the main polygons with sides of 7 m are segmented into a net with sides reaching 3 m, within which are smaller polygons, sometimes having sides of only 0·2 m.

(b) **The Origin of Closed Patterns** It must be emphasized at the outset that closed pattern soils are not specifically a periglacial feature, desiccation of clays may produce a similar if not identical pattern. This similarity is not just a case of convergence; it should not be forgotten that even in a cold environment, desiccation cracks often occur. Some are produced during freezing owing to the removal of water by suction.

We shall now review the various hypotheses which have been formulated and discuss how far they explain the types of patterned ground described above.

(i) *Theories of origin* The following summary is based on a critical review of proposed theories of origin, made by Washburn in 1956. The oldest theory is that of Högbom (1910), who explained patterned ground by frost heaving. The greater heave of the material with the most fines causes an outward thrusting of the stones, leading to a progressive sorting. This forms stone circles, and the accommodation of the adjoining circles to one another produces stone polygons. The same process operating on clay soils subdivided by desiccation cracks produces mud polygons. Another hypothesis proposed by Frödin, Taber and Poser is that of differential heaving. Inequalities of the vegetation or snow cover leave patches of bare soil where the rate and depth of ground freezing is greater. Ice segregations form here (partly by drawing water from the unfrozen ground), and heaving takes place forming a low dome. This raised surface gives rise to a lateral migration of stones, giving sorted polygons. Washburn proposes the theory of cryostatic pressure, according to which masses of soil, still unfrozen, are subjected to strong pressure by the increase in volume of neighbouring frozen masses, especially during the autumn freezing above the permafrost. This may lead to a deformation of the surface to form frost boils. Steche's hypothesis is that heaving results from the adsorption of water by colloids, occurring during the wetting of clays in a dry climate. This does not appear to play an important role in periglacial areas, for during the thaw, when the colloids might adsorb water, the centres of the polygons usually sink instead of rising as the theory demands. A fifth theory is that of Meinardus (1912), based on differential frost shattering. In moist areas, freeze–thaw is more effective and produces greater quantities of fines; this leads to ice segregation and heaving. It cannot account for the regular pattern of polygons, however, and explanations based on contraction due to desiccation or low temperatures have been current since the time of Baer (1837). Desiccation, reinforced by the effects of low temperatures, causes contraction cracks in which the stones lodge as they creep outwards on the surface of the soil. Desiccation cracks may hold concentrations of ice during winter. This process operates, but it can affect only clay soils which are subject to considerable contraction.

Another theory is that polygons are caused by convection, owing to differences in the density of water at different temperatures (maximum density at 4°C). Gripp, and later Romanovsky, held that these arise from the juxtaposition of cells of convection caused by the descent, during the thaw, of water heated to 4° and therefore at its most dense. But this hypothesis may be based on no more than simple analogy.

Differential frost shattering and the washing out of the fines forms the basis of another hypothesis. Patches of fines thaw more slowly than stony areas, so water produced by thaw flows through the latter washing out any fine material and accentuating the contrast between them. Washburn suggested yet another theory: that of migration due to changes in the consistency of soils during thaw. On the edge of ice segregations during thaw a large amount of water is formed, which may cause the soil quickly to reach the liquidity limit. This plastic soil may no longer be able to support the stones it contains, so they sink. The fact that ice segregations form in the same place year after year may help, though it is doubtful whether this can, on its own, account for the formation of polygonal nets. Finally, Corbel (1954) proposed sorting by vibrations due to seismic shocks. This winnowing action brings up the larger debris and moves it into desiccation cracks. The lack of any general coincidence of distribution between patterned ground and seismic areas is however, against this theory. In fact, no one theory can explain the different types of patterned ground. A combination of several processes is necessary; a combination which varies in the different types.

(ii) *The origin of some types of patterned ground* We shall begin with the less controversial forms.

Tundra polygons. Ice wedges play a vital part in the formation of tundra polygons. The higher parts of the surface, which form a net, mark the position of ice wedges. These have developed from contraction cracks resulting from intense freezing and have subsequently been widened by ice segregation. The ice wedges may not always develop far enough to form a complete network. For this to happen the material must be homogeneous (contraction then produces regularly spaced cracks), fine grained (the greater the amount of ice in the soil the greater the contraction) and very well supplied with water. Ice wedges are a very stable feature; they grow very slowly to a large size.

Ice wedges are sometimes composite, as Popov (1953) has shown: they show several successive wedges, one on top of the other, in the same vertical plane. A wedge widening upwards ends sharply on a contraction. Laterally, the ice wedges pass into ice lenses at the level of the contractions. This pattern occurs in alluvial plains which are still forming, and is due to the burial of a net of tundra polygons by alluvial deposits which at the same time form fossil ice. In this alluvium a new net of polygons forms, and so on. The remains of former tundra polygon nets frequently occur in Pleistocene alluvial gravels in western and central Europe. When seen in section in gravel pits they are described as *ice wedge structures* or *ice wedge casts.*

Mud polygons. Their formation is slightly different. Contraction due to ice formation is not responsible, for the linear contraction so caused is too slight to have produced clear-cut fissures forming a mesh, on average, one metre across. Here, the first stage in the process is the desiccation of clay materials. Under the effects of freezing there is some migration of water, so that parts of the soil become dried, causing shrinkage cracks. These have been produced in the laboratory using saturated loess.

These cracks may fill with water during the thaw and develop as ice wedges. In a climate with diurnal frosts, small stones moved by *pipkrakes* may collect in them, forming borders. Polygons of 10–15 cm diameter are known to have formed in 1965 in less than three weeks during the drying out of a temporary pool near Salar de Coposa, at 4300 m in northern Chile. The centre of the polygons, normally concave when formed by desiccation, may become convex because of frost heaving. Quite often, debris moves into the surrounding cracks during thaw when they are not quite full of ice. This leads to the borders thawing more rapidly than the centres. It explains the formation of small secondary polygons in the fairly fine-textured centres of larger polygons. It also explains why the pattern tends to be rectangular, the typical form of a desiccation crack network.

Stone polygons and stone circles. It is not possible to explain sorted polygons in terms of a single process. They result from the combination of two processes. One produces fissures, in the form of a polygonal net, and operates alone in non-sorted polygons (mud polygons). One of its main causes is shrinkage due to desiccation during freezing, as is borne out by the location of polygons in very wet ground. The second process is the surface migration of the coarsest debris, apparently in most cases due to *pipkrakes*, or needle ice, operating on the raised centres of polygons. This concentrates the stones in the borders, where they fall into open cracks due to contraction, and lodge there. In the borders, movement is least, so that plants are frequently concentrated there.

This theory assumes that the centre of the polygon is slightly higher than the border, so that there may be an outward movement of stones under the influence of *pipkrakes*. It is generally true in winter, owing to the maximum segregation of ice there. In summer, on the other hand, owing to the thaw, polygon centres sink back and become hollow. The initial impulse in polygon formation seems to come from differential heaving in heterogeneous material, a small amount of finer soil would lead to uplift which in turn would lead to the outward creep of stones towards the borders. Once the stones become concentrated there, the process is accentuated. In the initial stages, there are isolated stone circles, but as they encroach on one another a polygonal net is formed.

The role assigned to *pipkrakes* suggests that polygons develop only on a bare soil; Furrer, Bout and others have shown that this is the case. The link between shrinkage cracks and freezing also accounts for the existence, in the Swiss Alps, of transitional forms between the nets of desiccation cracks and regular hexagons described by Furrer (1954). The sinking of polygon centres which accompanies the general thaw, limits the lateral movement of stones on the surface to a short period, as Schenk has shown. If it is to be effective, this movement requires a fair slope, in other words a large amount of frost heave at the centre of the polygon. This in turn needs a good supply of water. Water supply is the basic factor and not the number of freeze–thaw cycles.

Vertical segregation which reduces the number of stones in the centre of the polygon has still to be explained. It is probable that two processes operating in different directions are at work, depending on the initia position of the stones, as well as their colour, conductivity, and the state of the soil during the thaw. Some stones, especially those initially just below the surface, migrate upwards to it through differential frost heaving. Others, especially, at lower levels, sink in the mollisol which is too plastic to support them in the thawed state.

Once formed, an area of polygons takes on a regular and stable pattern, a state of equilibrium which is maintained provided the climate remains constant. If the pattern is partially destroyed, it reforms very slowly, as shown by the field measurements of Michaud (1950) in the Alps, and Kobayashi (1956) in Japan.

(2) **Open Patterns**

These consist basically of striped ground, together with certain 'solifluction terraces' of a linear pattern. The latter are a transitional form to unsorted (amorphous) solifluction.

Sorting, in these cases, produces a pattern of parallel alignments, which are always found on slopes, unlike the closed patterns. It is generally believed that stone stripes are the result of sorting influenced by gravity and a classification may be based on this.

Two types may be distinguished. The first results in patterns parallel to the slope direction, as in typical stone stripes; in the second the patterns are perpendicular to the slope, as in stone-banked terraces or stone garlands.

(a) **Striped Ground (Parallel to the Slope)** The transition from striped to polygonal soils has been described in many places, both in high mountains and in the Arctic. With a slope exceeding 2·5°, polygons are no longer regular, but become elongated in the direction of the slope, for the effects of gravity added to those of lateral pressure caused by freezing lead to a more rapid movement downslope, causing the elongation of the polygon. The polygons become steadily longer and narrower and eventually open-ended. Between 2·5° and 7·5°, polygons are transformed into stripes.

The limiting slope values for polygons and stripes are not clearly established. They appear to vary with the nature of the material and the climate. Richmond, working in Wyoming, gives different values from those of Cailleux, a limit of 4° for polygons and 4–15° for stripes. The maximum slope for stripes varies, from author to author, between 15 and 30°.

The structure of striped ground is very similar to that of polygons. In plan, the bands of material are sorted by size, the size depending on the composition of the original material. In tropical areas, the bands are narrow: only 10–20 cm wide. In temperate areas, they are wider: 0·6–1·2 m (in Wyoming) for the widest of the fine bands, according to Richmond; but 10–20 cm at Chambeyron according to Cailleux. Little precise work has been done on their cross-profile. Richmond has shown that stripes of fine material, as deep as they are wide, pass gradually into the underlying unsorted material, and that stripes of coarse material (which stands vertically and is open work) rise 15–30 cm higher than the fine stripes. The coarse stripes extend a little less deep than the fine and end sharply against the unsorted underlying material. Another type of striped soil is formed of earth stripes whose structure is similar to the above, except that the material is all fine. Nevertheless, these stripes do show sorting: stripes of coarse sand, for example, may alternate with stripes of silt.

The sorting of the materials in striped ground depends upon two processes: cryoturbation and washing.

Cryoturbation combines both horizontal and vertical movement, adding movement of debris downslope by gravity to a lateral movement caused by the same processes which produce the sorting of polygonal soils. The fine material seems to move mainly by frost-heaving and by gravity in summer when it is in a soliflual state. The coarse material must move mainly under the influence of *pipkrakes*. Nothing is known of the relative speeds of movement of the coarse and fine materials.

Washing. The coarse bands being open work, act as natural drains. Water flowing through them during thaw washes any fine material out of them, making the sorting more pronounced. The fines are carried down to the top of the unsorted zone.

The relative importance of these two processes is unknown. It must depend above all on the amount of water available during thaw. Both processes act together in bringing about a downslope movement of debris.

There are also some less common types of striped ground. One, ascribed to wind, has been observed by Troll in tropical mountains, the Bolivian Andes and the Drakensberg. They occur only in fine material. The particles become aligned parallel to the dominant wind and are uplifted at night by pipkrakes. The earthy stripes correspond to lanes where the wind prevents vegetation growth.

(b) **Cryoturbation Steps** Cryoturbation steps (Fr. *microreplats de cryoturbation*) break the slope into a series of small steps, generally of unsorted or poorly sorted material. They form a distinct category from the much larger benches known as *goletz* or *altiplanation terraces*, which will be examined later.

The type showing sorting passes gradually into unsorted forms. Little attention has been paid to them and no clear theory of origin has been proposed. In particular, it is not known why they form in some places instead of stripes. Possibly they require steeper slopes, of the order of 20–30°, judging from photographs. Cailleux suggests that terraces form instead of stripes where there is a better vegetation cover.

These sorted steps form alternate bands of finer and coarser debris, running perpendicular to the slope, following the contours approximately, occasionally uniting and separating, hence the name garland soils. The coarser debris bands form steep rises of open work blocks, often sloping at their angle of rest, around 30–40°. The finer bands form the treads behind the stone risers, with a stony surface, even though fines may be abundant. Garland soils occur in typical periglacial areas with a vegetation well adapted to cold conditions. They have the appearance of elongated crescentic steps, several decimetres long and some metres wide. The vegetation is confined to the risers, while the treads are bare. On the latter, there may be some sorting leading to a concentration of stones on the surface as a pavement. Sometimes, if the tread is wide enough, it may be covered by polygons passing briefly into stripes at the foot of the riser behind.

The formation of true garland soils, such as are seen in the mountains of temperate areas, has been analysed by Netopil in Slovakia. During winter, snow blown by the wind collects in bands across the slopes. In between, the frost penetrates more deeply and destroys the vegetation. During the thaw, the bare soil bands, which have not been protected by snow, are subjected to intense needle ice formation. The fines move downslope but are stopped by the vegetation on the limit of the bare ground. A small step is thus formed, which extends upslope at the expense of the vegetation. The latter is under attack from below by being undermined, from above by burial. Frost heaving concentrates the stones as a pavement on the tread, summer run-off helping a little in the process by washing down the fines. These processes end by destroying the bands of vegetation, and concentrating the stones on the surface so that they form a mantle over the whole slope, steadily eliminating the terraces. The formation of terraces marks the beginning of the destruction of mountain pastures.

(II) Unsorted Patterns

These form a distinctive microrelief, in which the materials are not aranged by grain size. Raised and depressed elements are broadly characterized by the same granulometry. There are, of course, intermediate forms between sorted and unsorted patterns. These features have been much less studied and documented than polygonal ground.

(1) Earth Mounds

Though polygonal ground is generally bare, mound patterns occur in largely vegetation-covered areas and extend into the taiga. This group has several subdivisions and includes features from a few decimetres to several tens of metres high.

(a) **Earth Hummocks (Thufur)** These rise 0·2–0·5 m above a flat grassy or boggy surface, and have a diametre of 0·5–1 m. They are covered with tundra vegetation, often with distinctive species. Sometimes widely spaced, sometimes closely set, they are always formed of fine materials: clay, silt or sand.

Recent work has shown that earth hummocks correspond in vertical section to festoons or involutions. Polish authors have studied closely the type of involutions which probably represent former earth hummocks in section. They distinguish two main types: the first consists of free involutions (Fr. *involutions libres*), showing no indications of pressure, forming festoons which may be continuous or interrupted by stretching, with some folding due to sliding on the flanks of the hummocks; the second consists of pressure involutions (Fr. *involutions forcées*), which are usually the result of pressure and the beds are very often broken.

These hummocks are undoubtedly due to frost heaving operating from within the hummocks. Once the swelling is great enough, the hummock thaws more rapidly than the surrounding ground, and the pressure of the over-saturated soil within ruptures the vegetation mat and the contents flow out. The two situations which give rise to pressure and free involutions are as follows: pressure involutions form always in regions of permafrost, under the effects of pressure set up in the mollisol by the downward freezing from the surface in autumn. This unfrozen mollisol is subjected to very strong pressure when water is abundant. In very wet areas this pressure may be great enough for the remaining unfrozen mollisol to break through the frozen surface layer, where it soon freezes, to form a mound. Free involutions generally represent 'hummock fields', considerable areas of regularly developed earth hummocks. They do not necessarily require permafrost. Their origin is still somewhat obscure, but they are probably the result of differential frost heaving. Once a mound starts to form, frost will penetrate it more rapidly than the surrounding ground, but why it starts to form is unexplained.

(b) **Hydrolaccoliths and Pingos** These have similar outlines to earth hummocks, but are much larger, sometimes forming true hills which rise sharply from level plains. The name *pingo*, used by the Eskimo of the lower Mackenzie basin, has been used by several authors and adopted by the I.G.U. Periglacial Commission. It has the advantage of being purely descriptive whereas the other name used, hydrolaccolith, is genetic.

On average, pingos reach 12–25 m in height and 30–60 m in width. Their sides are always steep (20–30°). They may form an unbroken dome, or the dome may be breached by an open crater, 5–6 m deep and several metres in diameter. Pingos are always vegetation-covered and their surface soil or peat is the same as that of the surrounding tundra. Below the surface are fine-grained sediments.

Their structure varies. Some have an enormous lens of pure ice as their core, especially the small or middle-sized examples. In these the summit is rarely breached. Some are very old, dating from the ice recession in areas occupied by Pleistocene ice sheets. They do not seem to be developing today. Others, small in size, form in a single spring, split open and disappear; these are the true 'hydrolaccoliths', developing in places where water reaches the surface under pressure. The water freezes forming a lens of ice which raises the surface soil until frost cuts off the supply of water. They form always on permeable beds or fissures, and in hill foot locations.

The other class of pingo consists of a succession of fine sediments and beds of ice. Their structure is similar to that of silts swollen by ice segregations, their growth slower than the first type but they may reach a very great size, forming true hills. They originate in lake beds, where there are fine, unconsolidated sediments, liable to frost-heaving. The latter takes place by infiltration of water when the lake is completely thawed. By degrees, a mound forms under the lake, and grows until the lake has been sucked dry. The pingo has then reached its maximum size and is surrounded by a dry lake-bed.

The disappearance of the two types of tundra mounds, hydrolaccoliths and pingos, takes place in the same way. As a result of their growth, the summit splits, owing to the stretching of the surface layer. The thaw can then penetrate more deeply, and if the water supply is decreased, their destruction is sure; the thaw melts the ice and a crater is formed by collapse owing to the decrease in volume. The crater steadily grows until it forms a lagoon surrounded by the remains of the pingo in the form of a circular rampart.

Several workers, chiefly in the Canadian Arctic and Alaska, have tried to date pingos and think that their formation is related to minor climatic fluctuations. A deterioration of climate would be favourable to the formation of the ice lens, an amelioration to its disappearance.

In Europe, during the last few years, an increasing number of pools and boggy depressions have been interpreted as the remains of pingos (Cailleux, Pissart, Maarleveld). The climatic deteriorations represented by the Younger Dryas and the Warthe Stadial seem to have been favourable to their development in some regions. Some pingo sites have been recorded on gentle slopes as well as on alluvial plains with numerous lakes, like the pingos of the Arctic.

(c) **Ropy Bogs** In the middle of the Taiga, some bogs show relatively dry ridges or corrugations, several metres wide and up to a metre high. These are arranged in three ways. Circular ridges, in the form of anastomosing rings, occur in the bogs of flat areas. The centres of these bogs are raised by the accumulation of peat, so that the rings are concentric. There are also long ridges, nearly parallel, though branching, which are typical of sloping bogs. These ridges are perpendicular to the slope. Finally, there are ridges forming networks, resembling those formed by tundra polygons, but the hollows between the bog ridges are smaller.

Ropy bogs, or *string bogs*, are formed by differential freezing. In the early stages, the ridges correspond to places where frost heave is greatest: during the storms of winter, the snow is blown off the ridges and the frost penetrates more deeply, leading to still more heaving. Once the uplift is clearly marked, it increases automatically. The hollows alongside freeze first and the pressure of the ice helps to raise the ridges. Snow lies on them less and less; frost penetrates more and more easily. The upward growth of the ridges is limited only by the susceptibility of the peat to solifluction on thawing.

(2) Stepped Slopes

Stepped slopes (Fr. *sols de pente à microreplats*) include 'sheep tracks', terracettes, cryoturbation lobes, etc., a class of slope forms related to garland soils. Like the latter, they break the slope into small steps, but they do not show any regular sorting of the materials. They have been little studied in spite of their wide distribution in periglacial regions.

(a) **Terracettes** Though long in use, this term is not satisfactory; it should be replaced by 'stepped ground' (Fr. *sol à gradins*). They consist of small benches 30–80 cm wide, separated by steep rises 20 cm to 1 metre high, breaking the slope into steps. They occur entirely on steep grassy slopes, of at least 20°, and are related to earth hummocks, into which they pass as the slope flattens.

Their genesis has been little studied and is not understood. Few, apart from the Scandinavians, have been interested in them, and they have given confusing accounts, as they failed for a long time to distinguish between artificial forms made by animals and natural forms. It is probable that the steps originate from the slipping of sections of turf under the effects of thaw, which penetrates the bare soil outcropping behind each tread more rapidly. Terracettes form grass covered treads, separated by bare risers. They may be formed by superficial slips, set in motion by the rapid removal of material at the foot of a steep slope without the necessity for periglacial conditions, according to Meynier.

(b) **Turf Garlands, Sols à Bourrelets de Cryoturbation** These may be related to cryoturbation benches (Fr. *replats de cryoturbation*), but their form is less distinct (there is no steep slope on the downslope limit) and they are smaller. They do not form continuous benches along the contours, but rather crescents or festoons which are more or less interlacing. Usually there is no sorting of the material: boulders, stones and fines are mixed together. The vegetation is more or less folded by the downslope movement of the garland. If the movement is rapid, it may, by stretching the turf, cause fissuring. Sometimes the turf is broken, allowing material to escape in a small flow.

Their development, to which little attention has been given, seems due to a movement in the layer between the frozen subsoil and the zone of plant roots, a movement produced by the soliflual state of the colloidal material during thaw. Rapid movement may cause fissuring, perhaps involving the turf. Washing of the garland results and it is probably by this means that the transition to 'cryoturbation benches' is made. These are characterized by a sorting of material. If there is no fissuring, the thickness of the turf checks the descent. On the upper part of the garland, when the stretched turf breaks, the bare soil undergoes considerable frost heaving. The excess water drawn up by the growth of segregated ice, forms a liquid mud on thawing, which renders vegetation growth impossible. The front maintains its vegetation while the tread is bare. The different forms seem to correspond to different types of climate; they occur even in temperate regions.

(3) Unsorted Flat Ground

These are more widespread than polygonal ground, for they are not so exacting in their water requirements. In spite of this, little work has been done on them.

(a) **Mud Fields** Found only on clay formations and restricted to level ground; on slopes they are replaced by steps, though their limiting slope value is not known. The soil is formed of pellets of clay, giving a very porous surface and looking like a rough-cast concrete.

They are formed by the destruction of the colloidal cohesion of the clay by repeated freezing and the uplift of the surface granules by needle ice. The instability of the soil, because of this continual movement, gradually destroys the vegetation cover once needle ice begins to operate in soil exposed by a break in the turf. Islets of vegetation like miniature mesas are formed and then steadily destroyed. Mud fields are very liable to erosion by sheet wash resulting from heavy rain.

(b) **Block Fields** These consist of debris produced by the frost shattering of rock, and occur only on rocks yielding a negligible amount of fines. If fines are present, patterned ground or block flows result. Block fields may be found on flat surfaces or slopes.

They consist of angular rock fragments, from several metres to a few centimetres long, with no arrangement, but many large voids which prevent sorting and the formation of patterns. Any fines which form are washed down, but as soon as they accumulate, sorting occurs and patterned ground is formed.

(c) **Stone Pavements** The arrangement is not the same as in block fields. Surface fragments instead of standing on end, lie flat. This difference is related to debris size: instead of being fairly homogeneous and coarse, it varies from blocks to fines. The latter, which are fairly abundant, fill the interstices.

They are common in high mountains of temperate areas and attributed to 'nivation': a useful word which explains nothing. On this view the stones lie flat because of the weight of the snow, though no one has described the mechanism. The influence of snow may be indirect. Stone pavements are in all probability due to *pipkrakes* which concentrate the stones on the surface. They come to lie flat when the needle ice raises them above a wet soil. The influence of snow is limited to furnishing a supply of moisture as it melts, for the development of needle ice by night frost.

(III) Slope Deposits

In this category are included slope deposits of fairly coarse but unsorted material.

(a) **Stratified Screes** Stratified screes (Fr. *éboulis ordonnés*), which have been defined by Cailleux, always occur on slopes where they form the equivalent of stone or block fields. They are especially common in limestone areas, but have recently been described on other rocks.

They differ from ordinary screes in that they lie at lower angles, so that they cannot have been formed by gravity alone. Again, in ordinary screes the largest debris is found at the base; in stratified screes, the material decreases in calibre towards the foot, especially on rocks which are very susceptible to frost shattering. In section, they show a succession of finer and coarser scree. Their granulometry is distinctive; there is a little fine matrix in the coarser beds, but a considerable amount in the finer beds. They are distinguished from stone stripes by a smaller range in debris size and by its arrangement. In stratified screes, the succession of fine and coarse beds is seen only in a vertical section, there does not appear to be any such succession in plan.

Recently, stratified screes have been the subject of several discussions which agree that they are formed by a combination of processes. These probably vary in importance from place to place. Slope wash, which may remove the fines from certain beds, plays a significant part only in marginal areas such as the Mediterranean coastlands of France. In the stratified screes of more severe climates such as in Lorraine, its role is negligible. Gravity, it is agreed, cannot account for them on its own because their slope angle is too small. The debris slides over the smooth surface of snow patches which melt less quickly than the ice in the joints of the rock outcrops above them. The thawing of this ice breaks off rock fragments which glide across the snow and come to rest lower down, at a smaller angle than gravity screes, forming one bed of the stratified scree. The snow patch melts later. From one thaw to another the size of the frost-shattered debris varies, giving variations in the calibre of the beds. In general, it seems that stratified screes form at the foot of slopes which are retreating very rapidly, so that they are consistently associated with rocks which break down rapidly under freeze–thaw. The lower part of the rock face is increasingly buried by them, and the rapid disintegration of the rock checks the production of fines, though fines do occur in the lower part of the slope. The paucity of fine debris and the rapidity of accumulation prevents the formation of soil stripes.

Stratified screes generally form great thicknesses (several tens of metres) along the foot of steep faces of rocks particularly susceptible to frost weathering. They result from a rapid process which plays an important part in slope evolution.

(b) **Block Flows** These apparently chaotic accumulations occur in minor valleys, which they largely fill, or as sheets on slopes. They occur on slopes of widely varying angles. The material is very coarse, often with very large blocks, up to ten cubic metres, and with very little fine material. The blocks are characteristically on edge when they are contiguous and dip against the slope. In many Pleistocene examples, post-glacial erosion has washed out the fine material and left only the blocks.

Block flows (Fr. *coulées de blocaille*) result from the solifluction of heterogeneous material. The large blocks, because of their weight, should move down rapidly as, owing to the fine matrix, there is no friction with the underlying bedrock. In the case of flow down the talweg (block streams), lateral pressure on the blocks tends to line them up with the valley axis and stand them on edge. Probably movement takes place in two sets of conditions. In most cases, they consist of solifluction flows poor in silty matrix but rich in large blocks because of a predominance of macrogélivation. The silty matrix was later washed out by water percolating into the open material and flowing into the blocky flow. In other cases, it seems likely that there never was a silty matrix in any quantity. The blocks are pressed together and oriented parallel to flow, indicating that their position has not been altered by subsidence.

This study shows the great predominence of mechanical over chemical processes. The basic feature is the mobility of the particles, partly a result of frost shattering which destroys the cohesion of the bed rock, partly a result of the destruction of colloidal structure, which induces a soliflual state. Chemical action can be important only in certain limiting cases, for example under snow banks which produce abundant meltwater rich in CO_2. This is a nivation feature and belongs properly to glacial and nival geomorphology.

(B) The Distribution of Soils and Microforms

This discussion has a twofold purpose, to determine the precise conditions for the formation of the different types of ground today, and to define the geomorphological associations in which they occur, forming a type of morphoclimatic area. Unfortunately, such a synthesis presents great difficulties, for the genesis of some features is not understood and too little precise work has been done. Nevertheless an attempt will be made to ascertain the factors in the distribution of the different types of ground in periglacial areas and then sketch their climatic groupings.

(I) Factors in the Distribution of Ground Patterns

As in geobotany, one may distinguish between two main types of factor: the azonal factors which are independent of climate, and the climatic factors which combine to produce a certain association of types of ground.

(1) Azonal Factors

These are factors which modify the action of climatic agents locally and decide the kind of *micromilieu* which influences the formation of ground patterns. In a study of the climatic distribution of the latter, they are responsible for the exceptions, hence the need to study them first in order to eliminate them.

(a) **Rock Type** This influences the speed of the processes that we have seen at work in our study of ground patterns. Cryopedogenesis is, first of all, a function of the ease with which consolidated rocks are broken down by freeze–thaw. This depends not only on the speed at which they shatter but also on the overall granulometry of the debris produced, in that this controls their porosity. On porosity depends the structure of ground ice. Porous frozen ground is permeable so long as the interstices are sufficiently large and the temperature of the water is above 0°C; the saturation of its surface layer with water during thaw is unlikely. Porosity also decides the water-holding capacity of unconsolidated beds. Water-holding capacity is small in the surface layer during thaw with a porous frozen subsoil, or in a very porous surface bed, but very large in the surface layer of a fine sediment like silt.

For unconsolidated rocks, it is the original texture of the rock which determines the grain size of the loose debris produced; in consolidated rocks it is determined by frost shattering. In a homogeneous rock, frost shattering tends to produce well graded debris, grouped around 1 or 2, or at most 3 maxima; in chalk, granules of a few millimetres and silt; in schists, small plates of a few centimetres. This is of fundamental importance in the sorting and formation of sorted polygons. The granulometry of superficial debris is the result of lithological factors in given climatic conditions. It controls the nature of ground ice and the water content of the surface layer during thaw. Thus, it is necessary to classify rocks according to the size of the debris they yield under frost shattering, to determine their influence on the formation of periglacial ground patterns.

(i) Rocks producing homogeneous precolloidal and colloidal soils. such are marls, clays, schists, silts and lake muds. To some extent, peat has similar properties.

During thaw they become completely impermeable and contain a considerable amount of segregated ice. Their colloidal cohesion is broken down by the migration of the ions. They take on a soliflual consistency, and become full of water as the ice segregations thaw.

These rocks are associated with mud polygons and tundra polygons; thufur, hydrolaccoliths, pingos, palsen and ropy bogs; stepped slopes, turf garlands; and mud fields.

(ii) Rocks producing homogeneous material of the size of coarse sand, (0·2–1·0 mm), such as sands, and those sandstones whose cohesion is destroyed by frost. During freezing, this material is too porous to freeze solid; the voids are not completely filled by ice. During thaw the surface layer is dry because it retains a degree of permeability even when frozen deeply, for it does not develop ice segregations. It does not reach a state of flow, and so never forms solifluction terraces. If sands do occur in solifluction deposits it is by slipping or slumping. These rocks do not give rise to patterned ground but are very liable to wind erosion. The microforms they produce in periglacial conditions are partly azonal: dunes, sheets of aeolian or niveo-aeolian sands.

They act as resistant formations, compared with rocks which are very susceptible to frost shattering, producing large amounts of fine debris. Thus, in Champagne, outliers of Eocene sands have protected the underlying Chalk, forming the residual Monts de Champagne in the Quaternary.

(iii) Rocks producing debris with two granulometric maxima. During freezing, they are susceptible to two processes, the displacement of the larger material by needle ice and the heaving of the fines by the growth of ice segregations. During thaw, the surface layer becomes plastic because of the impermeable frozen substratum and the abundance of water from the ice segregations.

This is a situation very favourable to sorting, and it is in such materials that stone polygons, stone stripes, stone pavements and stratified screes develop. But these materials may also produce microforms which are not limited to them, such as earth hummocks and stepped slopes, or if considerable coarse debris is present, cryoturbation benches.

(iv) Rocks producing coarse material without fines. Such are crystalline schists, many granites, basalts and nodular limestones. The material is very open, does not freeze solid and remains permeable. During the thaw, there is no free water between the blocks. The essential processes are frost shattering and the action of *pipkrakes*. The characteristic microforms are stone roses, block fields and block flows.

(b) **Site Conditions** These control the supply of ground water and the part played by gravity in the movement of the materials.

(i) *The supply of ground water* This plays a major role because gravity acts through solifluction which is a function of the water content of the soil. Ground water determines the physical state of the soil, as well as the soil grain size, and the form of the ground ice.

Internal movements in the soil require a fluid state, which depends in part on the amount of fines, colloidal and precolloidal. This fluid state determines ice segregations, the degree of impermeability of the frozen bed, and water content during thaw. It in turn depends on the supply of water to the surface layer, for ice segregations are increased by the presence, under a bed of fine debris, of a considerable porous bed.

The form of the ground ice controls frost shattering and cryoturbation. The former is most active when one face is kept wet during freezing. Cyroturbation by needle ice, which occurs only in very wet conditions, may cause sorting and result in patterned soil in entirely stony deposits, as long as a steady supply of water is forthcoming. Thus, peculiar local conditions may lead to the existence of patterned ground well beyond its normal extension.

(ii) *The effects of gravity* The main work to determine the limiting slope values for different types of ground is that of Cailleux. This is a very complex problem, for the role of slope interacts with the influence of grain size, water holding capacity and climatic factors.

Closed patterns occur on almost horizontal surfaces. In other situations gravity distorts the pattern: the polygons are elongated or destroyed. Cailleux puts the limiting slope for regular polygons at 2·5°. Richmond, on the other hand, puts it at 4°. The former must relate to cases where there is more abundant fines so that a soliflual state is more readily reached.

Open patterns, mainly striped ground, occur on slopes of 7·5–26°, always on gentler slopes than comparable gravity screes. This reflects the great mobility of the material under periglacial conditions. Stratified screes occur on slopes of 5–33°; block flows on slopes of 3–24°.

The wide range of slope values covered by each is due to variation in the amount of fines, which controls the importance of solifluction. Thus, on limestones, the slope angle below which downslope movement is impossible seems, according to my own observations, to be 1° for chalk head, where chalk 'dust' may reach 50% of the total. For blocky jurassic limestone head which consists of about 50% stones, 5–20 cm long and only about 5% of silt, it is 10°, while for limestone blocks without fines it is 20°. These figures refer to Würm deposits in the Paris Basin.

(2) Climatic or Zonal Factors

The main difficulty here is that there is insufficient climatic data, and that which is available does not strictly relate to soils. Furthermore, the distinction between actively-forming, and fossil, features is difficult.

(a) The Freeze–Thaw Cycle This has been made fairly familiar through the work of Troll and his system of graphic presentation, *thermoisopleths*. On these, the temperatures for the whole year are shown on a graph, the months of the year being represented on the x-axis and the hours of the day on the y-axis. Diurnal and annual variations are shown together. Troll (1944) distinguishes two frost rhythms, diurnal and seasonal, and has tried to relate to them the size of the patterns in polygonal and striped ground.

(i) *The diurnal cycle* is characteristic of tropical mountains and some oceanic Arctic areas. Freezing occurs often but does not penetrate deeply, so that the rocks are subjected to a weak and shallow but oft-repeated process. Frost shattering does not produce coarse debris; it affects only the very surface zone of joints. The movement of surface debris by needle ice is intense, where conditions are moist, as they usually are. This leads especially to the production of polygons, which remain small because the frost is shallow and lateral sorting is checked. Typical, but shallow, periglacial soil patterns are produced.

(ii) *The annual cycle* is typical of high latitudes and most temperate mountain areas. The frost is more or less intense, always prolonged, and may go so far as to produce permafrost. It penetrates deeply, but the depth reached by frost is not the important factor; rather it is the depth affected by freeze and thaw; hence the importance of the annual range, which controls the depth thawed in summer, that is the active layer. The number of freeze–thaw cycles is inversely proportional to this range; in continental climates, conditions pass quickly from continuous freezing to continuous thaw, and in oceanic climates the reverse is true.

Two cases must be distinguished. In the first, a frost of moderate intensity occurs, in which the number of freeze–thaw cycles is still relatively large, and which penetrates to a depth of about one metre. This is very favourable to shattering of the bed-rock deeply and repeatedly. It is also favourable to sorting and to the development of polygons in particular. Finally, it promotes solifluction, for the frost is intense enough to produce a good proportion of fines. In the second case, a very intense frost giving a large annual range is accompanied by only moderate sorting because of the reduced number of freeze–thaw cycles. Nevertheless, it provokes strong solifluction because of the breakdown of colloidal structure. It leads to the formation of features which do not form in other conditions, such as tundra polygons which require intense frost, pingos which involve a massive segregation of ice, palsen and ropy bogs which need a rapid spring thaw, and hydrolaccoliths which are related to intense frost and the hydraulic properties of the permafrost.

(b) **Soil Moisture** This plays an important role both on account of its influence on the penetration of frost and its effects on the physical state of the soil during thaw.

(i) *Influence on freezing* This assumes two forms. A snow cover hinders the deep penetration of frost, hence the rarity of permafrost in temperate mountains. Areas with a thick snow cover are not characterized by frost weathering and patterned ground. Snow has its own effects however, producing other features: nivation landforms, such as nivation cirques, and avalanche chutes. Indirectly, snow operates in the moulding of the periglacial landscape by the steady water supply it provides through long drawn-out melting. It favours the action of needle ice. Water content during freezing is also very important: the moister the soil, the greater the change in temperature needed to freeze or thaw it. Given these temperature conditions, the efficiency of freezing is multiplied.

(ii) *Influence during thaw* Moisture content determines the physical state of the soil and hence cryoturbation. Snow cover, even if it hinders the development of patterned ground, does promote amorphous or unsorted solifluction on slopes. A moist soil in summer increases the effectiveness of occasional night frosts. However, dryness in summer is not without effect, it produces desiccation cracks which lead to the formation of mud polygons and it favours wind deflation on fine materials without a vegetation cover.

(c) **Wind** In addition to purely aeolian phenomena which are not limited to periglacial conditions, though perhaps well developed under them, the wind in combination with snow plays a significant role. It influences differential freezing of the soil by breaking up the snow cover. Areas covered by snow are still protected, while frost penetrates more easily where the snow is thin or absent. This leads to differential frost heaving by promoting ice segregation in the latter areas. Similarly, by blowing the snow off hummocks, wind conspires to accentuate them. It also produces niveo-aeolian deposits from the deposition of sand or loess on snow. When the snow melts, the sand remains, but in more or less uniform sheets and not in dunes.

(d) Vegetation Vegetation acts as an obstacle to soil movement, but one which is often overcome when the physical processes are sufficiently intense. When the processes are weaker a strong vegetation cover may check movement; the lobate form of solifluction tongues, with their terminal bank, is due to it. For a long time German authors have distinguished between *free solifluction* and *bound solifluction* (respectively unhindered, and hindered by vegetation). Sometimes the vegetation tends to reinforce soil structures; polygon borders are occupied by plants because there is less movement than in the centres. Isolated tufts of vegetation may favour the production of earth hummocks, for the areas between the tufts may heave because of the deeper penetration by frost.

The influence of climatic factors explains the distribution of different soil patterns, and periglacial microforms, in large associations, or provinces, which correspond more or less to the main types of climate described above.

(II) Climatic Associations of Soils and Microforms

These depend mainly on the rhythm and intensity of frost, and on humidity, especially snow fall.

(1) Dry Climates with Severe Winters

This climate, represented by northern Siberia and the islands north of Canada, has very cold winters, a continental annual temperature range, with relatively few freeze–thaw cycles and a low precipitation. Here the optimum conditions for tundra polygons occur, and they cover vast areas, especially on alluvial plains. Hydrolaccoliths on the slopes, and pingos on the plains, show their greatest development; the lakes and pools which lead to their formation are abundant. Solifluction flows are also widespread, to the point where the surface of entire hill regions is in movement in summer. These flows are encouraged by summer rain which arrives just as the soils are beginning to dry out after the thaw. Cryoturbation benches and goletz (altiplanation) benches are also found. Well developed polygonal and striped ground on the other hand, appears to bc rare.

(2) Moist Climates with Severe Winters: Arctic Type

The type area is Spitzbergen, where winters are severe enough for permafrost, but temperatures are not nearly as low as in Siberian winters. Annual temperature range is not so large, summers being cool with fairly frequent night frosts. There is a greater precipitation which is better distributed, so that there are quite abundant falls of snow. In summer, rainfall is smaller but fog is frequent, causing condensation. The existence of permafrost, the large number of freeze–thaw cycles, and the humidity, lead to the development of polygons. In this type of climate, solifluction flows are well supplied with freeze–thaw debris and with meltwater from snow. Frost shattering is accelerated by the frequent frosts in moist conditions (night frosts in summer). Features resulting from frost shattering, such as block fields, are very common; tundra polygons, hydrolaccoliths, pingos, and features produced by wind action are rare.

(3) Moist Climates with Severe Winters: Mountain Type

In this type of climate, represented by the Alps, and mountains of central Europe, precipitation is heavy compared with that in high latitudes, so that there is a widespread snow cover. The considerable diurnal temperature range leads to frequent summer night frosts. Though winters are severe their effects are offset by the snow. Finally, and most important, are the great local differences in microclimate, and the variations throughout the year. All this producces a sample of each of the forms developed under these microclimates and altitude ranges. Almost all forms are present but are often of limited extent because of variations in site conditions and erosion by streams. Block fields of all varieties, stratified screes (on account of frequency of steep slopes), hummocky ground and stepped slopes in grassy areas, turf garlands and block streams are especially frequent. Though not so common, stone polygons and stone stripes (as well as stone pavements, which are typical), are fairly frequent. All other forms do not occur, as they require a more severe climate.

(4) Climates with a Small Temperature Range: Arctic Type

This type of climate, found on Kerguelen Islands (lat. 50°S., long. 70°E.), has an absence of intense or prolonged frosts and of marked winters. It is typified by cool summers and by night frosts occurring at all times of the year, by high humidity and heavy rainfall, and by considerable falls of snow which do not remain long on the ground. Stone fields are widespread because the humidity promotes effective frost weathering, but with slight frosts, the size of the debris is small. Solifluction is also very active thanks to the constant humidity and the absence of prolonged frosts which would arrest movement. The action of needle ice, and frequent freeze–thaw destroying the colloïdal structure of the soil, lead to abundant solifluction terraces and block streams. Polygons are not common and are small; they are of the tropical mountain variety owing to the shallow ground frost. The climates of mountains in the cold temperate oceanic belt belong to this group. Here the cold is due to altitude, but there are no very severe frosts, the annual range is small though freeze–thaw is frequent and there is a high humidity. Their surface is characterized, in the zone just below the nival zone, by the same features, and in the zone below that again (the alpine grassland) by earth hummocks and steps.

(5) Climates with a Small Temperature Range: Intertropical Mountain Type

The main features are a daily freeze–thaw cycle with a small annual and large diurnal range of temperature, and a higher rainfall than in the polar areas, which is offset by a considerable evaporation rate. Condensation at night is important and leads to the formation of giant *pipkrakes*. The part played by nivation is lessened by the fact that snow melts rapidly below the snow line. Ground patterns and microrelief are very similar to those in the preceding climatic type. Mud fields due to pipkrake action are common, as are turf garlands, especially on clay soils. Surface frost shattering produces only shallow stone fields and there are no great scree slopes. The sorting of soils is intense but shallow, and is mainly the work of needle ice. The most significant process is cryoturbation on clays and shales.

(6) Sub-Periglacial Climates of the Taiga

On the whole, morphogenetic conditions are not typically periglacial but belong to forested regions with severe winters. However, especially in Asia, a large part of the taiga grows on relict permafrost which modifies considerably the processes working on the surface and introduces typical periglacial features such as hydrolaccoliths, and reinforces solifluction.

The climate has two characteristics. It is continental, with a large temperature range: intensely cold winters with severe frost and very warm summers. It is more humid than arctic periglacial climates, favouring peat bog development. Periglacial features which are due to the intense cold and relict permafrost are, ropy bogs, seasonal hydrolaccoliths and thermokarst, the latter occurring on relict permafrost thawed on the surface and overrun by the forest. It is not entirely due to the present-day climate.

Frost climate soils and microforms occur in large associations corresponding to variations in climate. Nevertheless, local factors or the presence of certain rock types may lead to an extrazonal extension of some of them, as in the field of biogeography. Polygons have been recorded in Austria at only 1200 m above sea level, on an embankment enclosing a lake. This is an extrazonal occurrence due to particularly favourable circumstances. Such cases are frequent and make mapping the extent of periglacial features difficult. It is necessary, therefore, to adopt the methods of other branches of physical geography, such as biogeography. In each case, the microform must be carefully placed in its context which is as much climatic as lithological, in a true ecological perspective.

CHAPTER 3

The Development of Slopes

THE study of soils and periglacial microforms gives us some insight into the processes attacking the bed rock and reducing it to material suitable for transport by slope processes. We may now try to understand how the relief is moulded by these processes which, when grouped into a morphogenetic system applicable to frost climates, should explain the characteristics of the periglacial landscape. This morphogenetic system is marked by the dominance of mechanical weathering (frost shattering), and by the movement *en masse* of the surface layer. The basic feature of the periglacial regime is the rapid evolution of slopes and this often completely dominates landscape development. Finally, we shall examine in turn the processes controlling slope development, both the evolution of zonal slopes and the intervention of azonal factors.

(A) PERIGLACIAL PROCESSES AND SLOPE DEVELOPMENT

As in soil formation, these processes vary, depending primarily on climate and the nature of the rocks involved. Furthermore, the combination of these processes varies within the periglacial field, resulting in differing conditions of slope evolution which give rise to a multiplication of forms. The morphogenetic system acts on the slopes through the shattering of the bed rock, mainly by freeze–thaw, and the removal of the debris by several agents: cryoturbation, slope wash, wind erosion and gravity (screes). Some of these agents are typically periglacial, as is cryoturbation, others are azonal, such as run-off. The final point is the transport of the material to the foot of the slope: on this depends the removal of the debris, which ensures the continuing exposure of the bed rock. Without this, the debris would fossilize the relief and stop its evolution. The morphogenetic system is an active factor, while the nature of the bed rock is a passive factor. The part played by each of the elements in the morphogenetic system is a function of the relations of climate and lithology.

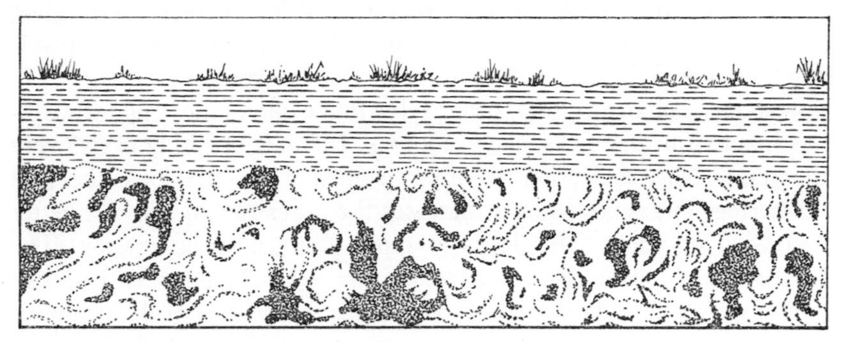

FIG. 10 Cryoturbation garlands, probably formed by convection, at Berry-au-Bac (Aisne) (*drawn from a photograph*)

Horizontal lining: chalky loess-like silt, probably aeolian and younger than the convection forms. Underneath is a mingling of chalky head and a brown interglacial decalified clay, churned up by convection.

(I) Rock Shattering

This is almost entirely the work of freeze–thaw; the role of other processes is negligible. Perhaps the splitting of rock by contraction under the effects of dry freezing takes part, but this has not yet been investigated. Shattering by impact or vacuum plays a part, but it is a minor one and limited to gravity screes. Occasionally, the heating of exposed rock by insolation may cause shattering but it assumes minor importance compared with frost. The operation of frost shattering depends on three factors: lithology, relief and climate.

(1) The Influence of Lithology

Lithology influences the operation of both micro- and macrogelivation. Microgelivation cuts across the texture of the rock and its effect depends primarily on the resistance of the rock to the pressure produced by the increase in the volume of water on freezing. In the area south of Allaket in Alaska, coarse-textured granites are disrupted into large blocks of 0·1–1·0 m, and fine-grained granites are disrupted to sand whose grain size is that of sand and silt.

In Champagne during the Quaternary, the white chalk was broken down to debris of silt to granule size, and marly chalk was broken to pieces 1–5 cm long, granules and silt.

The differential break down of rocks according to their facies gives great importance to the lithology, especially as cryoturbation depends largely on the grain size of the products of disintegration.

In so far as climate allows, macrogelivation exploits the zones of weakness inherent in the rocks, such as joints. Tectonic crushing is also very important. Microgelivation is often facilitated by previous chemical weathering; in granite rocks it increases the porosity and allows a better infiltration of water. This leads to rapid granular disintegration. The denudation of consolidated rocks under a periglacial climate is the result of intense macro- and microgelivation. When the latter is weak, the debris is coarse and such features as block streams, block fields and gravity screes are formed. Where microgelivation is important it continues to break down the fragments which it has split off in association with macrogelivation. The debris becomes progressively finer, producing an increasing amount of fines, as is shown in the reduction in the debris size of stratified screes downslope. Microgelivation facilities solifluction. The site and climatic conditions determine the degree to which each rock type is affected by macrogelivation and microgelivation.

(2) The Influence of Relief

If the fluctuations in temperature are large enough to cause intense freezing, frost weathering is greatest in damp areas. Rock with its joints full of water is more difficult to freeze but it is subjected to greater strain because of the greater volume of ice which forms in it, and thus shatters more readily. The formation of niches at the foot of rock faces is due to there being more moisture; when the foot of a slope is not buried under debris coming from above, it is undermined and retreats in the same way as sea cliffs. Local topography may also encourage frost shattering where moisture is provided by snow banks which persist into the summer. These snow banks are generally produced by drifting, or avalanches whose pattern in turn depends on relief. This differential frost shattering accounts for the formation of nivation niches, it also explains the differing character of slopes developed on different rock types in periglacial conditions and the irregularities in a single slope cut across several rock types.

(3) The Role of Climate

On this there is little data, only a few scattered observations. It is generally believed that frost produces only thin soils, at most a few decimetres thick. This is probably true of some periglacial climates, especially where temperature fluctuations are not marked. In such climates the frost penetrates only a little way and has no effect at depth, or the summer thaw affects only the surface layer and the effects of freeze–thaw are felt only a little below the surface. Again, in the mountains where slopes are steep, the rapid removal of debris does not allow the development of deep soils. Nevertheless in climates with a very great temperature range, this is certainly not true. In Champagne, for example, the white chalk, though very susceptible to the effects of freeze–thaw it is true, is thoroughly disintegrated, often to a depth of 4–5 m, and shattered to 10–25 m. Naturally, soils as deep as this can form only on relatively flat surfaces.

Under different climates the same rock may give different disintegration products, for the part played by macro- and microgelivation depends on climate. Macrogelivation occurs only where the frost penetrates deeply enough to freeze the water contained in the joints, and in areas of permafrost, when the seasonal thaw penetrates deeply enough to affect them. Thus, with a diurnal freeze–thaw cycle, a massive granite yields only a small quantity of debris by granular disintegration; under a severe climate macrogelivation springs joint blocks of several cubic metres. Microgelivation may also work very efficiently: in the dry Andes of northern Chile, for example, at Salar del Huasco and in the Puna de Atacama, night frost succeeds in reducing to sand and gravel, extremely hard volcanic rocks (ignimbrites, andesites and massive tuffs). Differences in texture are important in the honeycomb weathering of steep rock faces.

Frost shattering is a powerful process capable of breaking down the bedrock to considerable depths at a relatively rapid rate. It is probably the most important of all the types of mechanical weathering operating on the earth's surface at the present time. The work of freeze–thaw has two aspects: it directly influences the form of ablation slopes, and controls, through the calibre of the debris, the method of transport down the slope. Sculpturing by frost is seen very clearly on cornices and rock faces steep enough to cause the immediate removal of the loosened fragments (i.e. slopes exceeding 45°). It also takes account of lithological differences, however slight, stripping away some horizons more rapidly and leaving others to form an overhang. Joints give rise to chutes or gullies whenever they are accompanied by a slight shattering of the rock; the final result is a relief of delicately etched cornices and pinnacles with a characteristic castellated outline. This type of relief is not restricted, however, to periglacial areas, it is found throughout the temperate zone wherever severe winters are experienced. In such cases, areas of strong relief are not covered by a protective vegetation but are being sculptured by frost. Their development is nevertheless, both slower and different from that which took place during the cold periods of the Quaternary, when microgelivation was dominant.

(II) The Movement of Debris on Slopes

This movement may come about under the influence of several agents which depend on the nature of the climate and the grain-size of the debris, itself dependent on frost work. The most important of these agents are cryoturbation and solifluction on the one hand, and run-off on the other.

(1) Cryoturbation and Solifluction

These are the most typical agents. On slopes, cryoturbation depends essentially on the grain-size of the materials. The supply of water from below the surface, which plays an important part, is determined by the porosity of the soil; if surface water can seep down and circulate freely, there is no surface cryoturbation, as is the case with coarse sands or screes. Only cryoturbation by needle ice is possible, though even this is uncommon except in particular climatic conditions where rapid freezing occurs with abundant moisture present. Nevertheless, cryoturbation by needle ice is very active on the slopes of the arid Andes of northern Chile, above 4000 m. Gravel and granules move down slopes, turning such obstacles as vegetation tufts and boulders. The same occurs above 4500 m in parts of the Andes of Venezuela: on a slope of 10° the loss of material appears to reach nearly half a cubic metre per linear metre in a year, judging from the rate of infilling of a roadside ditch. Debris containing abundant fines not only retains the surface water, but draws up to ice segregations sub-surface moisture during freezing. Water from both sources is at the surface when thaw takes place and it is likely to produce soliflual conditions. Given debris of a suitable grain size, cryoturbation is most likely in moist conditions during the warm season. It promotes the movement of debris *en masse*: stone stripes, mud flows and block streams, and stratified screes. It tends to produce regular slopes, developing as a whole, retreating on a straight front, completely different from those produced by running water which evolve by localized incision and headward erosion.

(2) Run-off

Run-off is favoured by the presence of frozen ground as this is more or less impermeable, and in some places by the absence of vegetation. It is countered by the accompanying processes which are often more powerful, such as cryoturbation. The breakdown of colloidal cohesion by frost is an effective check, for the water instead of running over a clay surface combines with it to produce soil flow. The small amount of precipitation in many periglacial climates further reduces the importance of run-off.

In some areas, however, run-off is very intense in showery weather during thaw. Evapotranspiration is small and the retention of moisture by vegetation slight, so that the run-off coefficient is high and flooding severe. The bed of a stream may still be frozen with ice in parts of the channels and in cut-off lakes. Flooding occurs readily, leading to very violent *débâcles* which produce anastomosing channels where vegetation is scanty. Severe undercutting of the banks occurs. The channels change repeatedly as a result of ice jams and log jams. On slopes, run-off works very efficiently on ground just superficially thawed, dilated by frost or saturated during thaw; rills form but traces are quickly effaced by mass movements. When the ground is frozen, the concentration of run-off is unlikely because of its resistance to erosion; sheet flow therefore predominates. This is also true underneath patches of snow or névé. On clay rocks frozen very hard and thawing slowly, unchannelled run-off may erode a glacis. These occur especially in somewhat continental conditions with rapid thaw accompanied by showers (e.g. Toul area in France and central Europe generally).

By and large, slope wash works in opposition to cryoturbation, removing the fines which are indispensible to it. Cryoturbation on the other hand, smooths away developing channels which might concentrate run-off. So typical rainwash features develop only on materials unsuited to cryoturbation, such as sands. Elsewhere they fail to develop, but this must not lead one to underestimate the effectiveness of the process.

This opposition of run-off and cryoturbation explains the difference in landforms between the periglacial zone and those climatic regions where run-off plays a dominant role. It is a fundamental point in climatic geomorphology.

(B) The Evolution of Zonal Slopes

Different types of slope are produced by various combinations of the processes just considered. We shall now deal with them in turn: slopes moulded by solifluction, slopes formed by antiplanation terraces and slopes of stratified screes.

(I) Slopes Formed by Solifluction

This is a typical zonal landform which may be considered as a climatic index. All types of solifluction slope have one feature in common: they are little dissected, stream channels are few and far between. The slope is moulded as a whole, over its entire surface. This development as a sheet, combined with the character of periglacial run-off, leads to a much coarser drainage net than under temperate conditions. The establishment of solifluction over the slopes as a whole sees a reduction in the number of streams. The minor valleys already in existence are to a large extent filled in by solifluction debris and eliminated from the landscape; their existence is inferred from exposures. On the other hand, with the end of a solifluction phase, stream density increases again and new valleys are cut, but these are not necessarily sited on the beds of the earlier infilled valleys. It is possible that such a sequence of changes may take place in the course of a single cold period, related to changes in the relative importance of solifluction and run-off, or to the formation and disappearance of permafrost. This point is worth systematic investigation.

It is possible to distinguish between two main types of solifluction slope; first, slopes due to localized solifluction which are characteristically uneven (slopes with slip lenses, slopes with niches and flows, slopes with cryoturbation sheets, slopes of differential solifluction), and secondly, smooth slopes of solifluction sheets.

(1) Slopes of Localized Solifluction

These slopes (Fr. *versants à solifluction inégale*) may be divided into several types, based on origin and on the mode of operation of differential solifluction.

(a) Slopes with Slip Lenses (Fr. *versants à loupes de glissement*)

These lenses form a kind of step or bench on the slope, with a steep arcuate front 0·3–2·0 m high. Their width may reach 20–30 m, but sometimes may be only 4–6 m. Their length approximates to their width. Their longitudinal profile, like the transverse profile in the lower part of the bench, is convex, and broken by secondary steps parallel to the main front. Behind the front the surface, at first flat and then concave (Fig. 11), breaks the hill slope in such a way as to indicate the removal of a volume approximately equal to that of the bench. On the upper side, the bench is bounded by a curved scar, 0·3–2·0 m high, but this may be marked weakly or even be absent.

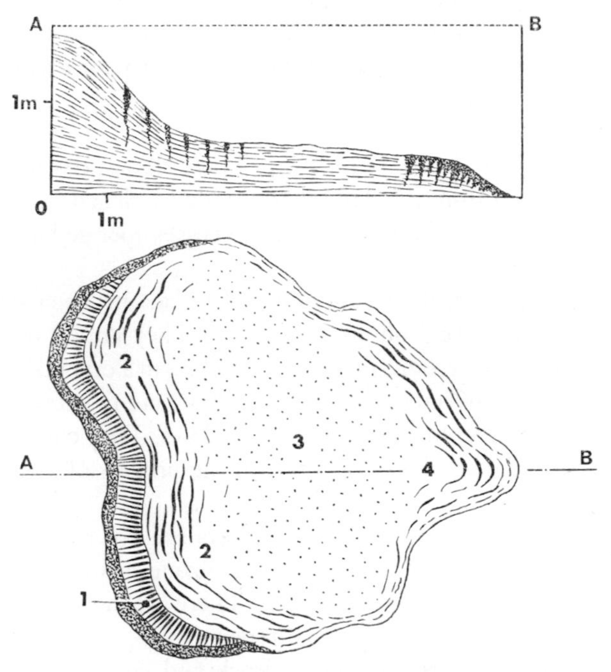

FIG. 11 A slip lens

Above: section along AB on the plan. Below: 1. slip scar 2. fissured area at the foot of the scar and its lower part, where water penetrates, wetting the substratum 3. flat surface of the lens showing wet mud in periglacial areas, marshy in temperate areas 4. Front of the lens, forming a step, fissured and moving over the substratum.

The slope as a whole has a characteristic relief. The steps succeed one another downslope and, when the hill slope is steep enough, there may be a piling up of steps at the foot. The steps dominate the lower part of the slope while the scars are more marked in the upper part. The steps overlap laterally and successive steps settle on one another, at first filling in the gaps between earlier steps, but later settling in a less orderly manner so that the surface lacks a pattern.

The steps are due to an uneven rate of movement, the tongues move more rapidly than the rest and their speed may reach 4 cm a month. They come to cover the turf or the tundra of a hill slope. The fluid soil forms a kind of pocket enclosed in the turf and the pressure which it exerts causes the turf to break and fold back on itself. When this happens the mud may flow on the surface. Solifluction steps are widespread, occurring beyond the limits of the periglacial climate. They may be found in temperate areas, but only on clays. They are nevertheless most widespread in periglacial environments, both in high altitudes and in high latitudes, for it is frost that produces fines in sufficient quantity for them to develop on many types of rock.

(b) **Slopes with Localized Mudflows** These slopes, developing today, have been described from the Arctic, especially by Sharp and Washburn. They also occur in areas where periglacial processes operated in the Quaternary.

In periglacial regions, these mudflows take place between stable areas, being sunk between levees on a debris slope. They are 20 to 30 m wide and divide into several streams downslope, ending in a cryoturbation sheet. Their surface is very irregular in detail but they tend to show a succession of arcuate ridges resembling small scale lava flows. They consist of a mass of debris, unsorted and rich in colloids, in the process of soliflual movement.

As in the case of stepped slopes, mudflows are not restricted to periglacial areas; they are found in the temperate zone, being common in the Alps, and even in the wet subtropical belt. There are, however, differences between the periglacial and the azonal types:

(i) Periglacial flows form on the bedrock and consist of freeze–thaw debris, while those of other zones consist either of unconsolidated deposits, usually moraines and clays, as in the Alps, or the clayey products of chemical weathering, as in the tropics. Thus they develop on quite different materials.

(ii) Their rate of movement also differs. Outside the periglacial zone, mud flows take place rapidly because an equilibrium has been disturbed. The process of flow extends over a few hours, a few days or at most a few weeks (e.g. in mountains of the temperate zone). It is the result of Atterberg's liquid limit being exceeded owing to a temporary soaking, and affects only clay areas. Periglacial mudflows on the other hand are slow, like solifluction, moving only a few decimetres or metres a year.

Mudflows have played an important part in some areas during the Quaternary. They have been described in central Germany and in France.

Baeckeroot has shown their importance in la Montagne Noire (N. of Carcassonne), and evidence for them occurs throughout the Massif Central.

(c) **Slopes of Cryoturbation Sheets** In this case the slope is regular, at an almost constant angle, but flattens a little immediately above low scarps some 0·5–2.0 m high, which succeed one another almost the entire length of the slope. These scarps slope at 20–40°, that is two or three times greater than the average for the whole slope. The materials forming the slope are not *in situ* but have come by cryoturbation from the upper part of the slope; they are unsorted, rich in fines, with many blocks on end. Eventually they cover the whole of the slope.

Like the slip lenses, this is a form of localized cryoturbation. The movement involved is very slow, a few centimetres a year, and this is reduced by local decreases in slope, which cause an accumulation of material.

A final type of uneven slope, moulded by solifluction, occurs frequently on ancient massifs, where the resistance of the rock to freeze–thaw varies. The Bruche valley (Lorraine), on metamorphosed Devonian rocks, affords good examples. These slopes consist of a series of irregularities, some concave, some convex, separated by smooth stretches or occasionally by small rocky projections. Here and there are solifluction dells (Fr. *vallons de solifluction*). This type of slope develops where the rock varies considerably in detail, in one place there is close jointing, in another the rock itself is less resistant to mechanical weathering, in yet another slight chemical weathering causes a more rapid disintegration by frost. Over an area of a few square metres the movement of material is more rapid and forms diffuse flows on the slope. Excavation of a hollow has begun and as it collects moisture, especially from snow patches, it tends to increase in size. At the same time the more resistant areas form projections as the more fissile material that surrounds them is steadily stripped away. Irregularities such as these are almost always found underneath solifluction deposits which have been built up into a smooth slope.

(2) Smooth Solifluction Slopes

In the case of these slopes (Fr. *versants de solifluction en nappe régulières*), the whole slope forms a single unit, most often in the form of a long drawn-out S, but sometimes perfectly straight. The finer the material covering the slope, the more constant and more gentle its inclination. On the chalk of northeast France where the debris does not exceed one centimetre in length, the slopes are only 2–3°, while on more resistant limestones, producing fragments of 10–20 cm, they reach 15°. These slope angles are directly related to the granulometry of the debris produced by microgelivation, as laboratory studies have confirmed. In some cases, other factors play a part, such as the chemical weathering of an earlier period, especially on crystalline rocks, which are more fissile if slightly weathered. This also makes them more porous and produces a larger amount of clay, facilitating solifluction. According to rock type and climate, unconcentrated run-off may play a secondary role of varying importance. It helps to produce summit convexity and to add colluvium to the deposits at the foot of the concave slope.

The slope is compound, consisting of three sections:

(i) the lower section, sloping at a very low angle, sometimes slightly concave, merging with the valley floor. This is a debris slope burying the foot of the valley side to a depth of 2–5 m. This gentle slope is more marked where material accumulates at the foot of the valley side because of the incompetence of the fluvial processes, than where the stream is capable of removing it;

(ii) the middle section, at a constant slope in most cases, and developed on the planed surface of the bedrock which is covered by a thin layer of freeze–thaw debris;

(iii) the upper slope, where rock outcrops, shattered by frost, form the source of the slope debris. This is the steepest part of the slope, which merges upwards into the convex slope of the interfluve.

These slopes are due to the continued action of freeze–thaw which shatters the bedrock and to solifluction which removes the debris. The flattening at the foot does not occur where erosion on the valley floor is vigorous enough to remove the debris so that the lower valley side is not buried. These slopes smoothed by a uniform solifluction occur on relatively homogeneous rocks. The time involved in their evolution varies according to the pre-existing relief, the resistance of the rock to freeze–thaw and the intensity of the solifluction process. They are very characteristic of the periglacial landscape; only the creep of fine debris due to intense chemical weathering in a humid climate can produce comparable slopes, but generally these are steeper and show a greater convexity.

(3) The Evolution of Solifluction Slopes

Some types of slope appear to evolve into others. The smooth solifluction slope is the ultimate form, the final stage in the evolution of slopes with mudflows and cryoturbation sheets. It is generally found on rocks especially suited to periglacial denudation, where the smoothing of the slopes is most rapid. The stages in its development may be reconstructed from an examination of present-day and Quaternary examples.

(a) **Initial Stage** Localized flows take place in existing hollows, mainly small valleys where the ground is moister because of the concentration of run-off and because downslope movement is more rapid. Incisions on the hillslope become the site of flows. Other sites are outcrops of rock which are more susceptible to frost weathering because they are wetter or have suffered tectonic crushing. The more rapid evacuation of debris develops hollows which serve to collect further debris from rock falls or solifluction. This initial stage is found especially on the more resistant rocks.

(b) **The Mature Stage** Frost weathering and cryoturbation have removed enough material to smooth the slope appreciably; the influence of minor local differences has become less important and the slope develops as a whole. The reduction of the areas between flows by frost shattering leads to the disappearance of localized flows. The debris is no longer concentrated in the more favourable areas but forms a single sheet covering the middle and lower part of the slope. Some irregularities still survive in the surface so that the movement of debris is not quite uniform, and slip lenses are formed, a patch of thick debris between two areas of rock outcrop producing a lens. Elsewhere, breaks in slope which persist for a great enough distance slow down the movement of the debris layer so that it builds up a cryoturbation sheet.

(c) **The Final Stage** Irregularities have disappeared and a smooth slope of constant angle has formed. Development continues, however, leading to a lowering of the angle of slope until an equilibrium is reached, an equilibrium which depends on the calibre of debris produced by freeze–thaw on the local rock. The steeper the slope, the more rapid is the removal of debris and the less chance of its being comminuted in the course of its journey down the slope. The more vigorous the freeze–thaw, the finer the debris becomes and the more gentle the slope becomes, for cryoturbation can move debris on feeble slopes so long as it contains abundant fines.

There is, however, a limiting slope value which is a function of cryoturbation and frost weathering. Below this angle the movement of freeze–thaw debris is no longer possible.

The continuing development of the hill slope involves its retreat parallel to itself, as long as the removal of the debris from its foot continues. Once the equilibrium value for the slope has been reached, it continues to develop by the removal of successive thin layers of bedrock, by frost shattering, and the transport of the debris by solifluction.

The final stage, which is reached when the streams are unable to remove all the debris collecting at the foot of the valley sides, sees the filling in of depressions by the mass of debris, and the evolution of the slopes which rise above this mass, towards an equilibrium value which is of the order of 1–5° for rocks favourable to solifluction. The final stage is represented by great sheets of perfectly graded debris whose calibre represents the maximum break down by frost. Above these rise very gentle hill slopes of between 1 and 5°. The area suggests a type of peneplain whose elevation is between that of the valley bottoms and the former interfluves. Such a surface was produced during the Quaternary on the chalk of Champagne.

(II) Slopes of Antiplanation Terraces

Goletz benches or terraces (Fr. *replats-goletz*) have been known mainly from Russian studies, almost entirely from the Urals and Siberia, where both contemporary features and forms inherited from the cold periods of the Quaternary, occur. Similar features have been recognised in Cornwall and Brittany by Guilcher (1950), in Devon by Te Punga (1956) and in the Ungava region of Canada by Derruau (1956). An increasing number have been noted in central Europe, in Czechoslovakia, Hungary and Poland, where they seem well developed above an altitude high enough for a severe climate. It is very likely that they are more widespread, many having been mistaken for cyclic valley benches; their definite identification requires good exposures but these do not always occur. The Americans reported a similar feature from Alaska, under the name of *altiplanation terraces* (Eakin, 1916).

(1) Morphology

The hill slope is cut into a series of benches which are almost horizontal, bounded by fairly steep fronts and rising one above the other like a flight of stairs. The width of the treads varies from several metres to several hundred metres. Benches much larger than this, exceeding a kilometre, have been recorded but they may be cyclic surfaces. The benches are arranged in rings around the summits. The highest ring is usually continuous but the others may be interrupted, forming discontinuous lines of benches. Their fronts are steep, the lowest angles being around 20°, the highest reaching 50° according to Russian work, but probably only exceptional cases exceed 40°. The height of these fronts varies, averaging 5–7 m in Siberia but sometimes reaching several tens of metres. Judging from Eakin's photographs, they would be at least 20–30 m in Alaska.

(2) **Structure**

These benches are largely composed of freeze–thaw debris. Their fronts are sometimes formed of bedrock covered by a screen of blocks. In most cases, the front is formed only of blocks; these are without fines and without any obvious arrangement, though the larger form the base and the smaller ones the top. Water emerges from the base.

The benches have the same structure as cryoturbation benches. The material becomes increasingly finer from the outer bounding scarp to the foot of the next scarp at its rear. At the same time the surface becomes moister. Sorting into polygons sometimes appears on the inner part of the bench though some benches consist entirely of block fields. They lack fine material and are pitted here and there by small closed depressions, 1–2 m wide and about 1 m deep. In other cases, patches of fine soil occur in the middle of the block fields.

Bench structure varies considerably with the different types of freeze–thaw debris. They all have one thing in common, however: the presence of very coarse debris, which only occurs in the frontal scarp. Goletz benches seem to form on rocks which are broken down by frost to ungraded debris, while smooth solifluction slopes occur on rocks producing well-graded and fairly fine debris. A severe climate also seems necessary, judging by the distribution of those active at present. Yet Quaternary examples have been described from the English Channel area, whose climate must have been very different from that of Siberia, Alaska or Ungava today, even if it was chilled by icebergs drifting down from the North European ice-cap.

(3) **Origin**

The very small proportion of fine material prevents the full development of cryoturbation. Other processes combine with it to produce goletz benches.

Their origin seems to lie in differential shattering by frost. This breaks up a mass of rock into large pieces which fall down and lodge on some irregularity of the slope, blocking the movement of fine material. At the spot where these blocks stop, they break down further, leading to the production of a small amount of fines which holds water. Thus the frost can more effectively attack the foot of the rock slope rising above this debris while it is wet. The bench thus formed, tends to develop of itself by autocatalysis, under a twofold process involving the sapping of the bedrock which rises above it, combined with the work of frost in causing the fall of fresh material on to its surface. As a result, the bench develops through the movement of debris in the central part where fine materials are abundant enough to cause cryoturbation. Part of this material reaches the edge of the outer scarp where it falls by gravity.

The evolution of goletz benches is still a matter for discussion. Danguin sees in them a residual landform due to nivation. Frost shattering is particularly intense on the edge of the névé patch but of little importance under it. During deglaciation the retreat of the névé limit was jerky and the goletz benches could mark the successive névé limits. Dr Tiulina on the other hand, believes that the benches are developing today without the aid of névé. Indeed, they may very well be forming by a combination of frost shattering, which reduces the rock to ungraded fragments, movement by gravity, and the washing out of fine material by snow meltwater in summer.

(4) The Evolution of Relief by Antiplanation

On the theory that they are relict forms related to the retreat of the névé limit, the lower benches are dead and in process of dissection by streams. Only the summit flat is developing, at the expense of the residual area which it surrounds. The evolution of the benches stops as soon as streams become organized and begin to dissect them. On the view that they are still developing through the action of frost, their evolution is the result of several processes. Each terrace tends to extend into the hillside by frost shattering and grow outwards as debris moves down its surface, becoming lowered because of the washing out of fines by run-off.

In any case, the series of benches is lowered as a whole by frost shattering and run-off. Their evolution implies a lowering of the general relief. The most probable overall effect is a steady progression of the different terraces in series, towards the heart of the mountain mass they surround. Each one expands by the destruction of the scarp of the one rising above it. For a general recession to take place, the loss due to this destruction must exceed the volume of debris arriving from the surface of the terrace immediately above.

There are two possibilities: either the lowering of all the benches combined with their centripetal progression, or their lowering by extending outwards, which theoretically demands a greater activity on the higher benches.

(III) Slopes of Stratified Screes

In the development of stratified screes, frost rapidly destroys the initial free face at the top of the slope. This destruction takes place on a straight front; there is no formation of niches, as Corbel has confirmed from Spitzbergen. In some respects one may talk of the pivoting of the free face on its base, producing a smooth slope of origin for the debris.

The lower part forms the accumulation zone at the foot of the free face, consisting of bedded scree. It is the scene of intense shattering which reduces the calibre of the debris and makes it easier to move. The very speed of the frost work often results in the burial of the slope. Screes 20–40 m thick are not uncommon in Lorraine. During this period of accumulation the increasing abundance of fines promotes solifluction and the dip of the beds gradually decreases from the bottom to the top.

Stratified screes do not show a limiting slope angle. The dip of the beds may decrease from say 25° in the lower beds to 10 or 15° in the upper. The slope becomes more gentle as it evolves. Sometimes, once the accumulation of stratified scree ceases because the rock slope at its head has been destroyed by frost, the deposit is affected by solifluction, as Dylik has shown in Poland. In Le Queyras (Upper Durance) there are widespread stratified screes dating to the Younger Dryas, which, though now fixed by vegetation, suffer from a rapid creep, bed by bed. They constitute a serious threat to construction work for they give rise to serious slips whenever they are carelessly cut.

As a rule, the slope of stratified scree is smoothly concave. This profile is due to the progressive decrease in debris size downslope. It merges smoothly into the surface at its foot.

(C) The Effects of Azonal Factors

In addition to slopes moulded by typical periglacial processes such as cryoturbation, there are also in periglacial areas slopes which are developed by azonal processes. Of these, the two most important are the free fall of debris and run-off.

(1) Free Rock Fall

Gravity screes are very well developed in periglacial regions, because of the frequent rock outcrops and the importance of frost shattering. They are formed of fragments which break off and roll singly down the slope. Their slope angle is determined entirely by the coefficient of friction of the debris; it therefore depends on those properties of the rock which control the size and shape of the debris. It must also be influenced by climate, which determines how the rock breaks down. From a theoretical point of view, it is probable that there are differences in slope values on any one rock type, between frost-produced screes of periglacial areas and the screes of hot deserts produced by temperature changes, for the nature of rock disintegration is not the same.

The distribution of gravity screes extends far beyond the limits of periglacial climates. They are common, and well developed wherever seasonal frost can attack a steep rock face. Gravity screes formed under a periglacial climate often show differences in detail from those of the temperate zone.

(2) The Evolution of Scree Slopes

These form below a steep slope, especially a vertical rock face.

(a) Initial Stage At first the form of the slope varies. In the upper part, pre-existing hollows or areas of weak rock collect the debris of frost weathering. These are frost niches, 'niches de gélivation', which grow by the parallel retreat of their steep head walls. In the bottom of the niche there is a thin sheet of debris with a concave profile; the niche is funnel-shaped and has a slope angle a little larger than the angle of rest for the material. Below, the chute down which the debris moves forms a very narrow gully, cut in the slope. The lower part of the slope, slightly less steep than the niche, is covered with a fairly thin layer of debris and has a transverse profile showing no concavity. At the foot, the accumulation of scree is cone-shaped, the apex being at the bottom of the chute. This apex rises as more and more debris is added to the cone, except in the rare cases where erosion is capable of removing all the debris feeding the cone.

FIG. 12(a) Periglacial slopes. Le Lac Noir, Kerguelen Islands (*after a photograph by Aubert de la Rue*)

Glacial Lake in horizontal basalts. Slope development is postglacial and therefore of short duration. The forms are young. The foot of the slope shows scree cones which are still separate but tending to join. Above each cone is the chute down which the frost debris falls. The height and almost vertical form of the face has not yet allowed niches to develop above the cones.

(b) **The Final Stage** This is usually marked by the burial of the foot of the slope by debris, owing to the absence of agents capable of removing it all. At the top, the retreat of the sides of the cirque-like funnel lessens their relative height; they retreat the more rapidly and end by cutting one another. The top of the slope is now formed of rock covered by an almost continuous mantle of thin debris, but for some time yet rock pinnacles separate the coalescing niches. They are reduced in turn, however, and the upper slope is then smooth; its slope becomes that of the angle of rest for the material. In the middle section, where evolution is less rapid, the areas between the scree chutes form rocky crests, often castellated, which are slowly reduced. At a certain stage the whole of the upper slope forms an inclined flat rock face strewn with debris, while the middle section has steep rocky pinnacles projecting through the debris. On the lower slope, the debris piles up; the cones coalesce to form a continuous glacis which gradually encroaches on the lower ground at their foot. The apex of each cone rises and gradually covers its feeding chute.

In the end, the upper part ceases to supply debris and the pinnacles are steadily reduced so that the hill slope is transformed into an inclined

FIG. 12(b) Scree slope near Holman Island (Post), Victoria Island, North Canadian Archipelago (rock type not indicated) (*after Washburn*)

Slope development is already well advanced. The original vertical face forms scarcely more than an alignment of pillars halfway up. These are the remnants of the spurs which separated the scree chutes. At the top of the slope, the intersection of the niches has produced a constant slope. The debris cover is thick at the foot but thin higher up.

plane. The relief at this stage is dominated by constant slopes (from interfluve to foot) and by conical hills. The steep slopes are preserved. The limiting value for slopes resulting from scree development is a little less in their lower part than the angle of rest for the debris, of the order of 28 to 39°. As screes can only form on steep slopes exceeding a limit of about 45°, the minimum slope on which free rock fragments will roll away, the top of the slope is a little less than this 40–45°.

When it has reached the equilibrium value, the slope is rectilinear, and only a little steeper at the top than at the bottom, because the limiting angle of friction in a state of rest is slightly greater than that in a state of movement. The limiting slope at the source of the debris is just a little less than that necessary to start it moving; the limiting slope in the accumulation zone is just a little less than that required to enable the movement of the debris to continue.

(II) Running Water

The effects of run-off are very secondary, being in any case much less widespread than scree formation.

(1) The Influence of Grain Size

Generally speaking, slopes under a periglacial regime do not offer very favourable conditions for the development of run-off. The regional run-off coefficient may be fairly large because of low evaporation, negligible transpiration and an impermeable permafrost layer. During thaw, however, the mud which forms on the surface is capable of retaining much of the water which is too intimately mixed with the soil to run away; it oozes rather than runs, carrying only the colloids and silt fractions. The washing action of water is effective only where large blocks are relatively important in the fine matrix, for they allow infiltration. Paradoxically, it is especially where fines are relatively scarce that they are most likely to be washed out. In coarse screes, the small proportion of fines is carried towards the bottom of the deposit as it accumulates. Most of the time, slopewash is a minor sporadic process whose effects are soon eliminated by major processes such as solifluction. Its action can be important only where no other process is operating to efface its work between times.

On slopes where cryoturbation is taking place, run-off plays no part in the evolution of relief. To this is due the low density of streams on this type of slope. Generally, it is only in the bottoms of the larger valleys that water is present in sufficient volume to form an organized flow and a river bed. On gravity screes, run-off is slight because the water sinks into the debris; it can play a part only in stratified screes which are rich in fines. Run-off operates only in a marginal area which does not evolve normally under the action of the dominant processes, which are essentially cryoturbation and gravity scree formation. This area consists mainly of sands too coarse to become soliflual; they are, on the other hand, mobile enough to be transported by running water. The existence of temporarily frozen ground or of permafrost is also necessary to allow run-off on this material, or all the water would seep into it. Similar run-off, during thaw, over sand still rendered impermeable in depth by frost, occurs in the temperate zone.

The resulting relief has been described by Malaurie at Disko in west Greenland. Since they are not subject to solifluction, slopes in sand are stable at as steep an angle as those of gravity screes, i.e. 35–40°, even if the sand is wet. On such slopes the base of the mollisol is not parallel to the surface; it is further below the surface in the middle of the slope and approaches it at the top and bottom. Summer rain percolates more completely into the middle part where the mollisol is thick, whereas a considerable proportion runs on the surface of the thin mollisol at the head and foot of the slope. Thus, according to Malaurie, there are two zones of surface run-off characterized by badlands, one at the head and the other at the foot of the slope. In the middle there is a more stable area marked by a belt of vegetation. Headward erosion from the foot of the slope extends the gullies into the middle zone, which develops by creep and spring sapping. The sand transported to the foot of the gullies in the upper part of the slope tends to extend upwards to the zone not dissected into badlands. The slope retreats parallel to itself so that its angle does not fall belwo 35–40°. As in the case of gravity screes, slopes moulded by run-off keep their steep angle until the final stages of their evolution.

(2) The Influence of Relief and Climate

The problem of run-off under periglacial conditions is an important one; it is also complex, for it is influenced not only by grain size, as we have just seen, but also by topography and climate. The influence of relief is important in the origin of certain forms of sheet flow which produce the *piedmont glacis*, recorded in several areas.

Very extensive piedmont glacis have been described by Enjalbert (1957) in front of the Mendoza Andes in Argentina. This may be compared with the great series of glacis in eastern and central Morocco, described mainly by Raynal. Their origin can be explained by a vigorous but sporadic unchannelled flow, and by large amounts of available debris. The characteristics of flow are very like those of other regions, but the load involved is much larger than in hot deserts where the speed of rock shattering is less. In Morocco, the climate today does not produce sufficient debris to continue building the glacis, which are being dissected.

In certain conditions then, unchannelled run-off may build up a glacis, under a periglacial regime.

Climate is therefore a factor in assessing the relative importance of run-off in different cold environments. Generally these effects are at a maximum in humid mountain areas because of the steepness of the slopes and the heavy precipitation. Nevertheless the role of running water in the evolution of relief in low lying periglacial areas has often been exaggerated, because of its importance during thaw in temperate areas. Conditions in the two climatic zones are totally different. One fact is quite clear about lowlands which experienced periglacial conditions in the Quaternary: many of the smaller valleys were subjected to solifluction, not the flow of running water.

(D) Differential Erosion in Periglacial Conditions

The overall development of slopes, which dominates the evolution of relief generally, is complicated by two factors which operate differentially.

(I) The Influence of Lithology

Rocks favourable to solifluction produce slopes which develop until they lie at very low angles. Periglacial processes cause a rapid removal of debris which soon reduces pre-existing relief to very subdued forms, with very gentle slopes and wide shallow depressions. In contrast, rocks resistant to cryoturbation generally preserve steep slopes which retreat parallel to themselves and cannot be reduced below a limiting angle of about 30–40°. In the final stages of their evolution, they still produce a strong relief, with conical hills or long constant slopes, sometimes capped by flat plateaux if the debris is not removed rapidly enough to allow the slopes to intersect.

In considering the influence of lithology, great importance must be attached to the initial relief, for on the relation between the actual slope, at the beginning of its development under periglacial conditions, and the limiting slope for the different processes, depends the type of slope development and therefore the pattern of its evolution. Nevertheless, even at the end of this evolution, periglacial denudation maintains a very varied relief which is largely a function of lithology.

(1) Rocks Favouring Rapid Slope Evolution

These are rocks whose debris may be rapidly removed by cryoturbation.

(a) **Limestones** The majority of limestones involved, particularly those which are weakly cemented, are not recrystallized, and their breakdown by freeze–thaw produces abundant fines. They include especially chalk and similar limestones. It was under the periglacial conditions of the

FIG. 13 Residual pinnacles in a ridge produced by frost-shattering of granite, Central Alaska (*after a photograph by Eakin*)

Castellated outlines due to mechanical weathering by frost, which is slow because the position of the rock is unfavourable to moisture retention. At the foot of the pinnacles, the debris is more thoroughly disintegrated by frost in the damper conditions of the soil surface so that it soliflucts and forms a smooth, fairly gentle, slope (about 10°).

Such forms are very common in areas which have undergone periglacial denudation. They occur on all compact rocks suspectible to frost work: limestones, sandstones (as in the Vosges and Saxony) granites, basalts, etc.

Quaternary that the Plain of Champagne was lowered in relation to the surrounding area.

Metamorphosed crystalline limestones and marbles are more resistant, as are the recrystallized limestones of coralline formations; being very compact and resistant, they are barely affected by microgélivation. Often, differential periglacial denudation strips the surrounding limestone from former coral reefs, producing cornices and perhaps pinnacles or castellated cliffs in hill slopes. Dolomitic limestones are also more resistant to frost than ordinary limestones.

(b) **Schists** Under the effects of freeze–thaw these produce silt which is favourable to the formation of segregated ice and cryoturbation. The slopes which develop on them differ little from those on chalk or clay. This explains the marked difference between the relief on schists in periglacial and subtropical areas. In Brittany, for example, periglacial processes have produced a gently undulating topography with slopes of 5–10° on schists, whereas in Portugal the same rocks give slopes of 20–25°.

(c) **Basalts** In some conditions, as yet not fully understood, coarse debris forming blockfields may be produced, in other conditions, fine silt. Probably an initial weathering, perhaps only slight, favours their reduction to silt. Vesicular or scoriaceous basalts are remarkably resistant to freeze–thaw.

(d) **Granites** Fine grained granites, especially if rich in felspars and mica, also produce very gentle slopes under intense cryoturbation. Frost breaks down the granite into fine debris where the comminuted felspars and micas provide the necessary fine matrix for soliflual movement. Such granites undergo complete granular disintegration under a frost climate, producing a periglacial granitic sand. This differs from sand formed by biochemical processes in its petrographic composition, which shows no appreciable change from that of the parent rock. Other granites give rise to blockfields.

In a general way, granites which have already undergone some degree of chemical weathering, however slight, offer a greatly reduced resistance to frost weathering. The core stones freed of the enveloping sand, are reduced by granular disintegration and shed shells which are themselves quickly reduced to sand. More rarely, granites split, usually along a joint in which chemical weathering had previously started.

(e) **Clays** These are readily reduced to a soliflual state not only by virtue of their facies but also, under periglacial conditions, by the destruction of the colloids, a feature which does not occur in most cases of soil flow under temperate conditions. The essential factor is the moistening of the clay bed and this is generally effected unevenly. Slope angles under which solifluction occurs are therefore very variable. As a rule their limiting value is not as low as that of slopes of chalk head.

(2) Rocks Resistant to Cryoturbation

Rocks resistant to cryoturbation and maintaining steep slopes under a periglacial regime are of two main kinds:

(i) those only slightly susceptible to frost weathering, which shatter into large blocks with little fine matrix. Such are the gypsum and diabase of Spitzbergen which form hills whose slopes evolve by scree formation.

(ii) those too porous to pass into a soliflual state. The most important are medium and coarse sands, and gravels. Slope development is by run-off, producing badlands when sands are dominant. Where gravels are important or in sands with little cohesion, the slopes are similar to scree slopes and remain steep.

(3) Slopes Formed of a Succession of Rock Types

When rocks of different facies succeed one another up a slope, the influence of lithology in causing differential erosion is not the same in periglacial as in other climates.

A bed of porous medium sand overlying a bed of chalk, very susceptible to frost weathering, gives a concave profile to a slope which has a free face at 5–15°, formed by the sand bed and retreating mainly by being undermined. The lower concave slope of chalk flattens progressively to 1–2°. The sand acts as a 'hard' bed, for it is less easily removed by denudation than the underlying silk.

A succession of limestones of varying susceptibility to freeze–thaw may produce an irregular slope under periglacial conditions. The less susceptible beds form abrupt steps which protrude through the sheet of angular gravel produced by the more susceptible beds which enclose them.

(II) Climatic Influences

These are primarily responsible for slope asymmetry in interfluves and minor valleys but the problem is complex and geological structure and lithology must be carefully investigated to ensure that they are not the real cause of the asymmetry. The processes operating at present and in former times must be determined by observation and measurement, and by a petrographic study of the deposits formed. The causes of asymmetry are many, so that the evidence often appears contradictory. Several climatic types seem to exist but their exact mechanism is not yet understood.

Three main causes of asymmetry have been suggested:

(1) Orientation

This leads to a differential operation of freeze–thaw and cryoturbation on the two slopes of a valley or of a ridge. It can, however, explain asymmetry only in valleys or ridges whose axes are approximately east–west. Thus in northern Siberia, on the lower Lena, slopes of sands and clays facing north are very steep, sometimes cliffed, and retreat by the undercutting of their base. The slopes facing south are very much more gentle and covered with solifluction beds.

In this case the difference in orientation causes the asymmetry. In very severe climates, thaw is less likely on the side facing away from the sun

(Fr. *l'ubac*), which remains steep. In less severe climates, the shaded side is more subject to periglacial processes so that it becomes gentle, while the side facing the sun (Fr. *l'adret*) preserves the characteristics of a non-periglacial morphology.

(2) Snow Accumulation

Poser has attempted to distinguish between primary and secondary asymmetry. Primary asymmetry, characterized by a steep slope facing north-east, represents the initial stage which occurs only at the valley head. Secondary asymmetry, with the steep slope facing west or southwest, results from a long period of development and is found in the middle stretch of a valley. The author's investigations have led him to reject this theory. It appears that the two types of asymmetry observed in Siberia are zonal in character.

(3) Loess Accumulation

Büdel explains the asymmetry of the valleys in the *deckenschotter* of southern Germany by loess accumulation. The axis of asymmetry is clearly north–south. The western valleyside is gentle and covered by a thick sheet of cryoturbated debris mingled with loam; the eastern side is steep and without an appreciable cover of superficial deposits. The presence of loam on the gentle slope only leads him to attribute the asymmetry largely to it, on the grounds that the presence of loess only on the leeward or western slope, and the resistance of the bedrock to solifluction, has produced differential cryoturbation, which has lowered the western slope more rapidly. This theory has been challenged by Rathjens (1952) and by Poser and Muller (1951). Their research suggests that solifluction, probably controlled by differences in snow accumulation and insolation, is the essential factor in the development of asymmetrical valleys.

If differential solifluction is the main factor, there are other minor ones which have been revealed by the work of Cavaille (1953) in the middle valley of the Garonne. In minor valleys close to the Tarn the solifluction flows of the gentle slope proved more resistant to undercutting than the molasse and, by forcing the stream bed against the steep slope, added lateral erosion by the stream to the effects of solifluction in producing asymmetry. In the main valleys the deposition of gravels has had a similar effect.

The origin of asymmetry valleys is thus complex. There are several types of asymmetry, all related to differential solifluction, but controlled by different factors in each case and resulting in varying relationships to orientation from one climate to another. In a general way, the very rapid slope development in periglacial conditions leads to the accumulation of large masses of debris at the foot of these slopes and its removal dominates the subsequent evolution of relief.

CHAPTER 4

The Work of Plurizonal Processes in Periglacial Regions

THE action of running water in the periglacial zone has certain characteristic features which result in distinctive landforms. Nor is this an isolated example. The morphogenetic processes stemming from low temperatures are also powerful enough to produce distinctive landforms in the spheres of wind action and coastal processes.

(A) CHARACTERISTICS OF FLUVIAL ACTION

As a result of distinctive climatic conditions, the removal by rivers of the debris produced by slope processes, and consequently the development of valleys and alluvial plains, takes place in a different manner from that in other morphogenetic regions. The work of the rivers depends on their regime which is in turn a function of climate.

(I) The Temporary Character of Stream Flow

This is linked either to a seasonal or a daily frost.

(1) Arctic Regions

The streams are frozen over by ice in winter, and often frozen solid. In northern Alaska, only a few of the very large rivers maintain a reduced flow beneath the ice. This is the so-called 'nival regime'; a better term would be 'regime with seasonal freeze' (Fr. *écoulement à gel saisonnier*), as this would convey better its true character. The streams begin to flow only after the thaw when a muddy ooze reaches them from the slopes and slowly melts the ice, or when waters arrive from southern districts already in a state of thaw, as is the case of all the great south–north rivers. Stream flow is limited to 4–6 months of the year. It often happens, as Cailleux and Malaurie have shown, that the floods following on the thaw take place on the ice of a river bed which is still frozen, with important geomorphological consequences.

(2) Mountain Areas

Conditions are a little different for the streams are rarely frozen solid on account of the very steep gradients, so that a reduced flow generally persists throughout the winter. In the Puna of Atacama, however, flow is intermittent, as in the Arctic, but the rhythm is daily instead of annual. A large diurnal temperature range often leads to the night freezing of small rivers of gentle gradient on the high plateau; the *rios congelados*.

The geomorphological consequences of this intermittent flow are not often of great significance. Generally, the periods of frozen streams coincide with the periods of slope immobility when the only changes taking place are those due to changes in the volume of ground ice. In the case of rivers rising outside the area, the results of the spring flood (*débâcle*) may be very great.

(II) Discharge and Run-off Coefficients

Discharge and run-off coefficients vary considerably with relief and climate. They are much larger in the mountainous areas with the greater precipitation and steep slopes. There are indeed great differences between the periglacial rivers of high latitudes and those at high altitudes in other climatic zones.

(1) Mountain Rivers

These have a greater discharge than rivers of high latitudes not only on account of a higher rainfall but also because they often receive water from glaciers lying at higher levels. Their run-off coefficients are also greater as a result of the frequency of steep slopes promoting greater run-off and the reduced evaporation owing to low temperatures and scanty vegetation. Mountain streams in a periglacial climate show little difference from those of other mountain climates. Their steep gradients and their occasionally large discharge makes them important agents of fluvial erosion. They actively develop their valleys, like other rivers, according to the general laws of river erosion. Usually they are competent to remove any debris from their floors. They ally periglacial processes to the general morphological evolution of the mountains, but the periglacial element does not impinge on the valley bottom, it affects only the slopes.

(2) Arctic Rivers

Arctic rivers are usually quite different. Their discharges are relatively small because of the low precipitation in periglacial areas, which in most cases is only between 100 and 500 mm. The scanty vegetation which absorbs little water must be taken into account, as must the evaporation, which is quite considerable judging from the sublimation of snow in winter and the presence of desiccation polygons. The frequency of strong winds is also important in this connection. Indeed evaporation is greater than is generally stated. Finally, river flow is seasonal as a result of deep freezing. Two types of river may be distinguished.

(a) **Local Rivers** Their catchment area lies entirely in the periglacial zone, and flow occurs only in the warm season. As an example one may take the Piassina of the Taimyr Peninsula, with 83% of its discharge during June, July and August, 90% from the end of May till the end of September. The total discharge is relatively small because of low precipitation which comes, however, mainly in summer, and amounts to 151 mm. There are no true floods, only a temporary flow which increases steadily by seepage from the ground soaked with water by the thaw. The mollisol acts as a sponge for the low rainfall, and releases the water steadily.

(b) **Allogenous Rivers** These have their sources in non-periglacial regions further south or in glaciated mountains. Such are all the great Arctic rivers: in North America, the Yukon and the Mackenzie; in Siberia, the Ob, Lena and the Yenisei. Run-off increases steadily from source to mouth, leading to the *débâcle*, the breaking up of the ice, which causes jams of floating ice against river ice which still survives downstream. Their volume is relatively large because it is derived from large basins which conform to the laws of run-off of southern regions of higher precipitation.

The Lena has run-off coefficient nearly equal to that of the Volga; that is, of a river of the forest and steppe. The water it carries away in a year is equivalent to 175–190 mm over its basin; the mean annual precipitation is 370–385 mm. This enables it to reach very large discharges; the mean annual discharge at Kyusyur being 13 900 cubic metres per second. For the Pechora River the figure is 4000 and for the Yenisei at Igarka, 17 400.

Very marked flooding occurs during the *débâcle*, which takes place in May in the middle reaches of the Siberian rivers and in June in their lower courses. In spite of the width of the valleys it reaches high levels, 10 metres or more. The fluvial regime is marked by a great annual flood, the extent of which depends on the degree to which the river is blocked by ice.

Arctic drainage is therefore different from the mountain pattern. The small rivers are, generally speaking, unable to carry away the mass of debris from the slopes, on account of their small discharge. This ceases to be true only in a few unusually wet areas in the Arctic, such as the west of Greenland. The large allogenous rivers, on the other hand, are very active, flooding great stretches and building up immense sheets of alluvium of distinctive type. It is possible to talk of a deficiency of drainage which does not follow the same rates as in the temperate zone.

Two distinct areas may be distinguished in considering the evolution of the periglacial landscape.

(i) the temperate or inter-tropical mountain areas, together with certain very humid areas in the Arctic, where drainage is by rivers which obey the rules of 'normal' fluvial erosion. Strictly periglacial processes are limited to slope development, occurring as part of the over-all evolution of the area under the control of the river system.

(ii) the Arctic regions, where flow is intermittent and where river work operates in a different way from that of permanent streams. Valley evolution is controlled by slope development which is intense, and by the distinctive work of allogenous rivers.

The Arctic drainage pattern has some distinguishing features. The interfluves frequently show a lack of drainage organization: lakes, marshes, disappearing streams are common. The form of secondary and minor valleys is also very distinctive. They are the *vallons en berceau* of French writers: round bottomed valleys with smooth concave sides, or *vallons à fond plat:* flat floored valleys, neither of which are due entirely to stream flow. The plains of alluvial deposition are also distinctive.

Although the larger rivers have sufficient flow actively to erode their beds, secondary streams are literally drowned under debris which they cannot carry away. In the lower courses of rivers draining a large enough catchment, the *débâcle* may lead to erosion. Ice floes are hurled against the banks and erode them so long as the river does not overflow. The floes collect in jams which temporarily block the river and build up pressure. When they give, a violent surge of water rushes along the bed eroding it, and transporting blocks which are much larger than those a 'normal' current would move. This explains the extraordinary size of some of the blocks found in periglacial river deposits and the large calibre of these deposits as a whole. The secondary streams on the other hand barely maintain their flow, as they are lost in debris. During the thaw, they spread out in laminar flow washing the surface, often flowing over ice which has not melted. In this way they transport debris in thin sheets, without shattering fragile pebbles, without causing much wear, as in the alluvial gravels of the eastern part of the Paris Basin or of the Charente. Both regimes may exist in the same river basin, as in that of the Seine for example. In the lower course, the large volume produced *débâcles*, with the transport of very large boulders and the deepening of the bed (to 30 m below sea level near Rouen), during the Würm. In the headwater zone, notably in Champagne, there was heavy deposition of well-sorted little-worn debris with horizontal bedding in large alluvial troughs.

(B) Characteristics of Wind Action

Wind plays an important part in periglacial areas, for five reasons. One is the frequency of strong winds and storms in the Arctic, especially on the coasts. These are particularly significant because of the low precipitation, especially snowfall. The effects vary: southwest Iceland, with its considerable precipitation, is little affected by wind erosion, though it is intense in the northeastern parts. Another factor is the reduction of the vegetation cover by the cold; this is increased by the wind blowing away the snow and exposing the ground surface in winter, leading to the destruction of the vegetation in Arctic regions; in mountain areas this mainly affects exposed ridges. Finally there is the concentration of water in ground ice by freezing which tends to dry out the surface layer of silty soils, and the production of abundant fine debris, especially silt, by frost weathering. This material is suitable for long distance transport by wind. All these factors vary in their operation but are most effective under the most severe climate, where wind strips the surface of snow and works on the fine debris, resulting from frost weathering, which has dried out by freezing. In summer, the very wet state of the surface of the mollisol checks wind action but does not totally prevent it; it occurs when winds are sufficiently strong to dry out sandy soils enough for them to blow about. The features due to wind are partly plurizonal, being found in other climatic zones; some are confined to the periglacial zone, or zonal.

(I) Plurizonal Features

These are experienced particularly in the cold steppes where the wind raises clouds of dust, which is deposited as loess. This affects sandy stretches, especially sheets of alluvium where the vegetation, as in hot arid regions, does not give adequate protection to the soil. Wind action is important mainly in autumn, when summer flooding has ceased and the first frosts have stopped surface run-off but the first snows have not yet fallen. The sandar of the ice sheets such as those in north Germany, Holland and Poland were areas of intense deflation. The same was true of some alluvial cones such as those of rivers coming down from the sandstones of the Vosges to the Rhine valley, and of certain moraines such as those studied in Brandenburg by Schulz (1956). Deflation may also occur on solifluction flows which are rich in sand as Schulz has shown. In this case it tends to impede solifluction by reducing the proportion of fines.

In periglacial regions, where there is sand, the wind causes intense corrosion, even in climates which are not particularly severe. Marcelin (1950) has drawn attention to it in the Nîmes area and in the region of the Lower Rhône. In places, notably in the Costière, magnificent wind-facetted pebbles are abundant. These consist of fine-grained resistant rock such as quartzites, diorites, and quartz, rocks little affected by frost shattering which destroys the effects of the sand blast. Cailleux has suggested a simple but effective test for wind-shaped pebbles: the wind alone cannot turn over pebbles exceeding 5–7 cm. Yet in a periglacial context one frequently finds blocks with undoubted wind worn faces, but much larger than this, sometimes 30 cm or more. They must have been turned over several times while they were being sand-blasted. Needle ice and solifluction have been responsible. The distribution of these large wind-facetted blocks is important in the reconstruction of periglacial climates.

The furrowing and pitting of rocks by wind abrasion is less frequent, for this takes place slowly. It operates on a scale of centuries where frost weathering operates on a scale of months, so that the effects of the former are likely to be defaced by the latter. Wind-shaped pebbles and blocks are common in very cold periglacial areas where the number of freeze–thaw cycles is small, as in Peary Land, in the extreme north of Greenland.

In the last century and in the early part of this, certain delicately etched cavities in sandstone have been wrongly interpreted as due to wind abrasion. In fact they have been produced by frost weathering which has detached grains of sand where their cement is weakest. The wind removed these grains. These effects may be seen especially well in the Vosges Sandstone, the Luxemburg Sandstone and some Swiss sandstones. The clearing of the cavities by wind eddies enables frost weathering to continue and produce pronounced cavities, but for all that wind action is secondary.

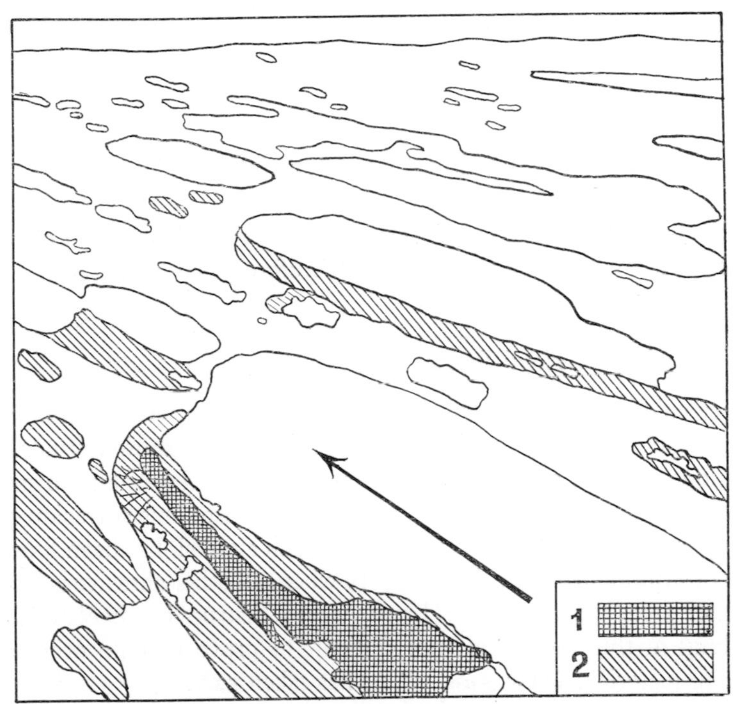

FIG. 14 Oriented lakes on the coastal plain of Northern Alaska (near Point Barrow) (*After an aerial photograph; Black and Barsdale, Journ. of Geol., 1949, Pl. IVa*)

The arrow indicates the mean orientation of the long axis of the lakes. This is not quite the same as the mean wind direction today, so that the lakes are already somewhat fossil. The wider beaches are all on the same side of the lakes, suggesting present day reorientation of the lakes because of the frequent and violent W. to S.W. winds.

1. Polygon fields: these show a preference for lake shores.
2. Floors of dried-up lakes.

The ordinary form of wind deposition, dunes, are not widespread in periglacial areas, the majority of those in central Europe, and on some sandy alluvial cones of Alsatian rivers such as the Moder, appear to date from the Late-glacial period and not from a really cold climate. The formation of dunes requires very mobile sand but this is prevented by the dampness of the mollisol in summer, its frozen state in winter, and by snow cover in periglacial conditions. One of the rare dune fields known in the Arctic is in Peary Land, where conditions are exceptional.

The character of wind deposition in a periglacial environment is determined by zonal factors and gives rise to distinctive deposits, such as loess and niveo-aeolian sands.

(II) Zonal Characteristics

In the periglacial zone, wind action has several effects whose nature depends on low temperatures and are therefore zonal in character.

(1) Corrasion by Hard Snow

In very cold conditions, snow consists of very small, very hard compact grains which are much more resistant than ordinary snow crystals. Observations made in extreme Arctic climates and in the Antarctic suggest that these grains when driven by the wind can cause some corrasion of the rocks or some polishing of them at least. Such a polish has been found on rocks protruding from the Antarctic ice where all other abrasive is lacking. In other areas such as Peary Land, where Fistrup has explained rock polishing in this way, it is very difficult to prove that no other more resistant material such as sand grains has taken part.

(2) Movement of Stones on Glazed Frost

In some sandy periglacial deposits in the Netherlands, Belgium and north France, there are scattered pebbles, 2–3 cm long, quite out of character with the rest of the deposit. In some cases at least, these pebbles could not have come down from higher ground (Guilcher and Cailleux 1950). They are found on the tops of isolated hillocks, entirely of sand; they must have been driven by the wind over icy ground, so that they were able to travel upslope. It has not been explained why they did not freeze to the icy surface.

(3) Sheets of Coversand and Niveo-aeolian Deposits

Dunes are rare and those that do occur are poorly developed and low (only 3–5 m); but in these cold areas sheets of wind-blown sand of quite another form are found. Deposition is spread out in a sheet marked by low swells some decimetres high and several metres or even tens of metres in wave length. The sand is usually poorly sorted: much less so than dune sand, and contains a high proportion of silt. It is unbedded. Edelman proposed that it should be called 'niveo-aeolian'.

These sands mingled with snow were laid down by winter snow storms, which accounts for the mediocre sorting, as fines of a considerable range of grain size may be blown along with the crystals of snow. The lack of bedding is due to the progressive settling of the mineral part of the deposit during the melting of the snow. The surface of these sheets does not form dunes, but only an irregular mantle with a suggestion of ridges and niveo-aeolian deposits help to subdue the relief. In the Sissone (N. of Rheims), where they were first described (by the author) they are slightly thicker on the west, that is the windward flank of the ridges. There they prevented solifluction on slopes of chalk which they have buried. Sheets of *coversand*, lacking dune form, are also common in periglacial areas, unlike niveo-aeolian sands they are bedded. Ters (1953) has described them in the Vendée Massif, where they are frequent on the ridges and higher parts of the interfluves. They thicken in the higher valleys which are buried under 10–20 m of fine cross-bedded sand, well sorted, in beds 1–2 mm thick, dipping or horizontal and usually cut by the surface of the ground. Wind-torn feldspars found in them suggest that they are derived from periglacial weathering. The coversands of Belgium and the Netherlands have been well described by Maréchal and Maarleveld (1955).

(4) Loess

Loess is a periglacial wind-blown silt. The grain size shows a maximum between 16 and 50 microns. Its development in a climate with weak chemical actions results frequently in a considerable $CaCO_3$ content, as much as 25%, though this is not diagnostic. Loess derived from completely siliceous rocks obviously cannot be calcareous, it must not be confused with other aeolian silts, which sometimes resemble it, such as those of the Argentine Pampas. In the dry temperate climate of the steppes, the accumulation of aeolian silts similar to loess is occurring today. As a result, in some areas such as northern China, the Hungarian and Roumanian plains and perhaps the Pampas, loess has been deposited in both glacial and interglacial periods so that it is several tens or even hundreds of metres thick.

In periglacial regions, loess is formed of fines from several sources, and not only from rock flour deposited as outwash, as was formerly thought. There is no necessary connection between glaciers and loess, but only a general agreement between the glacial periods and the periods of loess accumulation. Rutten (1954) has shown that, in Iceland, north of Vatnajökull, cover sands are deposited in stormy weather with north or S.S.W. winds, whilst in fine dry weather the wind lifts dust to 900 m and deposits it 80 km to the north as loess. Péwé (1951) has demonstrated that in Alaska the silt deposited by winds at the present time is a loess. This is formed of silt produced by the frost weathering of schists and basalt, picked up by the wind from the river banks and dried out flood channels.

Probably a large part of loess is derived from the fine debris of frost weathering, some of which has been moved by streams, some not. This would explain its distribution more satisfactorily than the theory of a glacial origin. If loess were of proglacial origin, the French loess would not be calcareous; it should be more widespread in Lorraine than in the centre of the Paris Basin, which is further from the North European ice sheet. Loess is always locally derived: that in the Paris area contains the foraminifera of the Normandy Chalk, that of Iceland is formed of volcanic debris. Loess may be transported some tens of kilometres but rarely more. It seems that an important constituent of loess, the silica fraction, which always exceeds 75% in a typical deposit, is produced by the frost shattering of sand grains, especially those which a preliminary ferruginization has made more fragile.

In Alsace, loess is more common in the north, furthest away from the Alpine glaciers. It is associated with large periglacial fans of sandy alluvium deposited at the foot of the sandstone Vosges, on which the wind has formed dunes and deflation hollows. In this case, the material has been produced by the disintegration of the Variegated Sandstone, shattered by frost, which took advantage of epigenesis by iron oxide penetrating along the cleavage planes of the quartz crystals. A sample of sand produced by the disintegration of the Variegated Sandstone, from which all material smaller than 50 microns has been removed, yielded a further 5% after a year of freeze–thaw cycles.

The correlation of loess deposition with the phases of periglacial climate raises many difficulties. Loess, by its very grain size, is readily reworked by solifluction or run off. Loess redeposited by water is distinguished by its closer texture, a slight decalcification, and above all by its lamination. In France, loess generally rests on a solifluction pavement, as in Germany, where Poser (1951) argued that loess accumulation went on throughout the cold period but that it had generally been more or less removed by the solifluction which it encouraged. Only at the end of the cold phase, when climate had ameliorated, did loess, which does not require very cold conditions, continue to be deposited though solifluction had ceased. This loess remains *in situ*. In Belgium and Holland, Gullentops and Scheys (1950), and Maréchal and Maarleveld (1955), have demonstrated the presence of three Würm loesses, the older two of which are not usually preserved, but have been removed by solifluction. In the neighbourhood of Vienna in south Germany, and still more in Hungary, a number of loess beds occur separated by soil horizons, sometimes gleyed, sometimes of a very organic grassland type, sometimes of a tundra type. It is probable that in these drier climates solifluction did not occur on a large enough scale to destroy all the loess, at least on gentle slopes. The presence of soil horizons does not necessarily mean milder climatic periods; they may record only local breaks in loess accumulation.

Loess and coversands have a zoned distribution. Everywhere the coversands occur nearer the Pleistocene glaciers, in areas of more severe climate, probably without a cover of vegetation. In Belgium, they occur north of the scarp limiting Hesbaye which runs north of Tirlemont and St. Trond. The loess, carried greater distances by the wind, has crossed the slopes, ridges and valleys which controlled the deposition of the sand. The example of present-day Iceland speaks for itself. I believe the accumulation of loess requires a cold steppe vegetation, that is a less severe climate than the periglacial climate. Before these steppe conditions set in, solifluction was general and was responsible for pavement at the base of the loess. Loess deposition implies a slight amelioration of glacial conditions; it would be post-maximum rather than solely Late-glacial as Poser claims.

The zones of loess and coversand deposition reflect the beginning of the vegetation readvance after the glacial maximum. Zones of accumulation are essentially related to the local or regional decrease in wind strength and to denser vegetation which traps the particles. In general, they form belts around the area of deflation. Cailleux states that in Iceland there are only local deposits of coarse material in central districts but that there are deposits of fine, mainly silt-sized particles carried by dust storms, in the outer zone. The distribution is the same in periglacial Europe. Sand occurs in the zone near the ice: Holland, and Germany in the Rhine valley below Cologne. The loess forms a belt further out: Paris Basin, central Belgium, southern Germany and Poland, this is broken only where there was not a close enough vegetation to fix the dust. There is some evidence of a similar scheme operating today in Siberia; there appear to be barchans in the northern part and loess further south, but detailed information is lacking.

These distinctions seem valid mainly in western Europe. In the Balkans and in Russia, as in the western United States, they are less clear. Even during the glacial maxima, a continual climate allowed the vegetation to persist right up to the ice front because of the warmer, sunnier summers. The cold loessic steppe seems to have been more permanent there. Indeed, a certain amount of loess transport still takes place in the steppe today. Instead of clear-cut periods with loess deposition succeeding periods without, there seem to have been variations in the intensity of deposition, which was almost continuous throughout the duration of the glacial period.

A loess cover, with its variable thickness, modifies relief considerably. Slopes producing eddies are the site of a particularly thick accumulation. As a result, loess may produce asymmetrical valleys. On flat surfaces, as in northern Jugoslavia, the original surface of the loess has low swells like those in coversands but less marked, reaching a height of 2 m (Milojevic, 1950). Finally, loess favours solifluction under suitable climatic conditions and may thus accelerate the reduction of slopes.

(C) Characteristics of Coastal Development

Coastal processes are considerably modified by frost. In one way the effects are negative: during the whole period when the sea is frozen over, the shores are protected from wave action. This must cause considerable quantitative changes in the evolution of the coast, but no one has yet studied them. It may be one of the factors promoting the growth of deltas in polar seas; all the large rivers of the Arctic are building them. The working season of the sea coincides with the time of arrival of the fluvial load. When the sea freezes it has not had time to destroy the deposits of the preceding summer. Furthermore, even in the middle of summer, ice floes persist on a considerable scale on many coasts, so that the strength of wave action is reduced. This last point may help to explain the importance of fine sand and mud on Arctic shores. Low coasts with lagoons and marshes are very widespread and cannot all be explained by the isostatic uplift of areas glaciated during the Quaternary. For this type of coast is found even where there was no ice sheet. It is true that periglacial rivers carry large amounts of silt derived from frost weathering, but special conditions, as yet little understood, favour its coastal accumulation.

One factor amongst others may be the temperature of the water, which is always around 0°C, and close to that of its maximum density, 4°C. Theoretically this should help to keep fine materials in suspension and permit their transport for long distances along the shore, and distribution along extensive stretches of coast. All these points require systematic study, which to our knowledge has not been undertaken in spite of their great practical importance.

Frost also has direct effects. The first is the destruction of cliffs. The beaches are subjected to the winter freeze up, which generally involves only one freeze–thaw cycle. It is, however, particularly effective because it operates on very wet materials. The foot of the cliffs and the strand to the level of free water below the pack ice undergo a very destructive frost shattering. The higher parts of the cliffs are affected by frost weathering in the same way as other slopes.

The retreat of periglacial cliffs is very rapid and is brought about mainly by differential frost weathering at the base, producing overhangs. On the whole, the profile tends to be convex in rocks moderately resistant to frost shattering and vertical in other rocks. Flores Silva (1952) in one of the few studies devoted to the characteristics of polar shores, describes fully the perpendicular cliffs in the granites of Graham Land. The debris is largely reduced by freeze–thaw, for the very calm waters due to the protection afforded by pack ice do not produce typical beach pebbles. Mud polygons may form between the ridges of angular blocks produced by the retreat of the cliffs. Corbel has also pointed out the importance of weathering in the evolution of the cliffs of Spitzbergen. It is possible that this accelerated retreat produces a platform at the level of the pack ice, and this might be the origin of the Norwegian *Strandflat*. A long marine standstill would be necessary, however, to produce so extensive a platform. In Norway, no pack ice forms at the present day, and probably there was none in the interglacial, while during the glacial periods the shore was covered by the glaciers. It is therefore not a likely area for a coastal platform to be produced by frost shattering.

The ice also plays a part in the evolution of coasts formed of unconsolidated deposits. Here again studies are few in spite of the frequency and widespread occurrence of this phenomenon. During the break-up of the sea ice by thaw or a particularly violent storm, ice rafts are driven ashore carrying embedded boulders. Certain unworn exotic boulders found along the coasts of western Europe may be due to this, but if one can exclude the possibility of their being ship's ballast, they may be used to identify some of the shore lines of the glacial period.

Reinhard (1955) has shown clearly the part played by ice rafts driven against the coast of Mecklenburg. These jams of sea ice occur one year in four on the average, with a northeast wind, and are dispersed by a southwest wind. The ice is driven up the beach, bringing with it pebbles and sand which are formed into ridges characterized by a microstructure of thrust faults. These ridges have a steep face towards the sea from which the thrust came, and a gentle slope towards the land they help to build up the upper beach. Generally, they are rapidly destroyed by summer storms, but some, which are too large, are simply washed and remain, somewhat defaced.

Similar ridges have been noted by me on the pebble beaches of the deep narrow inlets of eastern Sweden and also of some of the lakes. With the very limited fetch, only ice jams could have produced them. The banks of pebbles were 1 to 2 m high and reached up to 3 m above the level of the Baltic. Unlike normal beach ridges, their steep slope faces the open water, as Reinhard indicated. In Spitzbergen, similar forms have been described by Thompson (1953), under the name of sand ridges, with a height of up to 2·5 m and a width of 40 m. They consist of sand mixed with large blocks, without sorting or stratification, unlike beach deposits. Scattered over them are depressions due to the melting of buried blocks of sea ice. In the ridges are boulders brought up from the sea bed. Icebergs which come ashore bring foreign morainic material which forms clay patches in the midst of the pebbles.

Polar coasts show some marked characteristics in their evolution which give rise to distinctive forms. These have unfortunately received little attention; even an adequate terminology is lacking. Accordingly, I propose the term *plate-forme littorale de gélivation* – cryogenetic shore platform – for the platform produced by the retreat of a sea cliff solely under the effects of frost weathering; and *rides de banquise* – ice floe ramparts – for ridges produced on the upper beaches by jams of ice floes.

PART THREE

Glacial Processes and Landforms

CHAPTER 1

Glacier Dynamics

WITHOUT an adequate knowledge of the processes of erosion it would be impossible to understand landforms, or very often, to identify them correctly. So, before studying glacial geomorphology, it is vital to summarize what is known of glacier dynamics. This is not easy as they are less well known than those of running water or even the sea.

Direct observation is difficult. It is possible to instrument running water in order to measure its velocity or load at a given depth. It is impossible to apply similar methods to the study of glaciers. Again, the use of a scale model in the laboratory, widely employed in hydrology, where it has enabled general principles to be discovered or defined, has scarcely begun to be used in the study of glaciers. The very flow of ice is much more complex than that of water; it is essentially a viscous fluid and not a liquid. Ice, in its journey from the snowfield to the glacier snout, undergoes changes in its crystal form which complicate the problem of flow. Furthermore, the problem is not the same in a cold glacier as in a temperate one. This is the key to the evolution of the problem. For a long time, only observations on the surface have been available, from which it is difficult to extrapolate to the lower levels. However, in the last decade or two research has taken a new direction. To classical glaciology, to the study of regimes, have been added the study of the physics and dynamics of ice. So far this has been tentative and fragmentary; it is scarcely possible to do more than review recent results and critically to examine accepted theories in their light.

(A) FROM SNOW TO ICE

Glacier dynamics are complicated by changes in crystal form during movement. Snow, névé and ice can be distinguished by the shape and size of the crystals of H_2O of which they are composed. This is an example of metamorphism which takes place under conditions capable of observation.

(I) Snow and its properties

Snow falls in the form of crystals of H_2O, in a sense it is a kind of subaerial sediment, chemical in origin, the precipitation of one of the constituents of air (water vapour). As with many sediments of this kind, snow is not stable; its properties change rapidly after deposition, as a result of the transformation of its crystals. The crystalline structure of snow depends on two variables: its initial condition and the stage of transformation reached.

(1) The Crystalline Structure of Snow

Snow crystals while falling, are generally grouped together in a manner which is regular but complex. All the various forms are characterized by a relatively large surface area compared with volume. This facilitates, not only the agglomeration of the crystals into flakes, but also entails a high porosity which allows air to be trapped between the clusters. Sometimes these clusters of crystals may be very compact, the snow then forms irregular particles owing to the entanglement of microscopic elementary crystal forms. At other times, it takes the form of irregular globules with a spiky outline but without clearly defined particles, this is sleet, formed of snow partly melted and resolidified during its descent. Rounded globules also occur, with smooth outlines like drops, this is essentially rain which has frozen while falling. Hail has a similar form, the chief difference being that the centre of the particles is often solid while in the case of frozen rain it often remains liquid.

In considering the properties of snow, these differences of form are of great importance since more compact grains result in reduced porosity. Snow grains are always small, around a millimetre. Their properties vary with the conditions of precipitation and the stage of transformation reached.

(a) **The Influence of Precipitation Conditions** It is unusual for snow to fall under conditions of extremely low temperature. Such areas have a low annual precipitation. Most commonly, snowfall occurs at about 0°C. With very low temperatures, crystallization is rapid and the grains consequently small, their size is further reduced if the snowfall is accompanied by strong winds, as these restrict the growth of the crystals. With the temperature around zero, snow crystals and groups of crystals have more time to grow, especially if the fall occurs in calm conditions. If atmospheric temperatures vary vertically, two possibilities may occur. Where the upper layers are cold and the lower layers slightly above zero, precipitation will take the form of snow in the upper part but the grains will tend to melt as they fall. The result is compact grains of sleet. If, on the other hand, the upper air is a little above zero, while the lower layers are colder, precipitation takes the form of rain which freezes while falling.

Because of the close relationship between the crystalline structure of snow and the conditions of precipitation, it is possible to have successive beds of snow, differing both in structure and mechanical properties, laid down in the course of a single protracted snowfall.

(b) **The Influence of the Stage of Transformation** As soon as it has fallen, the structure of the snow undergoes a continuous metamorphism. Indeed, once it reaches a certain depth (only a few decimetres), the lower part is affected by the pressure of the snow on top, which continues to accumulate. This pressure is sufficient to cause settling and metamorphism (diagenesis), which begins immediately after the fall, under the influence of temperature changes. These set in motion the series of processes which in turn transform snow to névé and then to ice.

Two successive phases can be distinguished in the diagenesis of snow. During the first, the grains become smaller and increasingly equidimensional while the form of crystals changes. During the second, the grains grow larger while becoming rounded. The mechanisms which produce these changes are of two kinds, they result partly from the pressure of the overlying snow which usually produces fine-grained, compact, hard snow, and also from molecular transfer, which depends on temperature. At very low temperatures the only active process is sublimation, which is very slow. When temperatures are around zero, the transfer is brought about by melting and recrystallization.

These processes are controlled by variations in the weather after the fall of the snow. A temporary rise in temperature followed by freezing, hardens the snow and this rapid diagenesis leads to the formation of large grains welded together by frost. Since weather conditions are responsible not only for the original character of the snow but also the conditions of its metamorphism, the crystalline structure is linked closely to climate.

(2) The Physical Properties of Snow

The fundamental feature distinguishing snow from névé is its porosity, which depends directly on density. The latter may vary from 0·1 to 0·6; since the density of ice is 0·91, it is obvious that in snow the proportion of air may reach 90%. This has important consequences. Snow is able to absorb large amounts of water, and this is mainly responsible for modifying its density and also affects its metamorphism. Snow is also very permeable to air so that the latter can circulate pretty freely. The presence of this proportion of air results in very poor thermal conductivity. From this it follows that the melting of snow is due to insolation which is able to heat considerably the superficial layer of snow, rather than to the direct effects of temperature, because thermal waves do not penetrate readily. The density of snow is an important criterion in determining its porosity. At the time of its fall, the more spherical and sheathed in meltwater the grains are, the denser the snow.

The mechanical properties of snow vary with its temperature. At low temperatures, it is elastic: around freezing point, it is more viscous. To its plasticity is due its power to creep. The larger the snow grains, the less the resistance to shearing since the points of contact between the grains are then less numerous than when the grains are small.

To sum up, snow is subject to opposing influences. Compaction increases its strength, while a rise in temperature reduces it by enlarging the grains, but compaction favours metamorphism, which, under milder conditions leads to a phase of grain growth. Finally, compaction itself is favoured by higher temperatures, which accelerate molecular transfer. The dynamics of snow are therefore extremely complex.

Changes in the mechanical properties of snow, responsible for its morphogenetic action, are particularly marked under more variable climatic conditions in which frequent temperature oscillations occur around zero. This fact is vital to the explanation of nivation phenomena.

(II) The Transformation of Snow to Nevé and Ice

Névé develops from the snow of the preceding year, already strongly consolidated. Its textural properties are therefore different from both those of snow or of ice. This generalization does not hold everywhere, however, it does not apply in polar glacial regions where metamorphism is so slow that snow may persist for several years before being transformed

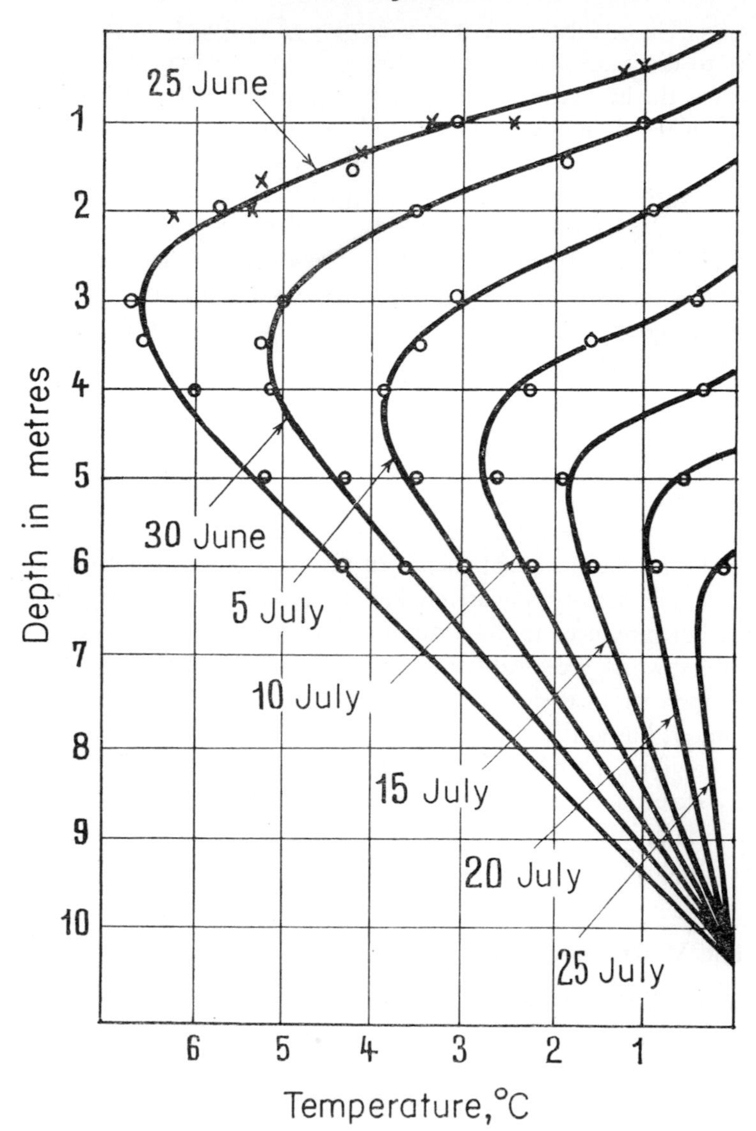

FIG. 15 Vertical distribution of temperature in the névé at the Central Station on Isachsen Plateau, (Spitzbergen) from 25th June to 25th July, 1934 (*after Sverdrup*, *Geogr. Ann.*, *1935*)

The relics of the winter cold disappear steadily under the influence of summer heat. At 3 m on the 25th June, the temperature is −7°C. On the 5th July it is only −3°C and on the 10th July 0°C.

into névé. On a global scale it is necessary to fall back on physical properties to distinguish the various stages in the metamorphism of snow. Density is the best criterion. In general, névé may be defined as having a density of 0·6 or more. In Greenland this density is reached only at a depth of 35 m. In other words, a density normally reached in the Alps after one year, is attained here only after 35 to 50 years. Density may also be used to distinguish ice from névé. The density of ice varies between 0·82 and 0·91, the range reflecting the proportion of air bubbles and in later stages, mainly dust. The time necessary for the transformation of ice is not known with any accuracy. As in the metamorphism of snow, the length of the process depends on climate.

(1) The Nature of the Diagenesis

The increase in density of water when solidified is caused by the rearrangement of the crystals. As the air is driven out, the grains gradually grow bigger, losing their original shape. In névé, air is still plentiful; névé is porous and its density is relatively low. In ice, air is no longer part of the texture but is reduced to the form of inclusions in the solid. It exists only as bubbles, which are steadily expelled so that the ice becomes more pure.

The increase in grain size is the basic fact in the metamorphism of solid water, but at the moment we have only slight evidence about it, in certain regions. In névé, grain size ranges from 1 to 10 mm. In ice it usually exceeds a centimetre. This increase in grain size goes hand in hand with an increase in density but the laws governing it vary from one climate to another, and are still imperfectly understood.

(2) The Mechanism of the Diagenesis

Again very little is known. Three processes together lead to the growth of grains and the accompanying expulsion of air. The first is the production of water, by local melting, which refreezes in the pore space, reducing the volume of air and increasing grain size. The second is the condensation of water vapour produced by sublimation through the pores of the snow or névé mass. Finally, under the influence of pressures created by glacier flow, plastic deformation and rearrangement occur within the solid, particularly at depth within the glacier. These three processes do not operate at the same rate, the first is by far the most rapid and it occurs within hours whereas the others require at least a week. This explains the slow development of diagenesis in the inlandsis where only the less rapid processes play an appreciable part.

5 *Glacial valley in the Alps: Zugspitze massif and the Höllental, Bavaria*

6 *Glaciers in the Mont Blanc massif*

In the foreground: séracs. In the trough: confluence glaciers with parallel ice streams and ogives, the latter soon disappearing beneath a continuous cover of ablation moraine. The glacier retreat has led to glacier confluences being made by ice falls at the mouth of the hanging troughs. To the right: avalanche chutes in the side of the trough, with, at their foot, cones of ice partly covering the lateral moraines.

(3) Glacier Structure

From a consideration of the glacier regime along with ice diagenesis, the structure of the glacier, that is the distribution of the elements within the mass, becomes clearer. In the upper part of the glacier (the accumulation zone), snow falling during the winter does not completely melt in the following summer, this results in the building up of successive layers of snow. The present year's snow forms the surface bed and is underlain by last year's snow, already transformed into névé. Below this the snow beds become progressively more altered. As for ice, this is only found at depths of 30–40 m, sometimes rather less in the Alps, but nearer 100 m in the inlandsis. In temperate glaciers, these beds of snow are generally separated by a thin layer of dust concentrated by the partial melting of snow in summer.

In the ablation zone of temperate or intermediate glaciers, conditions are rather different. By definition, ablation predominates over accumulation. Névé does not form. In winter, snow lies directly on the ice whereas in summer only the ice remains. All the ice has come from the source area, and therefore its diagenesis is far advanced. The structure of the glacier mass has changed. The characteristic stratification of the surface névé zone has been obliterated by the effects of pressure due to flow. Judging from the meagre evidence available, texture has been altered as well as structure, the grains tend to become elongated in the direction of flow.

(B) Glacier Flow

Although it was first recognized in 1544 by Sebastian Münster, very little is known about glacier flow.

(I) Observed Data

Existing data concern only certain aspects of the problem. The only glaciers whose movements have been studied for a considerable length of time and are relatively well known, are the alpine glaciers of the maritime type. In contrast, only sporadic observations have been made on other types, especially on the inlandsis. For example in Greenland, there

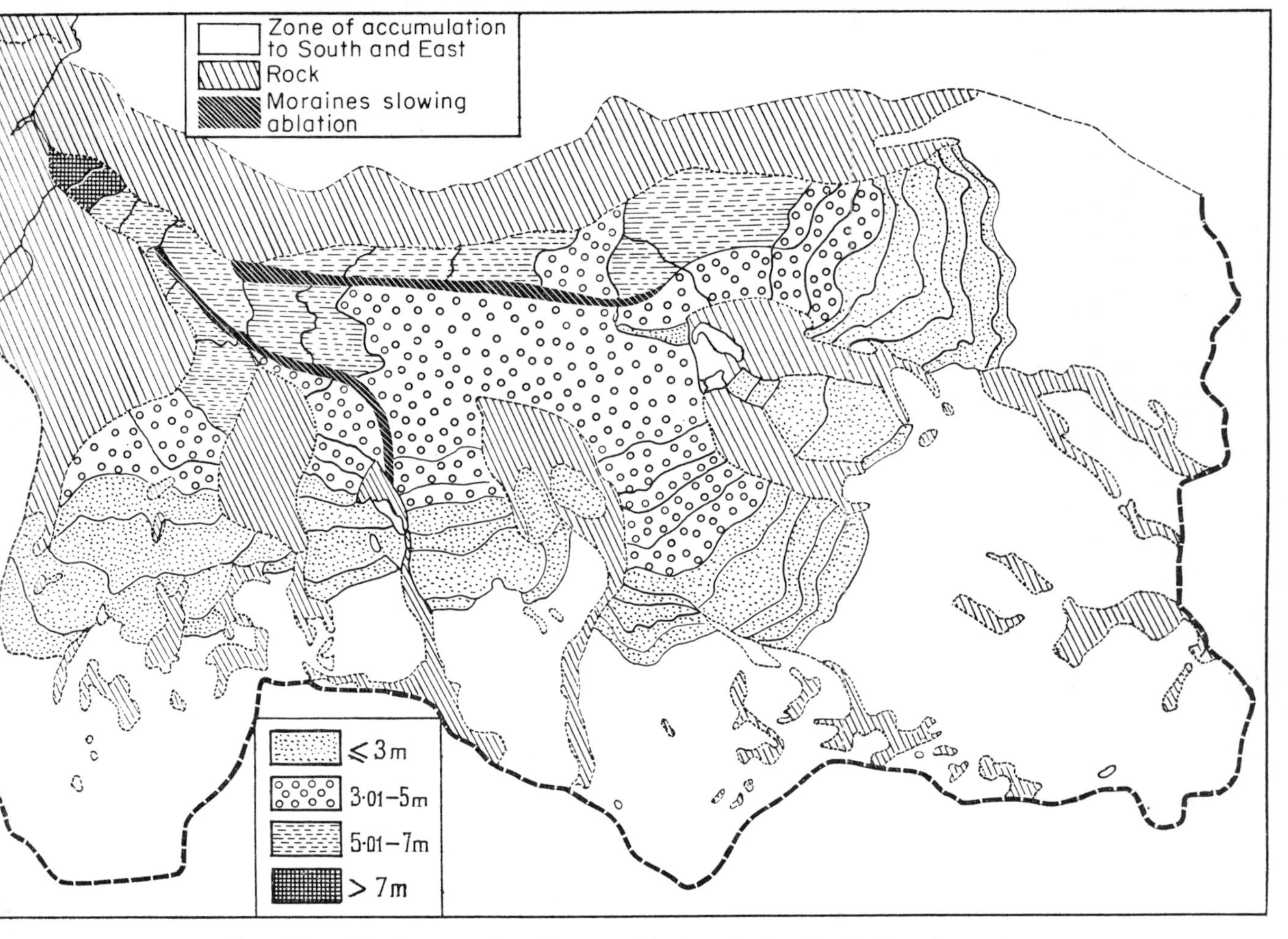

FIG. 16 Ablation on the Gorner Glacier, Switzerland (*based on the 1/50 000 map of the F.O.S.O.*)

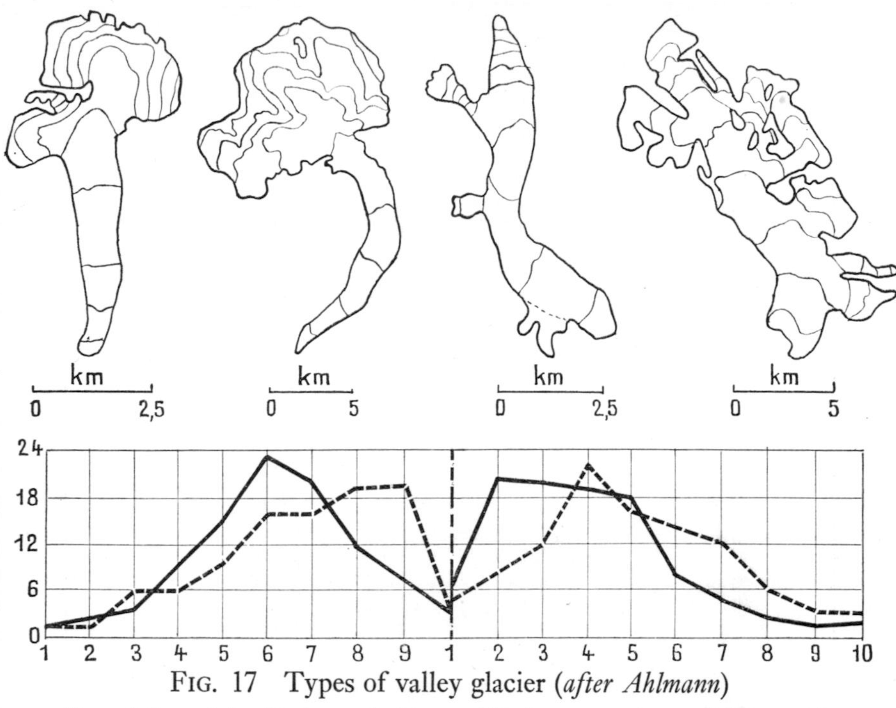

FIG. 17 Types of valley glacier (*after Ahlmann*)

From left to right: Vedretta de Forno (Alps), contour interval 125 m; Great Aletsch Glacier (Alps), contour interval 265 m; Sachen Glacier (Central Asia), contour interval 165 m; Fourteenth of July Glacier (Spitzbergen), contour interval 100 m.

is available only a series of comparisons between fixed points made at considerable intervals of time, or short but interesting observations on the outlet glaciers. As regards the mechanics of the glacier itself, observations are also often very scattered.

(1) Techniques of Study

The major difficulty here springs from the slow movement of glaciers, which is of the order of some hundreds of metres a year, at the surface.

(a) **Data on Surface Movement** These have been obtained by long-established methods. The oldest and simplest uses coloured and numbered stones or stakes arranged in transverse rows on the glacier surface. Their initial position is fixed by sighting from a reference point of the bed rock. Theodolite readings are then taken daily or sometimes more frequently. The study of the inlandsis is made difficult by the scarcity, or even

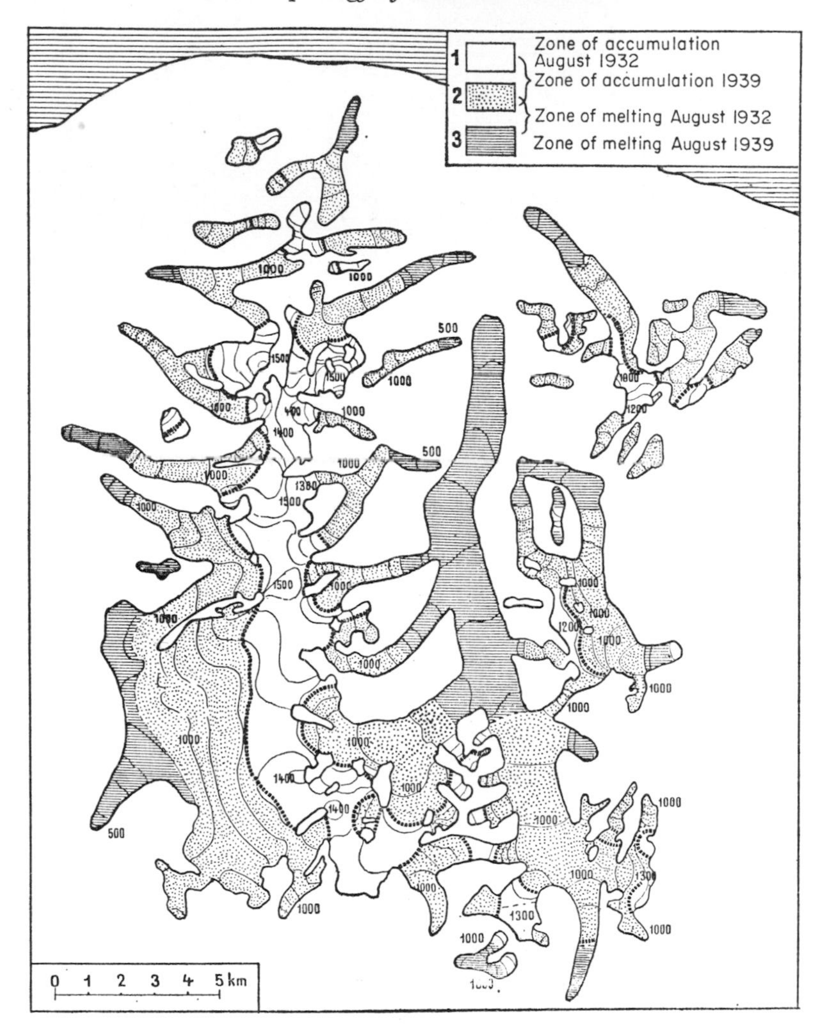

FIG. 18 Anastomosing glaciers: the glacier pattern on Clavering I., N.E. Greenland (*after Ahlmann*)

Contour interval 100 m; figures show altitude.

Mountain ice cap on the highest ground. Large valley glacier, with small valley-side glaciers coming down from the uplands to the valley floor but not always reaching it.

absence, of reference points to which a line of markers could be fixed. Position can only be determined astronomically.

(b) **Data on Movement at Depth** The oldest method has been in use since 1904. A bore is made down to the rock floor and in it a column of

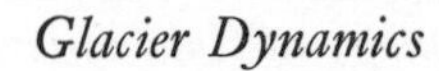

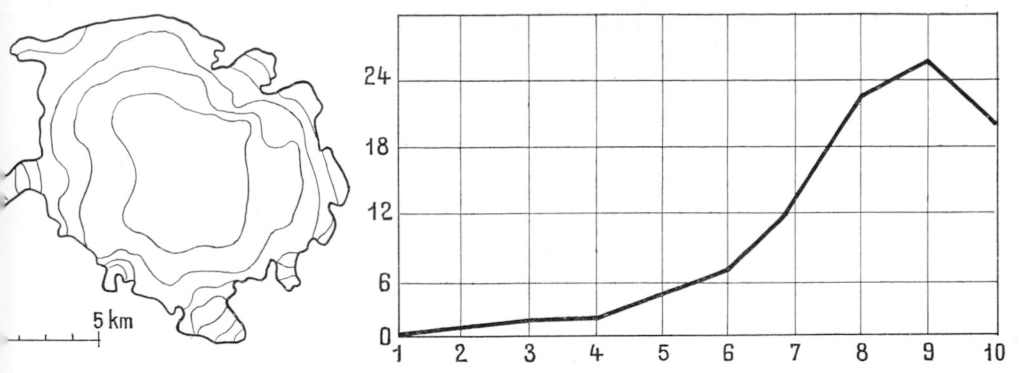

FIG. 19 Simple ice cap; Hardanger Glacier, Norway (*after Ahlmann*)

Left: schematic map, contours at 100 m; Right: frequency distribution of altitude.
An almost perfect ice cap, with slight development of outlet glaciers, which extend the curve on the graph towards the origin.

rods is inserted, these are left in position and their displacement systematically recorded. Since the total length of the buried rods is known, regular measurement of the part exposed enables one to reconstruct the profile of the rock floor and the thickness of the ice. In recent years, a modified version of this has been used by British glaciologists at the Jungfraujoch station, while direct observation has been made possible by the construction of tunnels under the ice to obtain water for the production of hydroelectric power, as for example, in the Mer de Glace.

There are several methods of indirect observation. One of these is the use of seismic soundings; another, using pollen analysis has had some success. Pollen carried on to the surface of the glacier by wind is buried under successive layers of snow and the spectrum records seasonal changes. Each bed is distinguishable and can be located by means of bores. Radioactive tracers might also be used but it is feared that the ice would prevent their location by absorbing the radiation. Natural radioactivity has been used; the proportion of unstable isotopes in fresh snow is determined and compared with measurements made on the various beds met in bores. Since the radioactivity is decreasing at a known rate, it is possible to date each layer of ice. This method has been used in Antarctica, especially by Lorius.

(2) Result of Study

The rate of flow of glacier ice is now fairly well known, at least as far as the surface is concerned. It is generally expressed in metres per year but it must be remembered that it varies with the season. The commonest speeds recorded in the Alps are around 40 m a year. That the rate of flow is progressively reduced in the lower parts of the valley glacier is generally accepted, for almost all glaciers terminating on dry land. Little is known of glaciers which flow into the sea. The calving of icebergs produces a void leading to a relatively rapid movement. Velocity also varies from one point to another along any one line transverse to the glacier. Thus there is generally a reduction in velocity from the centre towards the sides, the maximum occurring close to the glacier axis. Sometimes it is more complex, with several longitudinal zones of maximum velocity separated by bands moving more slowly. Such differences in speed between parallel bands are generally found when the ice is formed by several confluent glaciers whose ice masses are separated by medial moraines.

The relationship between velocity distribution at the surface and the characteristics of glaciers is still imperfectly understood. The thicker the ice, the faster it tends to flow. This does not appear true of the inlandsis, however, as flow is very slow in spite of its great thickness. The reduction in velocity towards the glacier limit, which is very general, is not solely due to friction with the rock bed; it is also due to the thinning of the ice. This also explains the reduction in glacier speed during retreat. It has also been established that rapid thinning of the ice is accompanied by a very irregular flow, which is attributed to an uneven rock floor. Again, this rule does not apply to the inlandsis whose outlet glaciers flow relatively rapidly compared with the movement of the ice cap itself. This is partly due to the calving of icebergs, partly to the concentration of ice streams by relief and, in Antarctica, to the increase of snow supply towards the margins, by blizzards.

Another factor apparently of considerable importance is the slope of the glacier bed, which is more or less accurately reflected in the slope of the ice surface. There is a correlation between slope and velocity (velocity increasing with slope). The great gathering grounds feeding glacier systems are areas of ice congestion where surface slope and velocity are small.

Yet another factor must be considered together with those above, the influence of the local regime of the ice mass under consideration. Thickness, slope and local regime can combine in many ways, sometimes working with, sometimes against one another. The surface velocity of glaciers is subject to periodic variations of changing rhythm. The greatest variations are those of secular rhythm for they are tied to variations of regime. As regards annual rhythm, measurements made in the Alps show a rate of flow for winter which is double that of summer. As to daily rhythm, only the precise measurements of recent years have made their study possible.

Although some authors refuse to accept it, this seems to be established. In northeast Greenland, Battle determined a rate of flow, during the day, of more than 1–2 cm, compared with a night flow equal to only 50–10% of this. Rates of flow at depth are almost unknown.

(II) The Properties of Glacier Ice

The essence of the question of the mechanics of glacier flow is whether it behaves as a viscous or plastic material. A viscous body subjected to outside forces is not capable of retaining its shape indefinitely; it tends to spread out. A plastic body on the other hand, will retain indefinitely the shape it takes on through deformation by outside forces. The viscosity of ice has been measured in the laboratory, like that of other materials. Its plasticity is equally well known.

The surface of a glacier varies considerably. Generally ice and névé do not adhere to bedrock but are separated from it by the *bergschrund* (Fr. *rimaye*), a fissure which may be from a few decimetres to 1–2 metres wide. It is not purely a surface feature. By reducing the adherence of the ice it diminishes the effects of mechanical erosion through direct contact. Ice does not grind all the hollows in the glacier bed.

The ice surface is sometimes smooth and unbroken, and without crevasses. Where valley glaciers are well developed, the ice displays a pattern consisting of V-shaped markings with somewhat rounded angles and apexes pointing down-glacier. These are the glacier ogives, they are formed of successive layers of ice, superimposed in stratigraphic order and outcropping because they lie oblique to the longitudinal ice slope. The amorphous bands which separate them indicate beds completely churned up. These are due to lateral additions by avalanches whose original stratification has been completely destroyed. The tensile stress due to friction along the glacier margin seems to me to be a further factor. When the glacier displays several sets of ogives side by side, it has been formed by several confluent ice streams. When two glaciers of comparable size unite nearly at right angles, the medial moraines of the main glacier are compressed as if crushed laterally while those of the tributary glacier fold in pleats and waves as if compressed longitudinally. Sharp distinguishes the following relationships in glaciers formed by several ice streams: *juxtaposed* ice streams, when two ice masses flow side by side at the same level and both reach the rock bed underneath; superimposed ice streams, when the ice of the tributary glacier establishes itself on top of the ice which is already in the main valley; and *inset* ice streams, where ice from the tributary glacier becomes sunk in the surface of the main glacier.

These points on the ice streams united in a single glacier are essential to an understanding of the form of the glacier bed, particularly the steps at valley confluences. They show that different ice streams mix very little, but tend to remain separate. Since this same phenomenon can be found at river confluences one hesitates to relate it either to plastic or viscous properties of the ice. It is the same with the behaviour of ice in relation to certain obstacles: in many cases the ice takes on the shape of the obstacle instead of pushing against it. Sometimes the ice cracks and breaks up into great blocks separated by large crevasses. Its surface appears chaotic, froming *séracs*, which are generally found on steep slopes where ice flow is most rapid.

Crevasses result from the fracture of the ice mass by forces applied too suddenly and too powerfully for plastic deformation; the resulting tension causes shearing. A study of the arrangement and appearance of the walls of crevasses indicates the relative movement of the blocks. Thrust planes can be seen dipping at less than 45°, often with a reverse slope rising down-glacier. They are frequently marked by stones, mud and debris of all kinds dragged up from depth and including blocks of 10 or even 20 cubic metres. In the ablation zone, such debris protects the clean ice underneath it, forming small steps sloping up-glacier like thrust planes. Other planes of discontinuity are roughly vertical. These are glide planes, and are smooth and fluted. They are produced by differences in the speed of movement between adjoining ice masses. The result of shearing and differential movement is to destroy the original stratification of the ice. Thus, observations indicate the great differences which may exist in conditions of flow. In the absence of studies on scale models, the mechanics of ice flow are poorly formulated and the relative importance of viscosity and plasticity is difficult to evaluate.

(III) The Mechanics of Flow

The mechanics of glacier movement are very much in dispute. Among more than 80 theories relating to the problem, not one can command a majority. Even the most serious studies are liable to at least two errors: firstly, the extrapolation of experiments done in the laboratory without adequate knowledge of natural conditions; and secondly, extrapolations based on extreme and oversimplified theories.

(1) Ice Texture and Basic Mechanics

Recent work on ice grains in temperate glaciers, particularly by Renaud, has shown that they are coated with weak saline. This interstitial brine is capable of remaining unfrozen at lower temperatures than the grains, since salts in solution lower the point at which water freezes. At about melting point the brine may become liquid and then promotes the movement of the ice grains in relation to each other. Hambourg had distinguished two basic types of plasticity:

(a) *microplasticity*, which is due to the tendency of ice grains to become drawn out in the direction of the forces acting on them. This elongation is achieved by the 'translation', or gliding, of thin laminae of ice which, joined together, form a grain of ice.

(b) *mesoplasticity*, which is due to intergranular movement owing to the semi-liquifaction of the interstitial brine. The lowering of the melting point due to the presence of salts causes the film of water near the melting point of the grains to increase in thickness.

The relative importance of these two processes is a function of the physical conditions in the interior of the glacier. In cold glaciers only microplasticity comes into play and then only slowly. But in temperate glaciers the two processes are at work, and are more active if the temperature of the ice at depth is at melting point. For this reason, the outlet glaciers of the Greenland ice sheet, which have a polar maritime regime, flow much faster than the ice cap itself.

(2) The General Nature of Movement

The problem of ice flow is complicated by the effects of pressure on processes acting at depth within the glacier and by the relative rigidity of ice. At a given point, speed is largely due to the thrust of the ice further up-glacier. There are several theories as to how primary movement takes place. The first is that of laminar flow, by which adjustment to pressure occurs along the contact surfaces of adjacent layers within the ice, giving a certain plasticity to the glacier. The second is that of extrusion flow: the increase of pressure with depth makes the basal ice more plastic and therefore more mobile so that it moves faster, with an upward component in the tongue. Heat generated by friction (*Avsiouk*) contributes to this process. So does the next factor. This theory concerns flow by gliding and rotation: shearing occurs in the depth of the ice, though open cre-

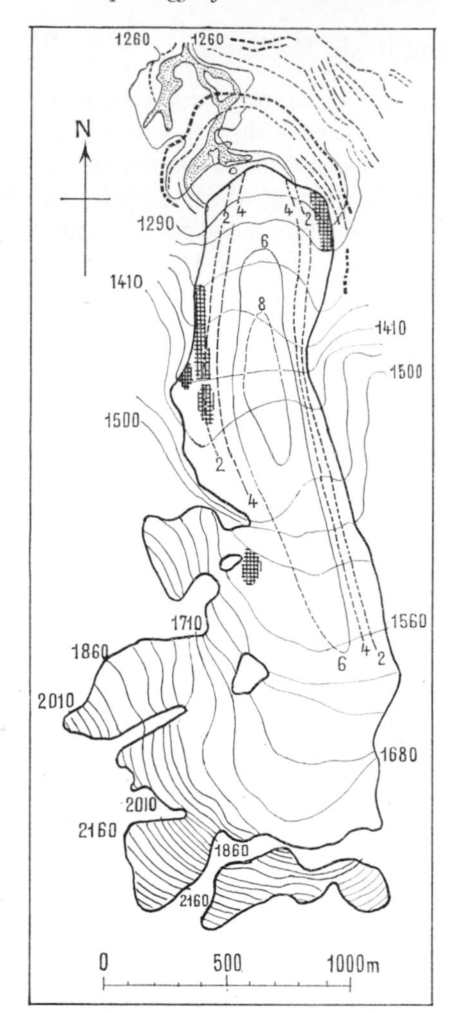

FIG. 20 Stryggedal Glacier, Norway (*after Ahlmann*)

Altitude in metres.

The lines with an oval trace on the glacier join points having the same rate of movement in cm per 24 hours, (averaged for 1st July 1923 to 21st August 1926). Note the decrease in speed towards the glacier sides and towards the snout.

vasses cannot form because of pressure, and blocks of ice are rotated upwards from the basal parts of the glacier.

Demorest distinguishes theoretically four different types of flow within the same ice mass. *Extrusion* flow and *obstructed extrusion* flow are controlled by pressure, plastic ice at the base of the glacier being forced outwards by the weight of the ice overlying it. *Gravity* flow and *obstructed gravity* flow are drainage controlled; the former could be considered as viscous flow. Given a mass of ice so thick that adherence to the subglacial rock floor is overcome, the ice tends to spread out under the force of gravity.

The two types of obstructed flow (assuming they exist) have an upward component and tend locally to increase the thickness of the glacier. The varied conditions at each confluence as a result of thickness, velocity and the dominance of one tributary over the other, determine the form taken by each ice stream.

Nye believes that flow is laminar. But if this is produced solely by plasticity and hydrostatic pressure, the existence of crevasses cannot be explained. Also, Nye has described two theoretical types of flow. Flow is compressive when velocity is greater upstream and diminishes downstream, so that longitudinal pressure is created and this hinders the development of crevasses. On the other hand, it might lead to fracturing and the development of thrust planes and ridges. Compressive flow could be produced by a decrease in velocity due to a reduction in slope or friction on bends, constriction, etc. The second type of flow, tensile flow, occurs when velocity increases downstream. This produces a traction stress which may exceed the cohesion of the ice and cause fractures which by tensile stress may become crevasses.

According to Nye, the topography of the glacier bed determines the type of flow. Where the long profile is concave, compressive flow is dominant. When it is covex, tensile flow will predominate.

Finsterwalder also distinguishes two basic types of flow. *Continuous* flow occurs when the ice remains unbroken, preserving the original stratification. In *discontinuous* flow, movement is by rigid blocks; the ice is broken up and masses of ice slide past one another at different speeds, separated by crevasses. This occurs at high velocities. In the first case, there is no apparent break in the ice but the maximum speed occurs at the centre of each glacier tongue and fine moraines are well drawn out in the direction of advance. Speed increases from the cirque to the lower middle glacier, at the end of which it is rapidly reduced. Here, only gravity operates, ablation having cancelled the effects of thrust from upglacier ice. In the second case, breaking point is reached and continuous flow gives way to discontinuous flow, three-dimensionally. Lliboutry has elaborated a complete theory of glacier flow and, like Nye, has expressed it mathematically. In his opinion, there are two kinds of movement: sliding, and plastic deformation. He believes that contact between ice and bedrock is very important. Heat generated by friction between ice and rock is poorly conducted by the ice and, as a result, temporary melting occurs locally to a thickness of several millimetres or even less. This film of water considerably reduces the resistance to movement, allowing slipping to occur, it also enables the ice to fit the irregularities on the glacier bed. This water, by entering the joints, would account for plucking, for by freezing there it causes joint blocks to adhere to the ice. Pressures are at their maximum on reverse slopes and at a minimum on their downstream face where the ice tends to become detached from the rock face, thus explaining the development of rock bars and over-deepening. An increase in supply when the glacier is not slipping, leads to a thickening to the glacier, causing a kinematic wave 5 to 6 times as fast as the movement of the ice. At any one point, the rate of flow depends on the velocity above and below it. It may cause movement which may be either compressive, or tensile with crevassing. The waves of pressure due to compressive movement travel much more rapidly than the rate of advance of the ice (up to 150 times as fast). The difference between dynamic and static friction, owing to delayed elasticity, accounts for the sudden spurts in flow.

Haefeli has made a critical study of the different theories and has shown that they are not exclusive and that the best of them needs to be further developed. He insists that continuous and discontinuous flow, may exist side by side in the same glacier, the latter being accompanied by crevassing. He believes that in a stationary ice mass which is impermeable and resting on a horizontal surface, vertical forces are equal to horizontal forces. He also agrees that there is a fundamental difference between zones of acceleration where the ice is subject to traction stress, leading to the formation of crevasses, and zones of deceleration producing compressive stress.

Conclusion

In the light of present knowledge, the following conclusions may be drawn. Compared with the laws of fluvial hydraulics, very little is known about the laws of glacier flow and there is no question of a quantitative interpretation. Before attempting to express the data in mathematical terms, it must be greatly increased. To the geographer, the most obvious distinction is that between continuous and discontinuous flow, both plastic and gliding.

During recent years, a French geophysicist, Lliboutry, has made great efforts to determine more precisely the mechanics of glacier flow by comparing very careful field measurements with the most advanced theory. He distinguishes:

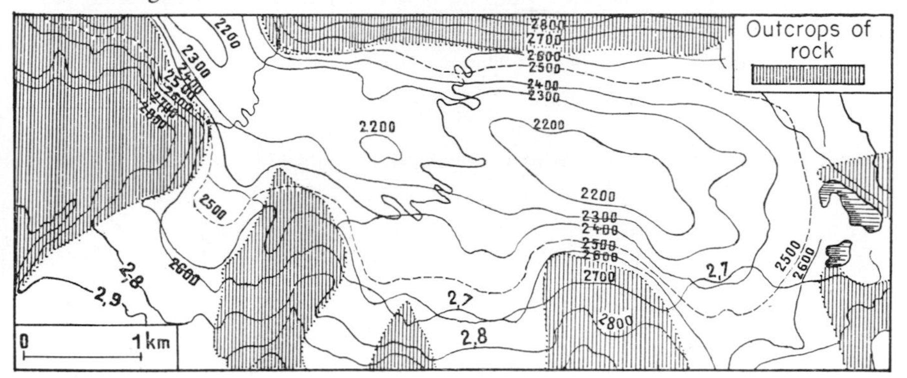

FIG. 21 Subglacial surface of the Gorner Glacier, Switzerland (*after Süsstrunck, La Houille blanche, 1951, p. 8*)

The contours of the glacier bed, numbered in metres, somewhat generalized and regular, have been drawn between points fixed by seismic methods. The surface contours, more sinuous, are numbered in kilometres.

(i) flow by plastic deformation which only develops when the ice is thick enough. This plastic flow is closely associated with the kinematic waves of ice which travel 5·2 times as fast as the glacier itself;

(ii) flow by gliding, where the glacier slips over its bed. This is expressed in surface tension, which may lead to shearing and the development of open crevasses. The rise in temperature reduces friction by causing pockets of water to develop between the sole of the glacier and the rock bed. The hydrostatic pressure of this water tends to lift the ice.

The two methods of flow may work together in the same glacier or interfere with each other. In a sector where gliding is dominant, the speed is controlled by the minimum speed of those sectors where flow is by plastic deformation both upstream and downstream. When ice, moving by gliding, comes into contact with ice which is not gliding, the pressure accelerates flow by plastic deformation and may even induce gliding. In detail this explains the jerky movement of the glacier considered in the short term. The sliding of a small mass of ice against another mass lying downstream, makes use of the elasticity of the ice. When the elasticity has been absorbed, it stops and only recommences with the movement of the mass lying downglacier. Finally, when friction is greatly increased by a large obstruction, wedges of dead ice or frozen moraine appear against the obstacle.

In my view, certain aspects of the theories outlined above are

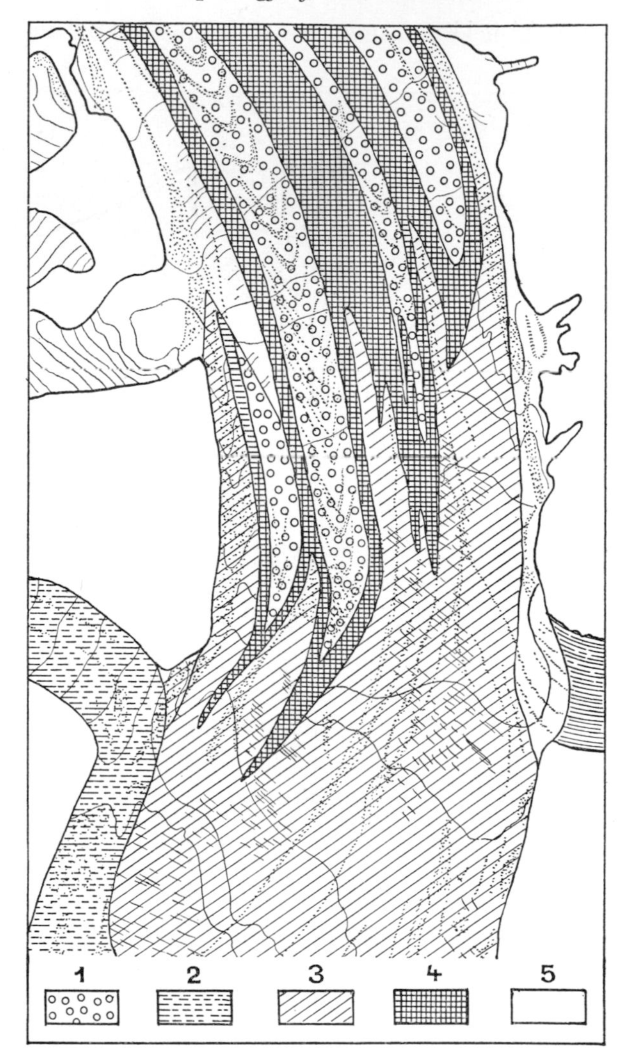

FIG. 22 Pattern of ice masses in the Aletsch Glacier (*after Vareschi*)

1. Areas preserving the original névé stratification (ogives) 2. Tributary glaciers with different pollen spectra 3. Area where ice masses are intermingled (ablation zone) 4. Stratification disturbed without the ice masses being mixed (edges of ice stream) 5. Marginal areas not studied.

Note the juxtaposition of ice streams seen clearly in the ablation zone. The fine lines represent contours at 30 m interval.

particularly important to an understanding of the geomorphological facts:

(i) The possibility of melting at the ice–rock contact; this water could enter joints and then refreeze.

(ii) The surface shearing of the glacier due to tensile stress, which, in major glaciers such as the Malaspina, is confined to the top few tens of metres of ice. According to Sharp this allows englacial moraine to rise towards the surface. Below this zone of shearing, flow at depth would be plastic.

(iii) Changes in pressure at the ice–rock contact; in conjunction with friction and consequently with the form of the glacier bed, promote an interaction between glacier dynamics and the moulding of the bed, able to create, according to the nature of the interaction, retroactions which may be positive (severe erosion) or negative (very weak erosion).

(iv) Plastic deformation with melting and refreezing allows, in conditions of compression flow, a close contact between ice and rock, with water penetrating joints and leading to plucking, while under conditions of tension flow there is a loss of contact between ice and rock resulting in the deposition of ground moraine in hollows in the rock.

(C) Theories of Glacial Erosion

Geomorphologists did not wait for recent developments in glacier dynamics before attempting to understand their influence on morphology. They began with a study of landforms in order to deduce the processes of glacial erosion. The danger in this is the possibility of arguing in a circle; starting with landforms and constructing a theory of their origin, then explaining their origin in terms of the same theory. The approach here will be different: to analyse the landforms and analyse the processes and then to confront the one with the other. A fixed standard, by comparison between processes and landforms seems indispensable.

In the present state of knowledge of the mechanics of glacial erosion, two major lines of thought have emerged, each tending to exclude the other and so hindering the advance of understanding. We shall examine each before indicating how they are affected by recent developments in the theory of glacier dynamics, inadequate though they may be.

(1) The Ultraglacialist Theory

Some authorities believe glacier ice to be the most powerful agent of terrestrial erosion, able to blot out former relief almost entirely, and remove a huge mass of debris in a very short time. Hansen, for example, has attempted to calculate the volume of material contained in the north

European moraines in order to assess the amount of erosion in Scandinavia. He concluded that, in addition to the excavation of lake basins and the Baltic, a layer averaging at least 25 m in thickness was removed from the entire surface of Scandinavia. This does not include the debris carried into the North Sea and the Atlantic and today hidden beneath the water.

Similarly, Kerr believes glacial erosion alone to be responsible for the deep troughs of British Columbia and southern Alaska. According to him, they have been incised to at least a depth of 600 m. Reid, relying on measurements of the solid load carried by the meltwater streams of the Muir Glacier in southern Alaska, believes that the average annual lowering of the surface of the whole basin is about 2 cm. At this rate a layer some 600 m thick must have been removed in 30 000 years, and it can easily be conceived that during the Quaternary glacial periods, though considerably shorter than the interglacial, the topography has been thoroughly remoulded, leaving scarcely a trace of the previous relief.

This extreme position has been held since the end of the nineteenth century and can still be found unmodified in recent work (that of Kerr, for example). It is, however, steadily losing ground as more and more cases are observed to run counter to it. Hansen's calculations are obviously too large, they depend on excessive estimates of the thickness of the succession of various moraines deposited by the north European ice sheets. They are rarely more than 30 to 40 m in thickness apart from the ridges of the terminal moraines and even these are often banked against pre-existing features which they envelop. Recent moraines consist in part of material reworked from older moraines or previous deposits carried only a short distance, as at Warsaw, where, though much of the morainic debris has come from Scandinavia, a large amount is Polish in origin: Oligocene and Miocene sands, Miocene Cretaceous clays etc. The relative volumes of these materials should be studied in relation to distance from origin – only then can the amount transported be estimated on a regional basis.

Further, the study of the Scandinavian and Canadian Shields has revealed traces of an ever increasing number of Pre-Quaternary erosion surfaces which have been modified only in detail. For example, around Flin-Flon some 650 km southwest of Hudson Bay, a Pre-Ordovician surface has been recognised, characterized by a semi-Appalachian relief of some 20 m. This relief is exactly the same where it is still buried by the Ordovician rocks, as where, after being exhumed, it has been covered by the Quaternary ice sheet. Similarly, in Finland, Tanner has observed that the Sub-Cambrian surface, buried by the Cambrian and later exhumed, continues unchanged beyond the Cambrian outcrop. Ljungner has made

7a Lateral retreat moraines in the Col Bayard, Hautes-Alpes

The ridged surface is quite typical, as is the land use. The material, coarser than the clayey substratum, is not cultivated. Debris size-range typical of moraines.

7b Differential erosion of valley fill, Ångermannelv, Norrland, Sweden (Subglacial)

Granvag: hillock formed of coarse os material (pebbles and sand) capped by slight remnants of mjälla. The os was buried in fjord deposits of the ice retreat. As these are finer, they lead to the exhumation of the os.

8a Subglacial deposits at Saint-Gorgon, Doubs, France

Deposits bedded and rounded by subglacial streams, and then deformed, probably by the melting of a mass of dead ice.

8b Würm ground moraine, Schülldorf, Slesvig, 4 km south-east of Rendsburg

Lack of bedding and especially of sorting. Silt mixed with blocks up to a metre or more. Material only slightly worn; the large boulders are of Scandinavian Granite.

8c Outwash deposits (Proglacial) in fron of the Würm terminal moraine a Fockbek, west of Rendsburg, Slesvi

Clearly stratified deposit, with well-sorte gently dipping beds. Few lenses. Shee washing with large variations in discharge.

similar claims for the Swedish plateau. Again, soft preglacial deposits, preserved in areas believed to have been scoured by ice, are known within the domain of former ice sheets as well as in that of local mountain glaciation. Baulig points out that in the neighbourhood of New York, deeply weathered rock, in places between 100 and 150 m. in depth, lies beneath the ground moraine. This suggests that erosion was not great. Easily eroded materials such as lake deposits or peat have survived around Junsele in the Swedish Norrland. They belong to the Saale-Weichel interglacial. In Corsica, in the upper Golo valley, the author has observed a great depth of granitic sand covered by a thin sheet of some 1 to 2 m of ground moraine from the last glaciation, on slopes of about 5°, in an open and subdued landscape, characteristic of preglacial chemical weathering. Figures for mean erosion, deduced from the solid load of meltwater streams, impressive though some may be, can be misleading: there is no guarantee that ice alone was responsible but, rather, it seems probable that on slopes and summits exposed to the atmosphere, an important part is due to periglacial processes such as frost, scree movement and solifluction.

The advocates of excessive glacial erosion have generally modified their views. Instead of a more or less uniform erosion to considerable depth, they advocate localized concentrated overdeepening, resulting in U-valleys, whence the name 'glacial valley school' by which they are usually known. One of their particular themes is a comparison between glacial and fluvial valleys. Glaciers naturally flow in river valleys and once they have melted, these same valleys are occupied afresh by rivers. The essence of the argument is to emphasize the importance of the succession of different erosion systems in the moulding of relief. To those belonging to the 'glacier bed school', glaciers are sufficiently powerful to profoundly modify the previous relief and to impress on it an entirely new character. Others (particularly de Martonne) would limit glacial action to a modification of the details of the earlier relief bequeathed by fluvial processes.

The 'glacier bed school' considers that the comparison is between the glacial valley and the river bed, not the river valley. The glacial valley lies entirely beneath the ice and the valley sides are simply the banks. This point of view, stressed by Davis among others, must not be forgotten. Like the river, the glacier develops its bed in relation to the dynamics of the flow and this development is so rapid that the effects of earlier systems of erosion rapidly disappear. Penck and Brückner systematically applied this idea in a study of the Alps. The Grenoble school in particular supports this view in France, the chief advocates being Allix, Blanchard and Blache. As regards dynamics the champions of this theory tend to compare directly the work of the glacier with that of a stream, the only difference being that of scale (dimensions and duration, velocity as a whole, 10 000 times less). Koechlin has attempted to apply the major formulas of hydraulics to glacier flow. But these authors do not adequately take into account the essential difference in physical state between water as a solid and as a liquid.

In fact, as recent work had clearly shown, the direct comparison between glacier and river is untenable. The difference in scale is vital to the processes involved and more attention must be paid to it. The difference in the state of the water is fundamental. The plastic flow of ice has no equivalent in the dynamics of running water and this is equally true of modifications of the crystalline state. As things are at present, it is impossible to accept uncritically the explanation provided by the 'glacier bed school'.

This comparison of the processes responsible for moulding the glacier bed with those of the river bed is one of the fundamental differences between the glacialist theory and that held by E. de Martonne.

(2) The Antiglacialist Theory

On the arguments summarized above, some authors have, since the second half of the nineteenth century, more or less repudiated glacier ice as a geomorphological agent. In their opinion, ice tends to preserve the former relief, hence the name 'glacial protection' theory. As in the case of the ultraglacialist theory, this has been progressively amended as the difficulty of fitting new facts into such a schematic framework became obvious. The results depart very considerably from the original theory.

(a) The Theory of Glacial Protection Whereas the ultra glacialists were originally geomorphologists, their opponents were glaciologists and geologists who attached little significance to morphology; indeed they ignored it.

Rütimeyer (1869) believed that when a glacier invaded a valley, erosion stopped, and that it was only after the ice had melted that erosion recommenced, by running water. Heim adopted this point of view though qualifying it somewhat. In his opinion, protection is only relative, in the sense that ice excavates less than the other agents of erosion, so that during glacial periods erosion is slowed down. He explains the Norwegian fjords as being due to preglacial erosion. The glaciers which later occupied them, protected them from destruction by infilling; this would explain the shallower water near the open sea (the threshold), but since the threshold is often formed of bedrock, this explanation must be received with caution.

The theory has been held by a number of specialists, chiefly in Switzerland and Great Britain (Freshfield). It has been adopted in France, notably by Kilian.

The landforms attributed solely to ice action by the ultraglacialists of the period, were explained by these authors in a different manner. Kilian held that the hanging tributary valleys were due to a later withdrawal of the protecting ice. Since the ice first retreated from the main valley, the valley has been deepened by postglacial erosion whilst the tributary valleys, protected by ice, have remained at their former level. Heim explained the subalpine, overdeepened lake basins entirely in terms of tectonic dislocation. Still more recently, Backlund has suggested a purely tectonic origin for the fjords of N.E. Greenland.

Brunhes, like Freshfield, has supported the theory of glacial protection and has attributed the major part of overdeepening and its related forms to the action of subglacial streams.

In the antiglacialist view of the time, the work of glaciers is limited to transporting superficial debris: they merely carried away stones falling on their surface, to form moraines. In this way the protective role of ice could be reconciled with the acknowledged presence of constructional forms.

A number of facts run contrary to this theory. In addition to landforms, which can be explained in several ways, some unanswerable objections can be made. In the moraines of northern Germany and Poland, there are many erratic blocks formed of rocks which do not outcrop anywhere in Scandinavia and which must have come from the floor of the Baltic. The ice sheet has apparently torn them from their outcrop and left them in the morainic belt where they are found today. Similarly, in the Veluwe push moraine near Arnhem in the Netherlands, debris from beds situated 10 to 20 km away, at 50 m below sea level, has been transported to an elevation of 100 m. Measurements made in Spitzbergen have revealed in glacial meltwaters a load of mud which implies an annual overall reduction of the surface by 0·1–20 mm. Since this consists of fine material, and superficial moraines are almost always coarser, this observation cannot be interpreted in favour of the glacial protection hypothesis. In the Alps, a removal rate of 2–10 mm a year occurs on rock faces, but this is in constricted valleys and is very probably a maximum value. In Iceland Thorarinsson has recorded a removal rate of 1 m in 180 years on the Hoffell Glacier (an outlet glacier of the Vatnajökull), on unresistant volcanic rocks, although the glacier was in retreat. In 1914–1915, measurements made on the Massa, right at the extremity of the Great Aletsch Glacier, have given an average annual figure of 500 cubic metres per square kilometre, equal to a layer averaging 0·5 mm and identical to the erosion achieved annually by the Rhône over the whole basin above Lake Geneva. Again, Carol, during a descent into the crevasses of the Grindelwald Glacier, was able to observe grooves and striae on bedrock produced by debris embedded in the ice, at a depth of about 50 metres.

These facts have forced the antiglacialists to abandon their original position and to modify their hypothesis.

(b) **Modern Versions** These no longer deny the imprint of ice on the relief and agree that there is a particular type of topography related to glaciers. But compared with the hypotheses of the ultraglacialists, who believe that glaciers alone are responsible for the excavation of their valleys, they prefer the idea that glaciers are only able to modify pre-existing landforms to a limited extent, scarcely giving them more than a particular finish. Their supporters use recently developed arguments based on the limited nature of glacial erosion in particular cases, such as the Pre-Cambrian shields and particular valleys.

For this reason, they point out examples of preglacial topography, later occupied by ice but only slightly remoulded. Richter has shown that cirques were very often river catchment basins. Sölch takes an extreme view. In his opinion, the majority of Alpine features are the result of river erosion and have only been slightly rubbed by glaciers. His view is transitional to that of de Martonne.

Boyé has expressed views which are in agreement with this school of thought, he considers the glacier primarily as a transporting agent, ice being too plastic and too soft to make a serious attack on consolidated bedrock. On the other hand, owing to its mass and relative rigidity, the glacier acts as a bulldozer, picking up during its advance, and pushing before and under it, all movable material from the subglacial surface. Again, the severe frost existing on the margin of an ice sheet shatters the rock. He envisages two main stages of development. First, during the growth of the ice sheet, a cold climate accompanied by intense surface frost shattering which prepares the material. Then, during the period of advance, this material is removed by the ice. This is the theory of periglacial deep shattering, whose chief merit is that it returns the glacier to its proper setting, both geographically and geologically, instead of treating it in the abstract, as the ultraglacialists tend to do too often. Boyé goes still further. He believes that, at least in some cases, permafrost develops during the advance phase. Later, when the ice has advanced, it provides thermal insulation and the temperature rises by the transfer of internal heat until the zero isotherm approaches the surface. Frost shattered rock is no longer cemented by ice, so the glacier is able to remove it. This explains overdeepening. This hypothesis has, however, still to be substantiated.

The interest of these modern versions of the antiglacialist theory lies in drawing attention to the relationship between a glacier and the other processes of the same morphoclimatic environment, particularly frost weathering, and in stressing the influence of the preglacial relief. Important elements of this point of view can be seen in various hypotheses which attempt a compromise between the two extremes.

(3) Compromise Hypotheses

Basically, these agree that the glacier is capable not only of transporting material but also of erosion and, thus, of shaping its bed to some extent. This erosion is not so great that the glacier bed takes no account of the main features of the preglacial topography, nor that any rock could be eroded, whatever the circumstances. These are two major hypotheses which are complementary rather than exclusive.

(a) The Hypothesis of E. de Martonne The main features of the preglacial relief control the action of the glacier and the resulting topography. This hypothesis has chiefly been applied to valley glaciers, particularly in the Alps.

In de Martonne's view, during the Pliocene, the relief of the Alps was very subdued, with shallow valleys and gently rolling surfaces from which rose residual hills whose relief was rather more marked, particularly in the Western Alps which were higher and more immature than the Eastern Alps. At the close of the Pliocene and during the Quaternary, a vigorous rejuvenation of the streams took place, the origin of which will not be discussed here. The resulting relief determined the action of the glaciers. Deep, narrow valleys with a stepped profile were incised in the older, smoother landscape. Headward erosion, in several waves, cut back into the mountains and is indicated in the longitudinal profile of the valleys by successive breaks in gradient, and in the cross profile by a series of benches. As this was in the initial stages, structure was still a major influence and the benches, though cyclic in origin, often coincided with outcrops of harder rocks, as did the breaks in the long profile. The effects of rejuvenation were felt even in the summit region where the gently rolling surfaces surrounding the highest points were dissected to form catchment basins.

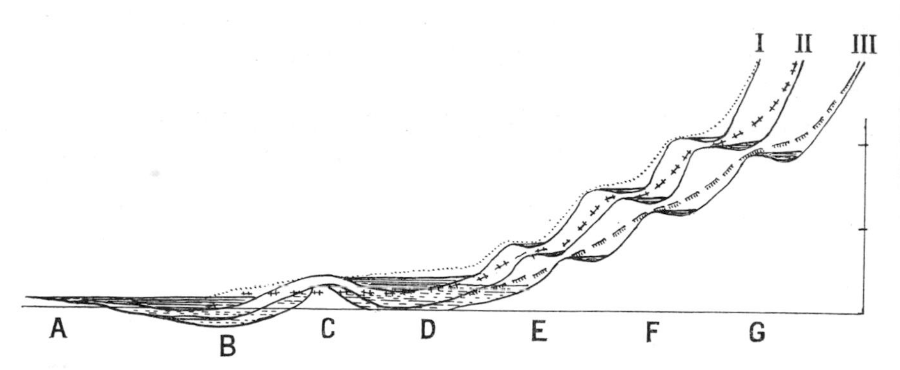

FIG. 23 Evolution of the long profile of a glacial valley (*after de Martonne, Traité, 5th ed., p. 911*)

I, II and III, successive river profile, (respectively): dots, crosses, and barbed dashes) and their glacial modifications (continuous lines); AB, terminal lake basin; C, rock bar; d, over-deepened trough with lake; E, F and G, successive rock bars forming the downstream limits of lake basins.

This deeply dissected topography controlled the work of the glaciers, which de Martonne interpreted correctly. In his view pressure is the most important factor and depends on the adherence of the ice to its substratum. On a steep gradient, séracs reduce this adherence. On the gentle gradients between, the pressure is almost that which would be produced by an equivalent thickness of ice; here, generally, the ice is thick and sluggish. From this it follows that the ice tends to accentuate initial inequalities in the relief of its bed; erosion is negligible on steeply sloping sectors but considerable on those sloping more gently. The former are almost immune, while the latter undergo severe erosion. The final result, which agrees with my own observations, is a succession of enlarged basins, frequently infilled by alluvium at a later stage because their floor lies at a lower level than the rock bar which encloses them on the downstream side, and a series of asymmetrical rock bars which have very steep faces downstream but have often a reversed slope on the upper side. The preglacial rejuvenation, working less rapidly up the tributaries than in the main valley, creates a break in slope at confluences. This is later exaggerated by ice and hanging valleys are produced. Cirques developing at former rejuvenation heads, begin the dissection of the summit plateau.

The theory of de Martonne covers the observed facts. As he himself has said, 'It is a logical explanation of the origin of Alpine landforms, limiting the role of glaciers to the deepening of their valleys while paying due attention to the importance of soil movements and the work of running water, both during preglacial and interglacial times.' In this lies its chief merit, it stresses the combination of successive processes in two different systems of erosion. By countering later extremist theories it has greatly advanced the study of Alpine landforms. In the light of later knowledge, it is possible to make some criticisms of the postulated glacier mechanics on which the whole theory is based. One might also ask if the morphogenetic scheme which underlies the theory really works in all areas where glaciated valley forms occur. Actually, beyond the areas once occupied by the ice sheets, to which de Martonne never attempted to apply his hypothesis, the glaciations are always located in mountains where the vigour of the relief multiplies the irregularities in profile and the breaks in slope. This nullifies any attempt at a theoretical discussion of the basis of de Martonne's hypothesis. Only when more is known through detailed study, can its value be assessed.

Some other authors have reached similar conclusions. One of them, Sölch, has also stressed the importance of the preglacial relief due to rivers but, in comparison with de Martonne, he minimizes the work of glaciers. Garwood produced a comparable hypothesis at about the same time as de Martonne, but his owed more to the idea of glacial protection.

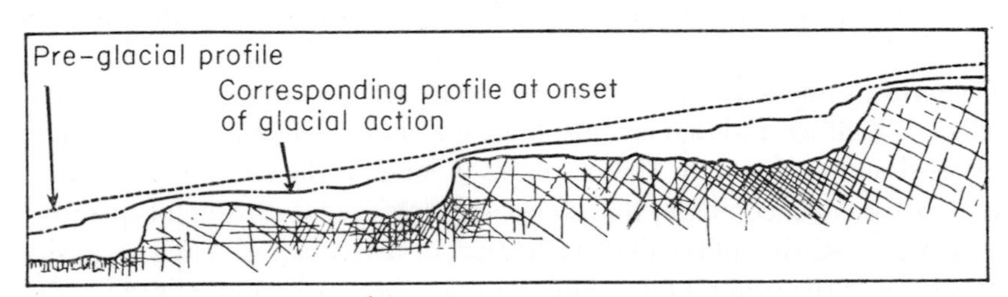

FIG. 24 Development of the long profile of a glacial trough with steps (*after Matthes*)

The continuous fine lines show the distribution of joints. In the close-jointed sections, plucking is dominant and leads to overdeepening; in the others, once loose surface materials have been removed, abrasion, a much slower process, takes place and roches moutonnées occur.

According to it, there are in each valley three sectors of steep slopes separating rock basins. Each sector is related to a new cycle of erosion dating from an interglacial. This oversimplified theory is not enough to explain an extremely complex situation.

(b) **Flint's View** While de Martonne has only attempted to interpret the effects of a local valley glaciation, Flint has been chiefly interested in the geomorphological role of ice sheets. His ideas have not found expression in the systematic form of a theory, but in a chapter of his textbook, which makes them less rigid. In synthesizing the work of his predecessors, he draws mainly on American work and to a lesser extent that of the Germans. When discussing de Martonne, one can talk of the Parisian school; similarly one can talk of the American school, but in a slightly different sense.

Flint, like the majority of present American authors, rightly distinguishes between two processes of glacial erosion, *plucking* or *quarrying*, and *abrasion*. The latter is caused by the scour of the unaltered bedrock by debris carried in the ice. It produces striae and silt (or rock flour).

The two processes are far from being of equal importance; plucking is dominant. It is greatly affected by the condition of the surface of the rock. Previous weakening, resulting from weathering or from joints and bedding planes, plays a most important part. The influence of lithology is the starting point of this study and Boyé's views on frost weathering fit into it.

The incidence of the two processes differs both in space and in time. Abrasion is dominant on reversed slopes facing upstream, on rock bosses developed on hard rocks. Plucking is extensive on the steep surfaces facing downstream. This asymmetry has been measured by Jahns on the granite hills of eastern Massachusetts. At the same time, Flint, following Demorest, came to the conclusion that pure ice has scarcely any abrasive effect on bedrock and that its morphological action depends on the amount of debris embedded in it. He reasons as follows: at the onset of glaciation, during the advance phase, the ice becomes charged with a great quantity of debris consisting of the unconsolidated, or partly consolidated, deposits which cover the ground (alluvium, products of weathering, jointed beds, etc.). This causes extensive abrasion. Gradually, as the supply of debris up-glacier becomes exhausted, the ice becomes cleaner and therefore less effective. As erosion reaches greater depths, joints become more widely spaced and plucking more difficult. This argument leads directly to the conclusion that, as regards ice sheets, erosion is always at a maximum near the margin. It also accounts for the great overdeepening by valley glaciers in mountain areas. Here tectonic forces have led to increased faulting and shatter belts where erosion by ice is greatly facilitated. These ideas are in agreement with those of Matthes who holds that rock basins are mainly structural in origin.

The great attraction of Flint's ideas is that they are not exclusive. They can be related to the hypotheses of other writers such as de Martonne and

Boyé who have also stressed the close connection between the glacier and previous events. But whilst de Martonne stresses the preglacial topography, Flint concentrates mainly on the conditions of the surface, thus making lithology the dominant influence. The three hypotheses are not contradictory but are to a large extent, complementary.

Conclusion

Four fundamental points must be made.

First, our knowledge of the mechanics of glacial erosion is still very limited. Analysis of the processes is not sufficiently advanced to provide reliable quantitative data. The mechanics of glacier flow differ according to the topography of the beds, the thermal type of the glacier and its regime. A basic distinction must be made between cold and temperate glaciers, one which coincides with that between valley glaciers and ice sheets.

Secondly, everything suggests that the effects of glaciation on relief are not uniform. An ice sheet does not mould relief in the same way as a valley glacier. Each differs according to local conditions such as nourishment, thickness and gradient. The processes which have been suggested as distinguishing characteristics are compressive and tensile flow, laminar flow, movement by rigid masses, sliding along thrust planes. It would be quite wrong to suggest that there is one glacier type repeating one particular process and everywhere producing identical relief forms. There are many different types of glacier combining a wide range of processes and accordingly able to produce widely differing relief forms. A discrepancy exists only in so far as our analysis may be based on too narrow *a priori* conditions, and thus be inadequate. The variety of mechanisms used by glaciers is at a maximum for valley glaciers because of the highly diversified relief, the variations in regime most often associated with a time lag less marked than the climatic phenomena, and the localized character of ice flow. This may also be true of an ice sheet, as in Greenland where the basic distinction is that at the margin, where the ice becomes thinner and sometimes divides into valley, or outlet, glaciers and in any case changes its thermal regime, passing from the cold type to the intermediate type.

Thirdly, the so-called glaciated landscape is not solely the work of glaciers. True, it is necessary to study the way in which the flow of ice tends to mould the glacier bed, and historically, it is to the credit of the 'glacier bed school' that it has posed the problem so clearly. However, it is not a one-way causal relationship of glacier and landform, but rather an interaction between the influence of glacier and the influence of lithology. As in all provinces of morphogenesis, we must have a starting point for erosion. In this case the starting point consists of the former relief and the influence of lithology. In so far as it thrusts these into the background, the glacier bed theory becomes an abstraction and is to be condemned as inadequate. The importance of the preglacial relief must not be underestimated in controlling or even causing the ice to flow, for its lower part, being in contact with the subglacial bed, is a major factor of morphogenesis. The principal merit of de Martonne's hypothesis is that it clearly stated the problem, even if the processes it depends on, turn out to be incorrect. The influence of lithology is no less important, though not so great in the case of ice as in other agents of erosion such as water. It is in relation to the processes peculiar to the ice that the lithological factor must be defined. Matthes, Demorest, Cotton and many others fully recognize this point.

Finally, there is the question of the time factor. The problem of glacial erosion is really the adaptation of the preglacial landforms to a new system of erosion which took place, in all known cases, in a short time, geologically speaking. Quaternary chronology suggests a multiplicity of glacial periods of short duration, probably only a hundred thousand years for the inlandsis and even less for valley glaciations. The discussion of Davis' idea of a 'cycle of glacial erosion' is of little value, as Baulig has shown. On the whole, glacial erosion has barely passed beyond the initial stage, that of adapting the former relief to the new system of erosion, thus underlining the importance to be attached to the preglacial relief. As de Martonne stated, this is not solely of fluvial origin. The refrigeration of climate leading to the growth of glaciers, is felt over a period whose duration depends on the distance of the area from the appropriate centre of glaciation. Between the phase of fluvial erosion and that of glacial erosion, there is a cold period, the duration of which varies from place to place, during which a periglacial system of erosion develops. This period is relatively short in the mountains, at least in the upper valleys. Its duration is much greater in the case of ice sheets, especially in their marginal zones. It must be added that the processes of periglacial erosion are particularly distinctive on moderate slopes and that the aspect which they give to the relief is much more characteristic of hilly regions than of mountain masses with very steep slopes. It may be expected that during the onset of glaciation, periglacial phenomena play a particularly conspicuous and distinctive part in regions adjacent to the ice sheets, but a little less spectacular around valley glaciers and in the more central parts of the former ice sheets, and still less in medium to high mountain ranges. The objection has been raised that periglacial phases may have been too short to have so great an influence. Nevertheless, various pointers, among them studies of nourishment of existing glaciers, seem to suggest that the ice advance has been very slow. Further, the system of periglacial erosion is very effective in moulding the surface, more particularly of the valley sides, rather than the talweg. This has an important bearing on the origin of glaciated valleys. Boyé has made a valuable contribution by insisting on the importance of periglacial deep shattering even if it is thought that some of his conclusions require confirmation.

In order to solve present problems in the study of glacial and nival landforms, it is not necessary, as some would wish, to decide first between the traditional hypotheses. It is much better to analyse the facts, and keep marshalling them by attempting a synthesis.

The study of a process, if possible quantitative, should be carried out as a team effort. Several typical glaciers, both ice sheets and valley glaciers should be chosen and a systematic study made of all their aspects, both their dynamics and geomorphology, paying careful attention to the interactions of the basic processes.

Instead of launching into a general theory of glacial geomorphology we shall study in turn, cirques and elementary forms, glaciated valleys, the beds of the ice sheets and ice margin deposits. After a description of the form of each we shall go on to discuss its origin. In this way we can set out more clearly the complex combination of factors which are not the same at all stages of the glacier's work, as much because of variations in the characteristics of the glacier itself (névé, trunk glacier, and dead ice at the snout), as of the different ways in which morphogenetic systems may succeed one another following the onset of glaciation.

CHAPTER 2

Rudimentary Forms

UNDER this heading are grouped those geomorphological processes operating during the early stages of the transformation of snow into ice and preceeding the action of the ice itself, both chronologically and dynamically. The basic forms of the glacio-nival zone are the work of snow and névé. As it is desirable to make a distinction between the two, we shall study first morphogenetic action of snow and then that of névé.

(A) THE GEOMORPHOLOGICAL ROLE OF SNOW

This relates to seasonal snow which melts before being transformed into névé. Two types of action are involved; one predominantly mechanical and the more important, the other predominantly chemical and dependent on the capacity of meltwater as a solvent. Since both processes are due to seasonal snow cover they are not confined to the glacio-nival zone proper; they are most active on its margins in a belt transitional to the periglacial zone.

(I) Avalanches

Avalanches are the most spectacular and violent form of mechanical erosion by snow. They are the direct result of gravity acting on unstable masses of snow. In many situations, they sweep downslope, uprooting trees and carrying away joint blocks and any unconsolidated materials, depositing the debris at the bottom in a confused heap. Avalanches are common in all regions with steep slopes and a thick snow cover.

(1) Conditions Leading to Avalanches

A mass of snow begins to move when the force of gravity overcomes that of friction, usually as a result of shearing. From this mechanical definition of the phenomenon, it is clear that four factors play a major role. The first, and a very important one, is the thickness of the snow. The coefficient of friction is not affected by the thickness of the bed, so that the thicker the bed the more easily the force of gravity exceeds the force of friction. The second factor, the internal cohesion of the snow, is closely connected with the thickness of the snow. Deep snow often consists of successive layers of differing character, at whose contact slipping and shearing easily develop. A rapid development of large crystals during the diagenesis of the snow makes a bed more difficult to compress but very friable and less plastic. This is 'old' snow. When fresh snow falls on its surface, slipping may occur; its weight may also break the old snow and its debris hasten the development of process. Thus, the addition of successive layers of snow tends to trigger off avalanches, especially if the second fall is massive. The surface of the first makes an ideal slip plane. Rain falling on soft snow, not yet hardened by freeze–thaw can also cause avalanches as at le Queyras and Ubaye in June 1957. The rain is absorbed by the snow as by a sponge, increasing its density, and may lead to an excessive gravitational pull. This process is hastened by the presence of an underlying bed of old or hardened snow.

A third factor controlling the coefficient of friction is the condition of the surface of the ground. Avalanches may occur even on gentle slopes, if the surface underneath is sufficiently smooth. If the surface is rough, the build-up of the snow only results in differential creep. The upper part of the bed is displaced by gravity a little more than the base. If, on the other hand, the ground is really smooth and the slope sufficiently steep, the displacement will also affect the lower part and will exert a mechanical action on the ground.

An avalanche may be set in motion by a combination of factors: topographic, such as the slope and condition of the ground, or climatic, such as the abundance and degree of stratification of the snow. Avalanches are more frequent in some climatic zones than others, and are especially so where winter conditions are more unstable. Massive snowfalls resulting from intense depressions. followed by spells of fine weather causing temporary melting of the superficial layer, leads to the hardening of the surface of the freshly fallen snow. Heavy rain following the snowfall is also favourable.

(2) The Geomorphological Setting of Avalanches

Slope and climate combine to limit the occurrence of avalanches to mountainous areas where slopes are already steep owing to other types of erosion. But all steep slopes with a considerable snow cover are not equally vulnerable. Climatic conditions may intervene. Dry regions (subtropical mountains and polar regions) are less liable since snow beds tend to be thin. Few avalanches occur. Again, the dry air and strong insolation cause hardening of the snow. In polar regions, wind helps to prevent avalanches by reducing the size of the crystals. The main geomorphological setting for avalanches is the mountains of the temperate oceanic zone where the atmospheric circulation causes sharp and frequent changes in temperature, and precipitation increased by relief, leads to frequent and heavy falls of snow.

Seasonal distribution is characteristic. Maximum frequency is reached between February and April when the snow cover has reached its maximum thickness and when incursions of maritime air are most common. Optimum conditions for avalanches occur in spring when snow cover is still considerable and the mean temperature is above zero. Particularly catastrophic avalanches usually accompany mild spells in winter.

Within the setting of climate, it is relief which plays the most important role in the location of avalanches. Yet, in the mountains avalanches are difficult to forecast. Where there are couloirs regularly used by them, the required meteorological conditions acting on the mass of snow and its stability may set off avalanches in places where they never occurred before. One can rarely consider the foot of any hillside to be completely safe from avalanches once the slope above exceeds about 10°. For this reason, avalanches are one of the greatest dangers in mountain areas. It also means that their geomorphological action has considerable importance, though it has been consistently neglected.

(3) The Geomorphological Role of Avalanches

This varies widely according to the type of avalanche. Thus, drift or powdery avalanches are formed of fresh snow, of low density; they occur shortly after the snow falls. Though their rapid descent makes them dangerous, their low density reduces their geomorphological importance. Sometimes, however, the entire snow cover is carried away, thus putting the avalanches into the category of ground avalanches, which do have an appreciable morphological effect. Often the wind created by one avalanche sets off others.

Avalanches moving in slabs, or by rolling, occur several days after a heavy fall of snow has, by its weight, broken up the superficially hardened snow bed lying underneath. These almost always take the form of ground avalanches. Wet avalanches follow a thaw which causes the snow mass to become top heavy. They are slow but very heavy owing to the high density of the saturated snow, and they are generally fairly large. They have considerable geomorphological importance as they scour the substratum.

There are, of course, many intermediate types and it is quite common for an avalanche to change its character during its descent. From the geomorphological viewpoint, there is a basic distinction to be made between ground avalanches and surface avalanches as only the former have a direct effect. The avalanche requires the existence of a steep slope. It is thus one of the processes affecting slope development.

In the mountains, avalanches tend to recur in the same places, in which case they are important in morphogenesis. In general, they make use of hollows in the hillsides such as gullies, cut out by small torrents, which they effectively sweep out. They are capable of carrying away all superficial debris in their track and thus expose the ground to the effects of frost weathering during winter so that the couloirs gradually become more deeply entrenched. This is helped by the fact that they tend to coincide with lines of structural weakness such as joints, faults or shatter zones. Classic geomorphology, preoccupied with 'normal' erosion, has confused avalanche chutes with stream gullies. Some of them are of course used alternately as avalanches chutes and stream channels from melting snow or after violent storms. During the flood of June 1957 in the Alps, when a marked rise in temperature took place, the same couloirs were eroded first by avalanches, then by torrential streams of snow meltwater and heavy rain. In their upper parts, these dual-purpose chutes branch towards the head like true stream beds but there is no real catchment basin. Occasionally the stream disappears in its lower part where it sinks into scree. Other chutes are used exclusively by avalanches and gravity scree if they are steep enough. They do not fork and fade out as the slope decreases. Often they cut into scree in which running water is lost. Avalanche chutes have not yet been fully distinguished from stream ravines. Classic theory has caused the role of torrential run-off to be exaggerated at the expense of avalanches as has been clearly demonstrated by Veyret in his study of the slopes around Mont Blanc. The floor of an avalanche chute is generally wider than that of a stream gully and the cross section is shallower and the rock more smooth. Deposited material remains angular and sorting is poor. At the mouth of the chute, debris accumulates on a bench or on the floor of the valley. Where the valley is narrow, avalanches come to rest against the opposite slope and the debris may completely block the valley floor. It is composed in part of snow from the avalanche which, being compressed, has become very hard and therefore melts slowly, occasionally forming névé which survives from one year to another. Some mountain glaciers have no other source of supply. As well as snow, rock debris caught up in the avalanche during its descent, collects in the form of a flattened cone. The deposits are generally poor in fines, being composed mainly of blocks with organic debris. When avalanches are very frequent, this debris builds up into what may be called an avalanche cone. This differs from an alluvial cone by its siting, which is frequently on a bench, with no relation to the stream pattern, but even more so in its form, that of a heap of material flung together in disorder like a rubbish tip.

(II) Other Forms of Mechanical Erosion by Snow

Formerly, snow was thought to have important geomorphological effects and a whole series of microforms have been called *nivation* forms or *cryonival* features. Actually these forms are not due to snow as such but to freeze–thaw. The role of snow is essentially passive.

(1) The Mechanical Action of Stationary Snow

Some authors believe that snow has a geomorphological action because of the pressure it exerts on the ground. Though this is true in part, it is not so great as is suggested. A careful examination shows that the snow very often forms arches and that it is in contact with the ground at a limited number of points only, usually on dry rock where melting is less active. Compressed vegetation recumbent on the surface, and nival pavements of stones lying flat on the ground with finer sediment beneath, are not due exclusively to direct snow pressure. The snowpatch, when thick enough, gives an ample supply of meltwater to the ground for many weeks as it melts. The ground is saturated and the fines are washed into the spaces between the stones which are gradually concentrated on the surface.

This soaking by the slow melting of snow is responsible for certain other processes which can be said to be indirectly dependent on the presence of snow. Indeed this saturation of the ground by snow is more effective than that caused by rain and more persistent. Its effect is increased when it takes place with a thaw in which the ground is frozen at a shallow depth and therefore impermeable. The term *cryonival* may be used in such conditions. Rapid refreezing at night helps to produce pipkrakes and sometimes, though not necessarily, solifluction.

(2) The Combined Action of Snow and Wind

Wind alters the crystalline structure of snow by reducing the size of the grains and by drifting it against obstructions. Snow drifts form which are particularly hard and very slow to melt in spring. The snow accumulates mainly in depressions, valleys which dissect exposed plateaux being the best example of this. The snow, blown across the plateaux, accumulates on the lee slope where the very slow spring melt promotes solifluction by keeping the ground wet. Where the snow cover is thin, the wind may remove it completely and attack the underlying surface. If the surface material is fine enough, chiefly because of frost, the debris could be carried away by the wind (deflation). In the lee of an obstacle or a sheltered area, the wind deposits its load of mixed dust and snow. The Dutch have given this type of deposit the name *niveo-aeolian*. During the melting of the snow, niveo-aeolian deposits undergo considerable settling which tends to even out the original irregularities of deposition. It is rare to find dunes in association with this type of deposit. Instead there are sheets, up to several decimetres in thickness, gently undulating, with shallow depressions. The hollows may be 20–25 cm in depth, rarely reaching a metre, usually closed and frequently elongated and sinuous. This is the mirco-relief described by Edelman. Niveo-aeolian deposits require for their development a considerable area, which during the cold season is bare of both vegetation and snow and has a dry, unconsolidated soil. If the ground is damp, it will freeze rock-hard, a condition more easily reached on coarse sands than on silt or of course, clay. Many authors consider that the loess and aeolian silts of the middle and younger Quaternary in Europe are niveo-aeolian deposits.

Snow crystals, hardened by frost, particularly at low temperatures, can have an abrasive action on rocks and may erode or polish them. Thus, wind erosion may occur where rock projects from a perennial snow cover, as Stahl has shown on Heard Island.

(3) Snow and Corrosion

Soluble rocks that have been continuously covered by snow for long periods display a surface that has been corroded and etched into numerous hollows and ridges. This can also be seen where the snow cover is seasonal. Two explanations have been advanced. One is that it is merely chemical corrosion by summer rain when the rock is bare of snow. The other is that it is a form of solution in which contact with snow plays a part. The term *lapiés* covers all types of bare limestone surface etched by furrows and having a corroded appearance. Some distinctions should be made. The most obvious is between lapiés buried under a mantle of soil and vegetation and those exposed to the atmosphere. Most lapié fields in the Alps belong to the bare type. Their distribution at a well defined altitude throughout the entire Alpine chain is considered by Rathjens to indicate their morphoclimatic origin.

In his opinion, lapiés are closely connected with snow cover. In winter this protects them from frost and prevents the destruction of the rounded crests, and the delicate partitions separating the fluting and the pitting, which may be deep and narrow. The lapiés should be closely linked with a definite climate stage – the postglacial.

Snow water plays an important part in the solution. Experiments made in Switzerland by Bögli, have shown that the CO_2 content of the air trapped within snow is greater than in the atmosphere. The CO_2 may have been derived from snow crystals and may have lodged because of its high density. Surface meltwater from the snow, together with rain percolating through it may easily become saturated with CO_2 and attack the subsurface.

Another important point must be considered: the persistance of the snow, which on melting releases water slowly so that it has more time to become saturated with calcium bicarbonate. This persistence is at a maximum in the hollows of the lapiés. The effect is cumulative. The initial hollows in the bare rock hold water and snow longest and tend to become deeper and deeper. The same applies to the parts of the rock which are most readily dissolved. The furrows are found there, while the areas between form the ridges. Once initiated the process tends to speed up by positive retroaction.

Corrosion by snow meltwater and shattering by frost do not operate in the same way, so that there is a certain contradiction in the form they produce. Corrosion etches and wears down a surface, lowering but seldom shattering. Frost breaks and shatters, producing more than it removes. It produces its characteristic microforms much more rapidly than does solution. Where it is intense it puts its imprint on the microrelief before corrosion has time to etch its own. Corrosion nevertheless is not hindered by frost, which actually enables it to work more rapidly. The effects of corrosion are to be detected therefore only by measurement of the process and not from the surface forms. Snow cover insulates the rock and prevents shattering by frost. Nival lapiés are therefore well developed because frost effects are weak.

(B) The Névé as an Agent of Erosion

Chemical solution by snow, with solifluction and frost shattering at the margins, closely connected with the presence of patches of snow or névé, have been used in conjunction with erosion by the névé and snow itself to explain the formation of cirques. The problem, now long under discussion, has been stated anew in recent years in the light of studies of the basic mechanisms operating on the periphery of banks of snow and névé. Even more than the problems of the glaciated valley, the problem of cirques emphasises the gulf between the glacialists and the antiglacialists. Before studying both lines of argument one difficulty must be overcome: the precise definition of a term so frequently and vaguely discussed as the glacial cirque.

(I) Cirques: Definition and Classification

The term cirque has a purely topographic meaning. It indicates a depression which is roughly semicircular, at present or formerly occupied by a glacier, and surrounded by steep slopes. This definition is imprecise and can be applied to objects differing greatly not only in shape but in size, so the need to classify cirques is obvious. The work of Maull forms the best starting point. He distinguishes the following types:

(i) *Gully* (*schlucht*) *and rock-niche* (*wandnische*) *cirques* which hang on steep slopes, and are small. They occur on the flanks of high mountain masses at the junction of avalanche chutes or on small breaks in slope.

(ii) *Funnel-shaped source cirques* These cut into watersheds and lie at the head of a glacier, hence their name (Ger. *Quelltrichter*). Generally their form is that of an inverted cone, without a flat floor or a well-marked break in slope.

(iii) *Basin cirques* (*Wannen-kar*) Their floor is flat or gently undulating and occupied generally by striated rock or *roches moutonées*. Their sides are steep and often consist of precipitous craggy spurs or form near-vertical walls. The floor of the cirque may rise towards its lower end, producing a low reverse slope which, when the ice has disappeared, impedes drainage and leads to the formation of a small lake (cirque lake). This reverse slope is due to a rock bar or *riegel* (Fr. *verrou*).

(iv) *Trough-end cirques* (*talschluss-kar*), at the upper end of a glacial trough which ends abruptly in semi-circular steep slopes. They usually form a sort of recess into which streams cascade, once the glacier has disappeared.

(v) *High-valley cirques* (*hochtal-kar*), with steep sides, a flat floor and a sharp break in slope at the downstream end where there is usually a reversed slope.

Apart from the last two subtypes, Maull's classification is based mainly on the form of the cirques and treats their topographic location as of secondary importance. However, the latter is equally worth studying. Two aspects may be considered: the local relationship of cirques to one another, and their siting.

Cirques rarely occur in isolation: they are usually found in considerable numbers in the same massif. There are two main patterns: in the first, they lie at approximately the same altitude, aligned along the flanks of the main crest. Sometimes they touch one another, some have recessed walls composed of several niches separated from one another by narrow ridges. These are generally larger than the average for the area and are the result of several simple cirques coalescing. They might be called composite cirques. In the second pattern, the cirques are strung out along the length of one valley at different altitudes, These are cirque stairways and in such a series the cirques are never of the same type, which suggests the site may be important.

The simplest and smallest cirques are always slope features overlooking the main valleys from the foot of the highest crests. The others, particularly basin and valley head cirques, are usually much larger and found in a different type of site. They are never found at the foot of the main peaks, but are generally overlooked by the simpler type of cirque. They are always at a lower altitude.

(II) Glacialist and Antiglacialist Theories

(1) The Glacialist Theory

Some authors, notably Lehmann and de Martonne, see the origin of cirques in the catchment basins of the streams which dissect the high mountain crests. Their basin shape leads snow to accumulate to a sufficient depth to become névé, and for this to move, under the force of gravity. Once in motion, the névé erodes the underlying surface and begins to modify the former relief. At present, this theory raises great difficulties. Why would the ice not convert the old valley of the preglacial stream into a trough? The glacialist theories always run up against contradictions: they may help to explain certain aspects of cirques once they are in existence but they do not explain their development from a non-glacial landform.

(2) Antiglacialist Theories

A considerable advance was made at the end of last century with the observations of Johnson. In his exploration of the bergschrunds (Fr. *rimayes*), which included a descent of about 50 m, he studied the very important effects of frost shattering. Up to this time, frost shattering was believed to occur only above the surface of the névé. Several writers have stressed Johnson's discovery and some have applied the concept of frost weathering to snow banks. Matthes, at the beginning of this century, observed that meltwater refreezes round the edges of snow banks at night, steadily reducing the debris to a finer state. He described the changes in the V-profiles of small valleys, due to running water and to U-shaped profiles fashioned by frost on the margins of snow banks. Between 1920 and 1938 much work was done on the results of periglacial and nivation action, enabling a detailed study to be made of the processes operating beneath and around snow banks. Recently, Souchez discovered, in Antarctica, a greenhouse effect produced by thin sheets of ice. Air temperatures never rise above zero, yet an intense frost shattering may occur beneath sheets of ice which exclude the air outside but allow the sun's warmth to reach the rock. As a result, the rock thaws out and its temperature vacillates around zero, leading to frost shattering. This may also operate in other areas of considerable insolation, as is often the case in high mountains.

(III) Origin and Evolution of Cirques

At present, the facts suggest that in order to explain the formation of cirques, an intermediate phase of periglacial action, slightly modified by the presence of snow patches, must be regarded as of fundamental importance. It is only after this phase that a glacier gradually forms in the embryo cirque and contributes to its growth, along with frost shattering.

(1) The Initial Phase

The situations where snow accumulates in winter and melts slowly in summer tend to be hollows. In the mountains, a hollow which has a 'cold' orientation and is near the junction of avalanche chutes is particularly favourable to the formation of cirques. In less dissected areas, a bench or small valley of any origin favours the accumulation of snow by wind drifting. In fact the form of snow patches is very variable since it depends on a microrelief in which running water is far from being dominant.

The importance of the studies by Lewis, in Iceland, is that they show the process is operating at the present time. The hollows containing snow patches are being deepened today in regions as varied as Spitzbergen, the Norwegian Fjeld, Iceland, the northern Urals and the Pyrenees. The details of the process vary according to climate and rock type. Thus in Iceland, Lewis has reported frozen ground beneath snow patches. Meltwater percolating through the snow succeeds in thawing it superficially. The two major processes in the morphogenetic system are the break-down of material by freeze–thaw and its transport by meltwater, Both are at a maximum on the snow patch margins where melting is most rapid and temperature fluctuations are most frequent. As the snow patch shrinks, the centre of action moves towards the middle. The process is, as yet not fully understood, particularly the question of freeze–thaw beneath the snow patch.

(2) The Névé Phase

Once the nivation hollow has deepened sufficiently, snow will persist from year to year and become névé. Round the borders of the snow patch, where bare ground is covered intermittently by snow, the processes described above continue to function. In the centre permanently covered by the névé, they will also continue as long as the snow cover is not too thick, but little by little their effect will decrease. During this time, the

FIG. 25 Nivation hollow (*after Lewis*, in Boyé, Rev. de Géomorph. dynamique, III, 1952, p. 35.)

Small collecting basin in Iceland. Note the characteristic form, the flat floor extending into the slope, the steep head wall forming an arc. Similar in form to a glacial cirque.

hollow deepens slightly, though the pace seems to slow down steadily whilst remaining active round the edges. The niche bites steadily into the slope, increasing the height of its headwall, while downslope it ends in a bevel edge. If blocks fall from the rock walls overlooking the névé, they can slide over its smooth surface and eventually accumulate in a ridge at its lower limit. These protalus ramparts (Fr. *moraines de névé*) may also form on seasonal snow whose surface has been hardened by frost. They have points in common with both talus and moraine. Generally they are asymmetrical in section with a gentle proximal slope and a steep distal slope (really a debris slope). The blocks may be of all sizes but, as in all screes, there is little or no fine material. Protalus ramparts usually lie at the foot of a steep rock wall but unlike ordinary scree, which they closely resemble, they do not make contact with the foot of the steep slope from which they have been derived; there is always a space left between, which is occupied by the foot of the névé. Since the thickness of the névé may vary from year to year, the proximal face of the protalus rampart is not simple and may consist of a series of ridges.

Névé remains motionless until it is thick enough for its mass to exceed the coefficient of friction. Since the floor of the niche usually has a slight slope, the vital element is the surface slope. Observations indicate that block slipping of the névé with an upward component towards the lip may occur to a greater or lesser degree in the lower part of the cirque. In some cases this may lead to the lifting of rock debris from the floor of the cirque; in others the lowest layers in contact with the rock appear to move but little and transport at this depth may be nil. At the present time it seems possible that some cirque glaciers are lowering the floor, while others leave it almost untouched.

In order that rotational slip, favoured by many English writers, may take place, the movement of the lower parts of the ice must be obstructed, as by a rock bar closing the cirque on its lower limit, or a very rugged substratum, and must be thick enough for plastic flow. This mechanism, observed in several Norwegian glaciers, presupposes a well developed cirque basin. It may account for their deepening but not their initial stages of development.

Formidable evidence suggests that freeze–thaw is a major factor operating to the depth of the bergschrund. This activity is very intense because of the abundance of water provided in summer by surface melting, as well as by springs. It is much less intense on the rock face above the glacier which is steep and subject to evaporation. However, Galibert believes that shattering along the entire length of the bergschrund is a sign of old age. In an active cirque the ice adheres to the rock walls which it covers completely with snow banks. The latter slide and fissure; their movement carries away joint blocks. In any case, it is by recession at the base that the headwall retreats.

Meltwater descending the bergschrund in summer, has other effects. The water may collect in hollows below the ice on the floor of the cirque. Under the weight of the ice above it exerts hydrostatic pressure on the ice, tending to separate it from the floor and make movement easier. It may induce shearing between masses of ice subjected to hydrostatic pressure and masses obstructed by rock. This processes might to some extent account for extrusion and rotational slipping which, by the removal of joint blocks from the cirque floor, causes the deepening of the cirque basin. Further, this action by meltwater is necessarily limited to a particular altitude; its dominant role would explain why, in any one area, cirque floors lie at roughly the same height, as many observers have noted.

The origin of cirques is a very complex problem as yet only partly understood.

(3) The Evolution of Cirques

In the majority of cases, it seems there is little or no sculpturing of the cirque floor, but an active attack on the headwall which retreats parallel to itself. The two processes are more or less separate; the headwall is sculptured by frost quite independently of the thickness or movement of the névé. The lowering of the floor only takes place under certain conditions which are imperfectly understood. Thus, the cirque walls retreat relatively faster than the floor is lowered; the slow rate of excavation of cirque floors explains why cirques fringing a particular range lie at an almost constant altitude. The rapid retreat of the walls explains the frequent formation of large composite cirques by coalescence with neighbouring ones. Rocky stumps aligned along the axis of some cirques may record this process during a prolonged period of ice retreat. The intersection of cirques reduces the divides between them to low jagged arêtes, frost riven and mantled with scree; at points of intersection, more massive pyramids may remain. This relationship between the rates of headward and downward erosion explains why some cirques may be very wide, yet bounded by low ridges.

Structure guides erosion. Incipient cirques are particularly well developed on certain types of rock where the destruction of a rock face by frost proceeds rapidly, producing a steep slope. The dip of the beds also exerts a considerable influence. Cirques which are eating into the front of a structural escarpment are unusually deep and have very high walls; the retreat of the walls against the dip is very slow but, on the other hand, from the beginning, snow must have accumulated to a great depth at the foot of the scarp. This local depth of névé develops semi-extrusive flow with thrusting, which will accelerate the excavation of the cirque floor. On the dip slope, however, cirques are numerous but small, of slight depth and very often in series, one above the other. Other lithological factors which exert great influence, are the bedding and the joints. Galibert has shown that in the Alps, cirque floors coincide with well-jointed zones of lenticular shape in granitoid rocks. Between Gandegg ridge and the floor of the Théodule cirque, the frequency of joints increases 4·5 times. Joints can often be seen on the wall parallel to the surface, they greatly facilitate the splitting of sheets of rock and the retreat of the walls. They may be due to decompression in which variations in the volume of névé would play a part.

The evolution of cirques is also controlled by morphoclimatic conditions. They are best developed near the limit of permanent snow cover, probably because meltwater is so important to their formation. However, this is true only of those mountains which experience large seasonal temperature changes, for example, it does not apply to the cirques in the Peruvian Andes where temperature changes are diurnal and incapable of releasing much meltwater. Here the origin of cirques seems closely connected with alternations of cold phases, accompanied by snow, and hot phases of snow melt, with development on a slope of fine scree, later swept away by névé (observations made with Dollfuss). The influence of orientation is also great. In the northern hemisphere, cirques are most numerous, best developed and come down to a lower altitude on north-facing slopes. The development of cirques follows the movements of the snowline. In areas glaciated by an ice sheet, cirques are deepened during the period of advance; at the glacial maximum they are found at the margins of the icesheet. In the Alps, during each glaciation, successive generations of cirques developed as the snowline fell. The lowest, found in the ranges near the ice limit, would date to the glacial maximum. Each generation would become reactivated, during deglaciation, at each temporary halt in the retreat of the snowline at a suitable altitude.

CHAPTER 3

The Development of the Glacier Bed

HAVING studied the basic forms of cirques developed beneath patches of snow and névé, we shall now turn to the influence on morphology of the glacier itself, considering only the central part of the glacier system and excluding the terminal ablation zone. As we have shown in the chapter on glacier dynamics, this is a special area in most valley glaciers where ice movement is considerably reduced and gives way to passive displacement. Recent advances in geomorphology have increasingly shown the importance and frequency of phenomena of convergence; many forms, superficially alike, may be due to different combinations of factors. Their identification presupposes a knowledge of the processes which have produced them; hence the emphasis placed on dynamic geomorphology. In the case of glaciers there is only one practicable method of studying these processes; to study the deposits and the condition of the bedrock surface. We shall therefore begin with a study of glacial deposits and the changes in the rock surface produced by glacier ice so that conclusions can be deduced about the processes in operation. Next we shall use these results in an attempt to understand glacial landforms and to decide in what way and to what extent, glaciers have modified former relief.

(A) EROSIONAL ALTERATION, DEPOSITS AND PROCESSES

Since the earliest work in glaciology, the former extent of glaciers has been deduced from a study of their mechanical effects on the bedrock and their deposits.

(I) Small-Scale Erosion Features

Glaciology lacks a general term for roches moutonnées, polished and grooved rock surfaces, and striated blocks, all of which are closely related. They are forms of the rock surface resulting from modification or transformation of its initial state by mechanical action. Glacially moulded forms are of many types but can be grouped into two main categories. The first includes those microforms and surfaces produced by scraping, scratching, planing and compression resulting in shattering. The second category consists of polished surfaces and roches moutonnées. These two classes each suggest a different mechanical action. Scraping indicates powerful mechanical abrasion, while polishing implies more moderate action, reduced abrasion, a gentle rubbing.

(1) The Scouring of the Bedrock

This is produced by friction between blocks embedded in the ice, and the bedrock. Under the effect of pressure and slow movement, the rock is scratched and rounded, sometimes even bruised. Several effects may be distinguished.

(a) **Grooves** These are rounded in section and frequently striated inside. They may be 5–10 cm wide and 1–5 cm deep. Under existing glaciers they develop where a sudden narrowing of the glacier bed results in lateral compression of the ice. Owing to its plasticity, the ice flows back towards the glacier axis and results in a concentration of blocks at the margin. The erosion of rock is more powerful if the blocks are hard. The grooves are, of course, parallel to the flow of the ice. On the bottom of the glacier bed, grooves give way to a different form – scratches. These may be fine at first but they become deeper downstream, developing into a small furrow which ends abruptly. This is due to a sharp change in the position of the block responsible for the scratch, probably because shearing changes the position of the ice mass in which the block is embedded.

(b) **Striae** Like grooves, they are caused by the friction of blocks in transport on the bedrock. They are, however, much more numerous and are found not only on the sides and bottom of the glacier bed but also on some of the morainic blocks. They have little depth, usually only 1–2 mm; they are also short, a few centimetres, rarely more than 1 m in length and their lack of depth makes them very liable to be destroyed. Their study provides much information on glacier dynamics. Together with other features, this knowledge is likely to advance our understanding of the mechanisms of flow when it has been applied to mountain glaciers which have recently retreated. Massive rocks which are not very hard are best for the study of striae. On pebbles and boulders they are sometimes all parallel to each other, in other cases they form one or more sets of parallel striae whose average direction coincides with the long axis of the stone. The variations between the groups of striae suggest changes in the position of the boulders or stones, indicating movement of the ice in slabs or separate streams.

Although most striae are glacial in origin, it has been observed that the friction of blocks embedded in ice floes on the banks and beds of rivers, the movement of boulders in solifluction flows, and even in avalanches, may also produce them. The former limit of glaciers cannot be based on striae alone.

(c) **Pressure Cracks** are much more rare. I have seen them only in quartzites, but they are particularly useful owing to the absence of striae and grooves on this type of rock. Viewed from above, they appear as fine, open cracks forming an arc of a circle of about 20 cm diameter, in section the crack is oblique and rises downstream. The concavity is oriented sometimes upstream and sometimes downstream, thus indicating the line of ice flow whilst gradient reveals its direction. They are formed by an ice sheet and can be explained as fracturing of the quartzite, a rock which is particularly brittle, by compression and decompression produced by large morainic blocks pressing obliquely against the bedrock. These pressure cracks can be compared with the crushed stones sometimes found in moraines. The stones may be split or even deformed, with gaping cracks round the edges which do not connect with the other cracks, as in tectonically crushed stones.

Striae, grooves and pressure cracks are all indicators of active erosion of the bed of the glacier. The resulting abrasion produces fines of silt size. This 'rock flour' probably takes part in the process of polishing and supplies the fine matrix of moraines. The friction under pressure by boulders frozen into the ice probably plays a part as yet unknown in the shaping of the glacier bed and in the reduction of the bedrock.

(2) The Polishing of Bedrock

Unlike the effects considered above, glacial polish is indicative of a very gentle mechanical action, a moderate friction by ice charged with fine debris, which is scarcely capable of removing any surface. As soon as etching begins, striae are formed. Polish seems to be the work of ice charged with very little coarse material and moving in plastic flow.

Roches moutonnées are surfaces polished by ice on very resistant rock with widely spaced joints, and are very smooth and rounded. There are no sharp corners and the forms have been reduced practically to stumps. Sometimes their smooth shape is disrupted along a crack or joint which allowed a block to be dislodged leaving a niche with a rugged appearance natural to the rock.

But not all rocks will take an ice polish in the same way. The best suited are homogeneous rocks which are neither fissile nor easily shattered, and are fine grained. But even on suitable rocks, roches moutonnées are far from being evenly distributed. Their density is high on the surface of the old shields once covered by ice sheets but they are much less widespread in glaciated valleys where they are often limited to certain clearly defined areas.

Ice polish and frost shattering work in opposition. It has been observed in Greenland that roches mountonnées along the edge of the ice sheet appear to be immune to frost shattering. Their smooth surface allows scarcely any water to penetrate them and so protects them. Moreover, it is very unusual for closely jointed rocks to take a good ice polish. When it does occur, the arrangement of the joints is unusual and prevents the plucking of blocks. The conclusion may be drawn that the presence of roches moutonnées indicates weak glacial erosion. This enables one to identify those parts of the glacier bed which have scarcely undergone any erosion, at least during the closing stages of the period when it was ice-covered.

For a long time considerable attention has been given to the distinction between glacial polish and wind polish, which also produces very smooth surfaces. Wind polish is often accompanied by a patina produced by the concentration of salts on the rock surface as a result of evaporation. This is totally absent on fresh roches moutonnées. Further, wind action produces cupules sunk in the surface of the rock, and well marked curving crests or keels.

Striae and grooves are an indication of powerful abrasion. They are particularly well developed on the beds of glaciers charged with debris. On the other hand, roches moutonnées and ice polishing indicate a much weaker erosion. For this reason, they are found in considerable numbers on the margin of glaciers with few moraines as is the case with the Greenland ice sheet. Striae and polishing thus have quite different geomorphological implications. This point must be underlined: ice polish is proof of the presence of ice but not of erosion by it.

(II) Glacial Deposits

Glacial deposits are all given the general name of moraines, a term which includes not only material carried by existing glaciers but also the deposits left by Quaternary ice. Surface moraines lie on the ice. These may be lines of debris along the glacier flanks, the lateral moraines, fed by avalanches and by scree. Their material is produced largely by frost action on the rock slopes overlooking the glacier. In composite glaciers, as a result of the juxtaposition of ice streams, some of the lateral moraines of tributary glaciers become medial moraines running down the middle of the glacier surface. Morainic material lying on the surface steadily becomes incorporated in the ice, some by falling into crevasses, some by being buried under fresh snow. Thus englacial moraines are formed. Very often this surface moraine does not penetrate deeply into the ice mass. Finally, ground moraine is found at the base of the ice. De Martonne believed that it consists wholly of surface debris which has fallen to the bottom of the glacier but in many cases, particularly in ice sheets, ground moraines seem to be much more the product of direct erosion of the glacier bed. Thus in Poland, northern Germany and the Baltic republics, ground moraine contains debris from a variety of rocks which outcrop, if at all, only on low ground, covered by the ice sheet to a depth of several hundred metres. It seems certain they must have been picked up from underneath the ice itself. Similarly, the moraines of some valley glaciers contain rock debris from outcrops which are confined to the foot of the valley sides which were covered by ice at the time the debris was picked up. De Martonne's views cause him to minimize the erosive power of ice, as a matter of course. At the snout of a valley glacier, the accumulation of all these types of debris builds up the terminal moraine. In the case of the ice sheet, the great extent makes it difficult always to delimit particular tongues of ice, and moraines are given the name frontal.

It is easy to study present-day surface moraines. Englacial moraines are known only from a few attempts at subglacial exploration, but they do seem to be much less common than de Martonne claimed. The study of ground moraine is even more difficult. Information is usually derived from an examination of the deposits left by glaciers (generally Quaternary), which have retreated. In making such a study one thing must be borne in mind, deposits left on the site of ice which has melted quickly may be one of two types: those at the base of the former glacier (ground moraine), or those formed of surface and englacial material which has been let down by the rapid melting of the ice (ablation moraine). This is an important distinction, as the two deposits originate under entirely different conditions.

Moraines, excluding those of the marginal zone have the following characteristics.

(1) Granulometry

Generally, the material is characterised by a very large range in debris size. It thus differs from the materials at the ice margin which are at least partly sorted by meltwater, and have sometimes been called 'washed moraines'. This absence of sorting explains the mingling of material of widely ranging calibre exactly as in deposits laid down in bulk by mudflows. Their granulometry is very similar; it cannot be used to differentiate ground moraine from such deposits. Ground moraine has a fine matrix of silt, together with some sand and sometimes clay. Typical ground moraine, of long glaciers descending well below the snow line, sometimes contains lenses which have been partially washed by subglacial meltwater. This will be considered later. Ground moraine may also contain large blocks, many about one metre, but sometimes even tens of metres. If the blocks are fairly large, postglacial or interglacial erosion can hardly affect them apart from removing the surrounding finer matrix, and they will then form erratic blocks. Usually their rock type is quite different from the underlying bedrock. Because of their size they will persist for a very long time before being destroyed by weathering.

The granulometry of present-day ablation moraine is different from that of ground moraine. The matrix contains less silt (i.e. less than 50 microns). It is possible that silt may even be completely absent and the deposit composed only of boulders and gravel. The rapid removal of debris from the steep slopes of high mountains leaves less time for frost weathering to break it down. Again, because of the relief, freezing takes place in somewhat dry conditions and is less effective. Superglacial material is to some extent washed by meltwater which streams over the surface of the glacier during the summer. This carries away part of the fines down *moulins* in the ice. There are important differences in granulometry between one moraine and another due to differences in the lithology of the glacier bed. Broadly speaking, colloids are rare, being found only where the rocks upstream of the glacier are either marls, clays or shales. The reworking of clay by the ice does not affect its character. Clays picked up by the ice are found completely unchanged in moraines so that it is possible to trace their origin. This method is particularly useful in identifying old erosion surfaces barely modified by an ice sheet. In this case the clays incorporated in the moraines are characteristic of chemical weathering under a hot climate (kaolinite, montmorillonite). Sometimes, material of silt size, and finer, is almost unrepresented and the moraine is sandy, the sand forming the entire fine matrix. Coarse granite, porphyry, sandstones and quartzite usually produce sandy moraines. Limestone, calcareous marl, slate, crystalline schist, and greywackes form moraines rich in silt. These differences in granulometry are very important. Moraines with a clay matrix, once in position, are very resistant to erosion by ice, partly because they become indurated and also will freeze massive, and partly because the colloidal cohesion renders them less liable to destruction by running water. Finally, compression by the ice increases the compaction of the moraine.

(2) Fabric

Generally, the texture is amorphous. The absence of sorting implies an absence of stratification. There are neither beds nor lenses differentiated by their granulometry, in ground moraine. The terminal moraines of a fairly large glacier are quite different; owing to the effects of meltwater they may show a rough stratification. Statistical studies of large morainic blocks show a slight majority with their long axes parallel to ice flow. This arrangement of the blocks with a weak preferred orientation suggests their lack of mobility in the ice. On the scale of the size of the blocks, the plasticity of the ice is only sufficient to allow their partial rearrangement to offer less resistance to friction with the bed or with ice moving in slices at different speeds.

(3) The Shape of Glacial Boulders

The shape of ice-moulded blocks is quite distinctive and often forms a sound basis for identification. The features usually measured are the indices of flatness and roundness. Ground moraine has a very uniform morphometric character. This is true both of the material of ice sheets and of valley glaciers. Only very small glaciers, in particular cirque glaciers, have a different material. The index of flatness is very low, around 1·5 or even 1·25. Frost shattered limestone usually has a higher index.

It seems that a glacier tends to reduce the flatness of the material it transports.

The index of roundness is low, but greater than for fresh rock debris. Histograms show a maximum between 0·050 and 0·150, the medians lying between 0·060 and 0·130. The shape of the stones as a whole is a subangular polyhedron, such as might result from crushing. This form has developed after being carried for a distance of 5–10 km, even in small glaciers.

Apart from the action of the ice itself, this shaping of glacial stones must be due to friction with the bed or other stones, which is also responsible for striae grooves and the rounding of the edges. The same pebble or block usually has several flat faces showing that it has changed its position several times. The ice must be sufficiently plastic to permit this change of position within it. This explains the existence, in ground moraine, of at least a small majority of stones parallel to ice flow. This proportion, which varies, is a function of the plasticity of the basal ice. Within the ice mass a crushing takes place; this is most clearly seen when, during a phase of advance, the glacier has reworked well rounded fluvioglacial material. On the other hand, in ablation moraine, rounded stones are far from rare and are sometimes very well rounded. They are quickly shaped by the violent action of meltwater in crevasses and caves in the ice. They are always mixed with slightly worn stones such as occur in ground moraine. Irregular histogram patterns are characteristic of ablation moraine.

Conclusion: The Processes

Many different processes at work within the glacier combine with one another to form a complicated dynamic system of which very little is known, and on which depends the particular morphological evolution reflected in the shape of the glacier bed itself. Two major mechanical processes seem to work together to mould the glacier bed. The effects of pressure are seen in the striae, the grooves, the fine scouring of massive bedrock, some shattering of boulders, the slight edge-rounding of debris, and a tendency to produce polyhedric blocks. This pressure is directly related to the speed of flow and the thickness of the ice. That glacier ice moves by plastic flow is proved by the way that striae can be seen to cling closely to the irregularites of the microrelief of the bed, by the weak orientation preference of morainic blocks and the polish found on roches moutonnées. These two processes are to a large degree in opposition;

pressure controls abrasion and the plucking of blocks, plasticity seems closely connected, though in a way not yet clear, with ice polish, a phenomenon which represents the preservation of relief.

Because of differences in the conditions of ice flow and of structure, it is necessary to separate the study of the formation of the bed of an ice sheet from that of a valley glacier. The area modified by an ice sheet for example, is very much greater than that of a valley glacier. Since the case of ice sheets is simpler, we will deal with them first.

(B) The Development of the Ice Sheet Bed

At present we will not consider the ice margins where the results of melting are dominant, or any modifications of the bed of the ice sheet during the Late-glacial recession.

Frequently, very systematized accounts of the relief of the areas covered by the Quaternary ice sheets are still met with; a central zone of ablation, generally on the old shields (such as Labrador, or Fennoscandia), with accumulation on their fringes (around New York and the Great Lakes lowland; the Germano-Polish plains and White Russia). This theory is correct only in part: accumulation is certainly most marked in the border areas where it takes the form of marginal moraines, but on the actual bed of the inlandsis areas dominated by erosion are closely associated with deposition belts. Thus, ground moraine includes local facies. Numerous examples indicating differential erosion on the bed of the ice sheet include parts of N.W. Russia and, in North America, the area S.W. of James Bay.

(I) Basic Landforms of Ice Sheet Erosion

These landforms are simplest, and the geomorphic processes are most readily understood, in areas of relatively homogeneous structure. Three main groups may be distinguished.

(1) Knock-and-Lochan Surfaces

This type of relief (Fr. *les surfaces bosselées*) is the most common in formerly glaciated regions of the crystalline rocks of the old shields which are, on the whole, more resistant to erosion, being both very hard and homogeneous. It forms rolling plateaux of limited relief, of the order of some tens of metres, and is found in central Finland, on the interfluves of Norrland in Sweden, in central Labrador, around Quebec, north of the Great Lakes and in Newfoundland. These plateaux of moderate altitude are little dissected, yet have considerable relief. This relief is without pattern and without clear controlling lines except those of tectonic origin. In some places the surface consists of roches moutonnées, sometimes grooved, in others, of rugged slopes arranged more or less like a stairway. Moraine is found in the intervening hollows: it is always full of great blocks and poor in matrix, sandy and infertile. The moraine is never thick but forms a discontinuous, irregular skin.

Hills on a massive rock such as granite are slightly asymmertical. The stoss slopes are the more gentle, convex and very smooth, with few irregularities. Lee slopes are much steeper and more irregular, developing stairways and roches moutonnées, with small patches of moraine alternating with steps. The asymmetry has been produced by the action of the ice sheet. On the stoss side, this has mostly taken the form of abrasion. On the lee side erosion by the plucking of joint blocks has been dominant.

(2) Drumlins

These hills are separated by marshy hollows like the former. They have nevertheless many important points of difference and are easily distinguished from them. Drumlins are aligned parallel to each other and fairly closely to the direction of ice flow. They are clearly elongated in shape and the stoss end is wider and higher and often convex. In length they reach 1–2 km, in breadth 400–600 m, and in height 20–30 m. They occur in swarms formed of many individuals; there are around 10 000 in the area to the west of New York.

Some authors have confused drumlins with osar and eskers. To understand these forms its is essential to keep them strictly apart and to use the term drumlin only for hillocks with a core of bedrock more or less covered with ground moraine or excavated from ground moraine. The drumlin is therefore either a pre-existing landform modified by ice or one created by glacial ablation. Generally, solid rock forms the stoss end which has a very thin cover of moraine, while the tail is essentially composed of moraine. Drumlins always lie close to the ice margin as in Ireland, the New York area, around Milwaukee, the lobes of piedmont glaciers, the inland margin of the Canadian north. Many workers, particularly Wennberg, have demonstrated that individual ice streams exist in the submarginal zone of an ice sheet.

The considerable part of the surface formed of drumlins developed in the ground moraine must be considered in relation to their submarginal position. They belong to the area where accumulation is dominant. This is what distinguishes them from the hillocks of the knock-and-lochan terrain of the plateaux such as in Swedish Norrland, where there is never any moraine moulded on the preglacial relief which has been retouched by ice.

Sometimes rounded and stratified proglacial gravel deposits form drumlins. These have been shown to have been formed by the ice covering and eroding its former proglacial deposits during an advance. Drumlins may pass into fluted forms on a similar scale sculptured from ground moraine or proglacial deposits. They may then resemble a gigantic corrugated sheet. These forms show that drumlins are mainly erosional in origin, formed as if by gouging.

(3) Areas of Ground Moraine

We are not here concerned with small patches of ground moraine, which are found almost everywhere on the bed of the ice sheet, but with extensive spreads. Their distribution as well as their facies has an areal pattern, they are particularly well developed just outside the areas of intensive glacial erosion and in the submarginal zone where they dominate the relief.

The surface form of these morainic sheets is most monotonous, undulations succeed one another without any pattern. This featureless terrain occupies low-lying plains but may also occur on plateaux where it is rapidly dissected by post-glacial erosion and its drainage is improved. In this type of constructional topography, differences in scenery are usually due to changes in soil and ecological conditions which are reflected in the vegetation and exploitation. This uniformity has many times led workers to overestimate the thickness of a sheet of ground moraine; because it occurs in the depressions as well as the ridges of the plateau, it has been assumed that it forms the whole landscape. This is far from the case; the moraine is often only a thin cover on pre-existing relief, sometimes only a few metres thick.

The basic landforms on the bed of the ice sheet which are simplest and easiest to interpret suggest than an ice sheet adapts itself to its bed, so that pre-existing relief plays an important part.

(II) Adaptations to Structure

The effects of the ice sheets on relief are undeniable. Some forms result from the remoulding of the glacier bed in relation to structure.

(1) The Nature of the Adaptations

The inventory of adaptations of the bed of the ice sheet to structure is far from being complete, indeed little thought has been given to it, and its drawing up is complicated by the survival of pre-existing forms. Nevertheless, some writers have investigated it and it is possible to draw some conclusions from their work, as well as some examples, which we will try to explain later.

Davis interpreted some lake basins as being the result of differential glacial erosion, calling them roxen lakes after Lake Roxen in Sweden. Vogt has shown that in parts of Quebec and Ontario, rock basins correspond to areas of deep weathering of the bedrock and that erosion has been guided by differential weathering of an earlier period. In other cases this explanation is not valid; the sound rock and the parts of it involved do not seem to be liable to differential chemical weathering in the manner required (Lakes Donald, Cawatose, Corbeil and others). The basins must therefore be the work of ice.

On the margin of the Greenland ice cap in the eastern parts of Ata Sund, Boyé has observed landforms which he explains in a similar way. The area has been entirely covered by ice before the postglacial retreat. The relief consists of structural cuestas with a steep scarp slope and a gentle dip slope; it is in close accord with structure. Boyé rejects the theory of an Appalachian type of relief. He claims differential erosion by ice operating with periglacial deep shattering. I have been shown similar relief in Norrland (Sweden) by Castelli.

The ice sheets have therefore initiated or accentuated a relief due to structure. In some cases, this is due to differences in lithology and resembles features developed under other climatic morphogenetic systems. In others there is nothing comparable except under climates where mechanical weathering is dominant, that is periglacial, and to a lesser degree, arid climates. This is especially true of those processes which exploit only the joint pattern, and leads us to consider the mechanism involved.

(2) Mechanisms

Two basic considerations help to explain the forms of differential erosion by ice sheets.

(i) The importance of periglacial phenomena during the ice advance. It has already been shown that the growth of ice sheets is primarily due to an increase in cold. Their slow rate of advance means that periglacial conditions must have prevailed in the area overrun by the ice throughout the period of its advance. There are undoubted proofs of this. Though the extent has not been precisely determined, there is no doubt that frost shattering has prepared the way for glacial erosion, just as nivation operated first in the development of cirques.

(ii) The combination of the two main processes responsible for glacial erosion: abrasion, predominating on slopes facing the advancing ice, and plucking predominating on the lee.

Frost shattering is a very powerful force capable of detaching large joint blocks of rocks, such as gneisses and quartzites, which are little affected by other denudation processes. A remarkable example is afforded by the greenstones intruded into the *schistes lustrés* of Le Queyras in the French Alps. Under climatic conditions other than glacial, these are picked out by differential weathering to form the higher points. They do not weather easily and break down only slowly; they are well jointed but the joints are several metres apart, so that their debris cannot be carried away by streams. Though their outcrop forms only 2·5% of the total surface they form a large part of the moraines, especially the large blocks (80% of those exceeding 1 m at some points), but a much smaller proportion of the fines. In spite of the reworking of the moraines, the present alluvium contains few blocks (less than 10% of material below 24 cm). A comparison of the petrographic composition of the moraines of various debris sizes with the local outcrops shows clearly the influence of glacial plucking. The latter has been all the more active as the greenstones, confined to the highest ground, have been the preferred sites of cirques. Though other morphoclimatic systems were unable to exploit the widely spaced jointing of these rocks which produce material too large for transport, ice, whose power in this respect is almost unlimited, has experienced no difficulty in removing it. It is most effective in the surface layer subject to annual freeze and thaw. Though powerful, because it operates over the entire slope, the removal of the debris by solifluction is slow, it presupposes the existence of the slope. Denudation by periglacial processes has probably been a modification of former relief. The work of glacier ice itself, scarcely seems capable of large scale excavation unless the rock is already segmented. When the joints are arranged so that joint blocks are stacked up like childrens' blocks, the slopes facing down ice are the scene of rapid demolition, probably by plucking, which leaves the rock no time to acquire polish, fluting or even striae.

(III) Conclusion: The Morphological Role of Ice Sheets

The complexity of the processes, the variety of conditions of flow, and the limitations of our knowledge, should breed caution and lead to the rejection of premature theorizing.

Outside the areas where deposition has been dominant, there are two associations of landforms. The first contains fjords and fjells. Fjords are very deep valleys opening to the sea and partly invaded by it. Troughs, rock bars and rock basins occur, forming a relief characteristic of the glacial valley. The word *fjell* is Scandinavian, meaning mountain; it has been adopted by French geographers to describe a high plateau, of low relief, formed of roches moutonnées and dominated by residual ridges fretted by cirques. The fjell is dissected by the fjord valleys and these two very different landscapes occur side by side along the coast. Together they form the relief of an old massif, retouched by ice after uplift and marked rejuvenation. As to the cirques, they have been shown to be due not to the ice sheet but to the climatic changes during its growth and decay. Some date from the advance stage and have been subdued by the ice sheet which rounded their rims and produced roches moutonnées on their walls; the others date from the retreat and continue to evolve today under the influence of local glaciers. In some cirques, these glaciers have quite recently disappeared as a result of an amelioration of climate.

Fjord and fjell relief forms only a small part of the area formerly covered by continental ice sheets. In the central parts, the typical surface is the knock-and-lochan plateaux, with roche moutonnée hillocks separated by hollows containing a thin film of ground moraine, while in areas of more varied rock types, landforms due to differential erosion may be seen. The latter become more common towards the limit of the region and, at the same time, areas of locally dominant erosion occur side by side with areas where deposition is dominant. In the submarginal areas glacial deposits become more important. Drumlins characterize some lobes of the ice sheet. This regional association is much more widespread than that of fjords and fjells. With the exception of Labrador, it exists throughout the area covered by the North American ice sheet. There is a close relationship between glacial landforms produced by an ice sheet and the large physiographic regions based on structure. The fjell complex is best developed on the border areas of the old asymmetrical, strongly-warped massifs rising abruptly above the sea, whilst the other association is found mainly on the gentle slope of the same massifs and their margins, with a broad adjustment of type to structure. The work of an ice sheet follows closely the pre-existing geomorphology. Demorest has claimed that, in certain cases, an ice sheet played a protective role, the greater part of the ice sheet floor being remarkably free from moraines, apart from glacier tongues located in the fjords and their surroundings. This is probably an indication of weak erosion. Similarly, Tanner's work in Karelia and southern Finland has shown that the Fenno–Scandinavian ice cap has barely altered a series of erosion surfaces, scarcely retouching the Precambrian surface, which is buried by Palaeozoic beds further south.

By concentrating on an analysis of processes, the importance of each factor in shaping the landscape can be more precisely determined. One factor is the influence of former relief. This is most important when the ice has invaded an area of considerable relief, in which the general asymmetry of the relief has a tectonic origin. Another factor is that of structure, which is a simple relationship in the case of jointing, but more difficult to assess in relation to former relief in the case of phenomena of differential erosion. A third factor is the zonation of processes within the ice sheet. This combines naturally with the other factors but tends to give importance to the processes in relation to their distance from the ice front, probably because this influences the dynamics of flow. Finally, the effect of glacial sequences, that is the advance and retreat of the ice sheet, must be taken into account.

The many ways in which these factors combine may have very differing results, but they need appear contradictory only in so far as we lose sight of the interactions between such diverse and often opposed influences.

(C) The Development of the Valley Glacier Bed

The valley glacier raises the same problems with regard to the shaping of its bed but the relative importance of the factors differs.

(I) Characteristic Landforms

Local glacier ice has much the same effect on bed-rock and makes similar deposits to those of an ice sheet. But the characteristic landforms are very different. Trough valleys, rock bars, hanging valleys and cirques are confronted by knock-and-lochan surfaces and asymmetrical hills. Landforms common to both types of glacier are rare. Drumlins and osar are exceptional in glaciated valleys, occurring only in the piedmont lobes. The main morphological feature which areas of continental glaciation have in common with those of a valley glaciation, is the form of the valleys found on the steep outer slope of the old shields which have been vigorously dissected by the outlet glaciers of the ice sheet. The characteristic landforms of a glacial valley, whether occurring on the margin of an ice sheet or not, fall into three main groups: troughs, rock basins and bars, and terminal basins, each of which has its subdivisions.

(1) Troughs

It is usual to contrast the U-profile of a glaciated valley with the V-profile of a river valley, but this is only true in general terms. Frequently, glaciated valleys have a profile in the form of a more or less regular V, such as the Béchine in the Vosges. U-valleys which are not glacial in origin are even more frequent; in the Vosges, the valleys of the Moder and the Zorn among others. Even if the U-valley and the glaciated valley are not synonymous, it is still true that one of the most frequent forms of the glacier bed is the U-profile. This is best developed on massive, resistant rocks on which scree has not developed after the disappearance of the ice. Rocks such as compact limestones, granites, gneisses, heavily metamorphosed schists and basalts are amongst the most favourable. On these it is not uncommon to find a flat valley floor, (very flat, as it is generally covered by a more or less thick sheet of alluvium, postglacial or proglacial, dating from the retreat phase) overlooked by steep walls. When the bedrock is not concealed, the junction between floor and wall is slightly rounded. Compared with other forms of U-valley, well developed glacier beds are marked by the extreme steepness of their sides and the flatness of their floor. In a periglacial environment, the valley side also consists of a steep rocky shoulder but it has been fretted by frostwork. It passes under a talus of scree, which is inseparable from the development of the rock face above.

Truncated spurs are a common feature of glacial troughs. The ridges between the tributary valleys instead of falling into the main valley in a rounded, convex slope, more or less continuous with its floor, appear truncated along a steeply inclined plane, that of the trough wall. Frequently this feature is not consistently developed through the length of the trough. Magnificent truncated spurs can be seen along purely fluviatile valleys such as the lower valley of the Dreisam in the Black Forest.

More characteristic of glacial erosion are composite forms. These demand a combination of factors rarely seen in other morphogenetic systems.

(a) **Confluence Steps or Hanging Valleys** These are associated with the best developed trough forms but are by no means found in all glaciated valleys. A tributary trough ends above the floors of the main trough, at times on its near vertical side. The terms hanging valley and confluence step underline the two essential features involved. The difference in level between the tributary and the main stream is very variable even along one main valley. It is usually around 100 m, rarely reaching 200 m in the Alps.

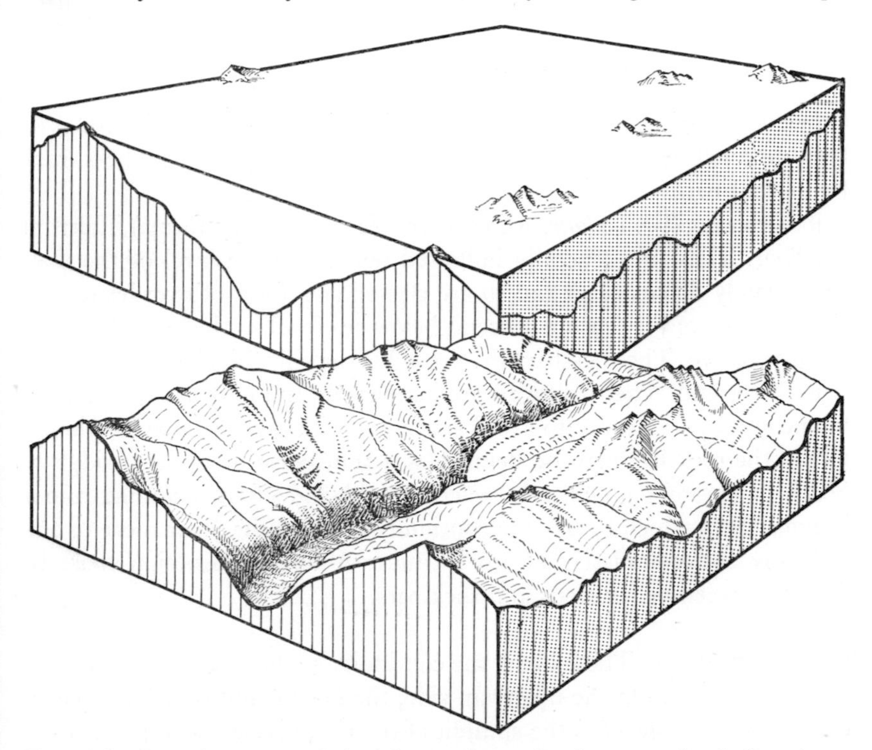

FIG. 26 Development of glacial troughs under ice completely burying a mountainous area (*after Flint*)

Examples are Alaska, South Island of New Zealand, Labrador in the Quaternary, etc. Above: During the glaciation, only a few nunataks protrude through the ice. Below: Details of the surface. The slopes are only smoothed, but the entrenched valley has been converted to a trough. The sharpest crests represent the former nunatkas.

Hanging valleys are found only along the sides of the best developed troughs and only along the main valleys. Some of the best examples are found along the northern slopes of the Alps, the Norwegian coast and the west coast of the South Island of New Zealand.

(b) **The Trough in Trough** This consists of a wider trough at a higher level in whose floor a narrower trough is sunk. The cross profile shows two very steep slopes, one above the other, separated by a bench which is interpreted as the old trough floor. In this type of trough, it is very unusual for the older trough to be well preserved. Its walls are generally defaced by scree, or by the work of avalanches and streams. The benches which separate the two generations of troughs are more or less continuous.

(2) Rock Basins and Rock Bars

Other irregularities occur in the floor of glaciated valleys and have even been detected below existing glaciers. These include, among others, rock basins and bars.

Rock basins (Fr. *ombilic*, which is restricted to valley forms) interrupt the floor. They are generally hollowed out below the level of the floor immediately downstream and so are classed as a form of overdeepening. But their floors very rarely descend below sea level so the overdeepening is only relative. The rock bar (Fr. *verrou*) is the sill which closes the basin at its lower end. The two forms are inseparable and only exist in relation to one another. In order to avoid confusion with other somewhat similar forms, the rock bar may be defined as a transverse or oblique ridge or bench (sometimes notched in several places and often including minor irregularities) which breaks the continuity of the valley floor more or less suddenly and completely at any altitude. A basic distinction must be drawn between valley steps and rock bars.

(a) **Valley Steps** These break the continuity of the valley floor but have no reverse slope. On the upstream side, the floor is not overdeepened; it ends at the same level as the summit of the rise, giving the appearance of a step. There is merely a sharp break in slope in the longitudinal profile; a remarkable example is the valley of the upper Vecchio in the Monte d'Oro massif in Corsica where the basins are only a few hectometres in length and less in width. Their floors dip very gently and are separated by steps, forming a series of small subvertical rises, which give an average gradient of 30° to 40°.

(b) **Rock Bars** In contrast, these are characterized by a local reversed slope which may affect part, or the full width, of the valley floor. The rock basin lying above the bar is sunk below the level of the top of the bar which closes the valley. The valley floor above is therefore overdeepened in relation to the bar, which forms a col. The bar may take several different forms. Sometimes it is only a part of the trough which is roughly graded. In these cases, the walls of the trough above the rock bar are continuous with those above and below it; the bar affects only the trough floor.

There are several types of rock bar. They may be oblique or transverse to the valley, continuous or partial according to whether they affect all or part of the floor. Partial bars may be medial or lateral according to whether the bar is joined to one slope or is isolated in the centre of the valley. Continuous rock bars may or may not be trenched by a gorge, and this incision may be later than, or contemporaneous with, the presence of the glacier.

Finally, there are composite bars consisting of a series of interconnected bars, but these nearly always belong to one of the main divisions, valley steps or rock bars.

Rock bars and basins are an important feature in the landscape. Behind continuous bars which have not been trenched by a stream, the elongated or round basin is occupied by a lake, or flats on lake infill. The greater part of glacial lakes at moderate elevations are of this origin. These variations control the siting of communications, areas of farming, and hydroelectric development.

(3) Marginal Basins

Around the margins of formerly glaciated mountain areas there are usually large basins which, since the departure of the ice, are occupied by lakes. Such is the origin of the girdle of piedmont lakes around the Alps, a feature which is not peculiar to the Alps but is found in Patagonia and New Zealand also. A study of the distribution of these lakes shows that they are sited where the main valleys open out from the mountains, their upper part is formed of a drowned trough and is continued downstream by an alluvial plain mainly postglacial in age. Although a rock bar often forms the lower limit of rock basin lakes, this is not the case here. The lower end of the lake is usually outside the mountains on the foreland, so that wherever the extension of the glacier has been great enough, they mark the zone of contact between the mountains and the foreland. Although the slopes which overlook them at the upper end are due to erosion, those at the lower end are always in part constructional and, at least in their upper part, formed by arcs of terminal moraine. These forms are

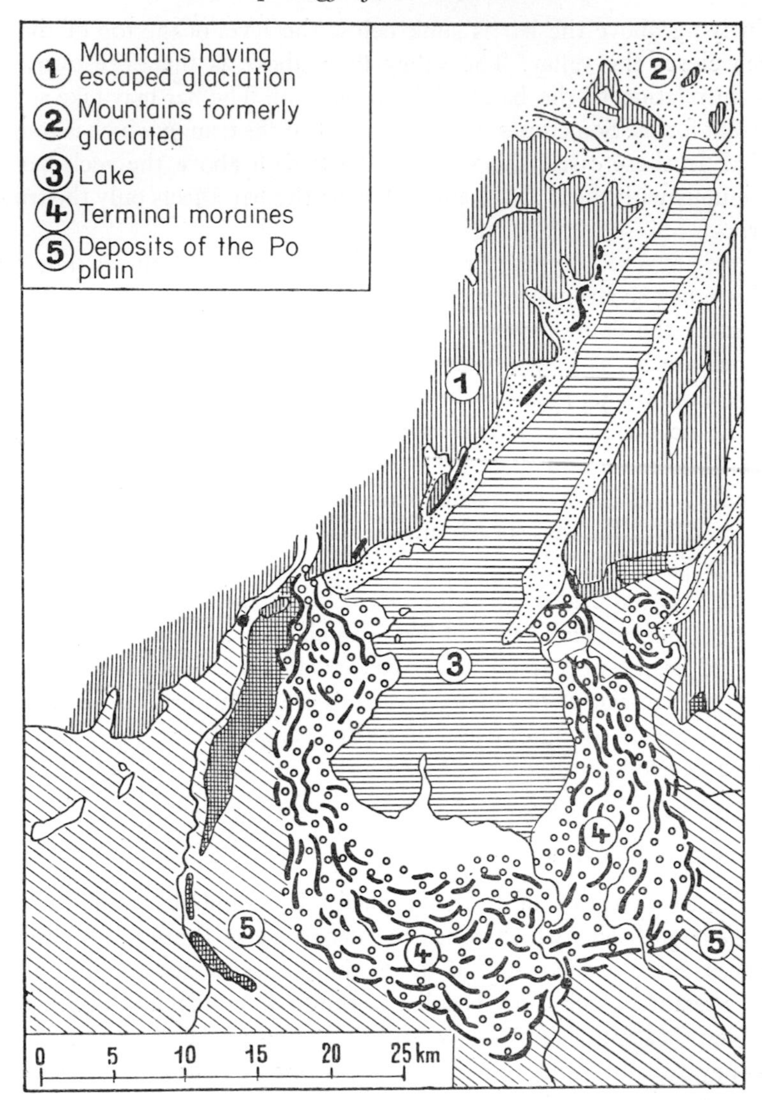

FIG. 27 An overdeepened terminal basin: Lake Garda (*after Koechlin*)

transitional to the ice margin. Several types of piedmont lake can be distinguished.

A subdivision may be based on comparisons between the depth of the lake and the height of the morainic dam. If the depth does not exceed the height of the moraine crest, one is dealing with a purely marginal form which does not owe much to glacial deepening but is essentially constructional in origin. These are terminal basin lakes which are not limited to the hill foot but may be found within the mountain chain at the lower end of the trough. Examples in the Alps include the majority of the Bavarian lakes – Chiemsee, Würmsee, Ammersee etc. All the other lakes are much deeper, the morainic dam having only a supplementary role; their great depth results from deep excavation of the bedrock by the ice. The lake has submerged a typical U-profile. These are the lakes of overdeepening and their floors descend far below the level of the solid threshold which is more or less buried under the morainic debris at the lower limit. The great Swiss subalpine lakes belong to this class. If the glaciated mountain mass falls directly to the sea, marginal overdeepening does not create lakes but another closely related form, the fjords.

The topography of many fjords is similar to that of the piedmont lakes. These are marginal, overdeepened basins invaded by the sea. Their sides are steep and soundings reveal a typical U-profile. Towards the open sea, the floor of the fjord rises so that the greatest depths are found in the fjord itself. Judged by their morphology and their position, the fjords can be put in the same class as the piedmont lakes. They are differentiated from the latter only by the fact that they have been invaded by the sea, so introducing an additional factor in their development.

(II) The Development of Glacial Valleys

In contrast with the erosive work of the ice sheets, the formation of troughs and their irregular floors requires a powerful localized action, whether it is caused by valley glaciers or by individual ice streams within the inlandsis moving in pre-existing valleys. If one might hazard a comparison, it would be between the sheet flow and channelled flow of water.

Two problems need analysis and discussion in turn: the formation of the typical trough and the origin of the irregularities in its profile.

Not all glaciated valleys are troughs. However, since some of them are, it is necessary to examine them in detail, to analyse the processes involved in their evolution, and to explain their genesis. It will then be possible to decide why some valleys occupied by ice are not transformed into troughs.

Typical troughs are not found everywhere, so before considering their formation, it is necessary to consider carefully two essential features.

(a) **The Distribution of Troughs** Troughs are found in areas affected both by valley glaciers and by ice sheets. Within the areas of valley glaciation, the finest troughs are distributed in relation to two main factors. The first is their position with regard to the mountain chain as a whole. In the Alps, the typical large troughs, continuous, wide and deep, occupy the outer zone of the chain. They are found in the large, longitudinal valleys between the Prealpine massifs and as deep trenches between the central ranges of the chain. In the great longitudinal valleys and the Prealpine gaps (*cluses*), rock bars are very rare and the trough forms are very regular and graded. Further upstream irregularities are common, trough forms less common and even less typical. There are, however, exceptions such as the magnificent system of well graded trough valleys at the foot of Mont Pelvoux to which Blache has recently drawn attention. These exceptions can be correlated with particular rock types and with deeply entrenched valleys surrounded by high ridges, a situation little different from that of the Prealpine troughs.

The second factor in their distribution is the rock type in which they are cut. The finest troughs do not occur on all types of rock. The part played by postglacial erosion must of course be taken into account and this is all the more active because the sides are so steep. It is nevertheless true that the best developed glacial troughs are developed on compact rocks with widely spaced joints, such as massive limestone, granite, basalt and gneiss, strongly metamorphosed schists and sometimes compact sandstones and quartzites.

In areas glaciated by an ice sheet, troughs have a very irregular distribution in two types of region. The most numerous and most typical mark the steep borders of the old shields close to the coast. The others, less numerous and not so well developed, are localized on suitable rocks on the margins of the mountain massifs that have been entirely covered by an ice cap; such are the Finger Lakes in the north of New York State.

This analysis of the distribution of glacial troughs suggests that the latter type is related to individual and powerful streams of ice.

(b) The Morphometry of Glacial Troughs Typical troughs show a very satisfactory statistical correlation between their width and depth. The deeper the trough, the wider it is. Koechlin had stressed this relationship based mainly on glaciers in the Alps and the Himalayas. However, it is also true of east Greenland where the tributary glaciers at the head of the Franz Josef Fjord are 5 to 6 km wide and around 1500 m deep. But this exists only as a statistical correlation which covers the existence of important local and individual variations. Though it is still insufficiently investigated, the morphometry of troughs suggests a correlation between them and the size of the glaciers which occupied them. This relationship is more marked in the main trunk glaciers on the periphery of glaciated mountain areas than in the lower valleys. It is complicated by lithology.

In conclusion, the morphological analysis of troughs suggests the strong influence of pre-existing relief on their location, through its effects on the direction of ice flow. This influence is particularly strong in the case of the inlandsis. Finally, it appears that the glacier tends to shape the trough according to its own laws of dynamics, interacting with the resistance offered by the lithological conditions.

It is on the subject of this interaction that theories differ. The glacier bed school reasons mainly by analogy with the action of water in the river bed; they see only a difference in scale between the processes involved, water moving more rapidly but with a much reduced thickness, the ice being very much slower but very much thicker.

All the glacialist theorics assume implicitly that the ice does not stagnate in a depression, but flows on over the threshold, implying extrusion on a large scale. In what follows, we accept this hypothesis on the understanding that while it has not yet been proved untrue, major overdeepening might be explained in another way; for example by deep frost shattering followed by an ice advance which removes the debris to the very front of the glacier or its immediate neighbourhood.

Blache believes the principal factors controlling glacial processes to be partly the tendency of glaciers to grade their valley in relation to their discharge, little hindered by lithology, and partly the fact that the erosive power of ice is closely linked to its velocity so that motionless ice is practically incapable of erosion, even of unconsolidated weathered material.

Koechlin believes that development of the glacier bed tends to produce a cross profile which can reach equilibrium in terms of the relationship between breadth and depth. In the case of small glaciers, this profile of equilibrium will be parabolic in form, but for large glaciers it will be a flat floored trough. The erosive power of glacier ice depends on two factors: speed and pressure, themselves controlled by other factors which vary in a relatively independent manner (thickness of ice, variation in discharge, and the slope of the rock floor).

Considering next to what extent these hypotheses will explain the trough form, let us return to the mechanism invoked by Koechlin and develop it. It is important to take account of pre-existing relief and of the existence of gaps between the glacier and its bed. Preglacial relief decides the formation of the glacier and its control continues until it has been sufficiently changed by the work of ice. This problem has not been considered sufficiently to allow firm conclusions to be drawn. If the preglacial valley is deeply incised, ice will build up rapidly to a considerable thickness, assuming the supply is adequate, and its movement may have an important effect on the floor. In these conditions, ice action may begin to modify the former relief. Conversely, an open, shallow valley requires a much longer time before being overwhelmed by a great enough thickness of ice for pressure to be effective. It is probable that there may be cases in which the velocity of the ice at depth being nil, the pre-existing relief would remain unaltered. This is clearly demonstrated in the Vosges where the relief of the upper western slopes has been entirely modified and transformed into typical troughs because the valleys are sunk more than 200–300 m below the adjoining interfluves which lay above the Würm snowline. In other cases, the landscape has not been stamped as glacial; instead, the valleys remain open with flat floors and gentle slopes covered with thick, deeply weathered soils, probably Pliocene in age. A slight modification by solifluction occurred in the periglacial conditions of the Late Glacial but this was not extensive owing to their short duration. It can be concluded that these palaeoforms, by not allowing a sufficiently thick concentration of ice to become mobile, have been protected by the glaciation at a time when ice stream elsewhere in the neighbourhood did become sufficiently concentrated to effect considerable erosion. It is certain that this occurs even in the inlandsis where the central parts of the sheet, flowing slowly by plastic deformation, protect the underlying surface.

A second process might equally be invoked, whose role has often been underestimated, in spite of the stress laid on it by Lewis. Along the margins of a valley glacier, the ice is far from being in close contact with the bedrock in all places and at all seasons. A gap exists, as on the margins of the cirque. Only cold glaciers seem never to have this void. But the outlet glaciers of an ice sheet and valley glaciers, which are responsible for the erosion of troughs, apparently do not permit frost shattering along the length of these voids, such as occurs in cirques. When rock conditions are favourable however, it results in lateral wasting operating unceasingly on the subvertical rock walls. But when the rock is resistant, abrasion is dominant and results in the development of grooves in the surface, with polishing, which in turn reduces erosion. Autocatalysis operates in the direction of preservation, but the destruction of the rock margin depends largely on the original slope of the valley side.

Next, the theories of Lliboutry on ice flow in valley glaciers may be considered. In a glacier where meltwater appears seasonally, it may make its way down to the contact of the ice with its bed, where, under pressure, it remains liquid for several weeks, reducing the friction of the ice. The seasonal fall in temperature causes it to freeze again with a corresponding increase in friction. The plucking of blocks frozen to the ice by the freezing of the meltwater which had found its way into fissures, is now possible. A similar mechanism would work particularly well in regions with marked seasonal changes of temperature. It would decrease in importance in the equatorial zone. In the Andes of Venezuela, in spite of severe tectonic shattering of the rock, which would help their removal, troughs are rarely well developed and overdeepening is exceptional. Finally, we must examine Boyé's ideas on periglacial deep shattering and periglacial gorges. Periglacial deep shattering has very probably played a part by breaking down the surface bedrock and facilitating its removal later by the glacier. However, since it has not itself modified the preglacial relief, it has not directly affected the condition of ice flow. If we take into account these complementary processes, the formation of a trough is perhaps largely a function of the thickness of the ice. It is probable that a shallow glacier whose form is mainly due to the preglacial relief, effects little erosion and may sometimes protect the surface below. Its bed tends to develop a parabolic cross profile, because erosion is more powerful in the centre where the ice is thickest, and it decreases towards the sides. This explains the relative rarity of well developed troughs in the high massifs. The incision of a stream in the floor of an open valley by rejuvenation would have allowed a trough to develop only in the gorge where the depth was adequate for pressure to build up and slopes are steep enough to allow the formation of a lateral void. On the edges of the incised gorge, the benches would have had only a thin cover of ice, in some cases, playing a protective role.

In the case of gorges sufficiently deep to carry the required thickness of ice, another threshold would appear if the increase in plasticity under the effect of pressure is as great as Koechlin suggests. Increasing thickness creates increasing pressure which in turn exerts increasing thrust on the bedrock, leading to either the removal of joint blocks or to abrasion, according to circumstances. But the increase in pressure has another and opposite effect, an increase in plasticity which tends to reduce friction. Thus, below a critical thickness, an increase in pressure accentuates erosion. Above a certain level, plasticity operates to reduce erosion, it also helps to close joints and crevasses in the ice and thus impedes the penetration of summer meltwater and the effects of refreezing which have been invoked above. The curve of intensity of erosion as a function of thickness has a maximum. As long as the negative effect of increasing plasticity due to the effect of pressure does not become dominant, a simultaneous widening and deepening of the bed takes place. Once the threshold is passed, only the widening would continue, as a result of frostwork on the flanks, deepening being inhibited by the increase of plasticity. In this way the relationship between depth and width of a trough may be explained, a variable relationship which depends on the amount of work effected in each case by erosion, as well as on the resistance of the rock. Note that topography plays a very important part in the development of lateral excavation. This may be negligible if high mountains overlook the glacier, as the retreat of the slopes supplies enormous masses of debris for a relatively slight change in relief.

Having analysed the formation of glacial troughs, we may now turn to the many diverse factors of secondary importance in their development. They can also be explained by another theory than that just outlined. Truncated spurs testify to the importance of lateral erosion which has caused the retreat of the trough walls. Lateral sapping explains the development of hanging valleys and confluence steps. It is particularly on this point that the two major hypotheses oppose one another. According to de Martonne, confluence steps represent cyclical breaks of slope; the tributaries have not been affected by the recent rejuvenation responsible for the incision of the main stream. To the supporters of the glacial bed theory, all is the work of ice and is tied essentially to freeze–thaw in the marginal gap. The tributary glacier has lowered its bed less than the trunk glacier, because of its smaller discharge and lower velocity. The confluence step is the measure of this difference in deepening. In reality, however, the two hypotheses do not exclude one another.

In areas of valley glaciation, variations in discharge are less marked towards the lower part, below the snowline, since tributaries are few. Conditions are optimum for the grading of the bed. Elsewhere, the ice streams are powerful and this tends to produce a trough no matter what the former relief may have been. Again, below the snowline, frost action on the trough walls is very powerful owing to the extent of the summer thaw. As regards ice sheets, topographic conditions associated with position are dominant factors; troughs may be explained in two ways. In submarginal zones individual ice streams tend to occur, they are usually channelled along pre-existing valleys which are deep enough and trend in the same direction as the main movement of the ice sheet. These valleys develop in the same way as the troughs of valley glaciers. Another possibility is that these valleys, particularly if incised into a mountain mssiif, may have been occupied by valley glaciers before the formation of the ice sheet, and have become troughs before the growth of the latter.

The deep piedmont erosion has occurred at the lower ends of well graded troughs. The overdeepened lake basins which mark it today can be explained by the progressive thinning of the glacier by melting. In the marginal zone the ice is no longer active and capable of erosion. Thinning, with its accompanying changes in dynamics, cause the sector of erosion to be replaced by a sector predominantly of deposition. Little erosion of the bedrock takes place and its surface rises downstream, forming the rocky threshold which encloses piedmont lakes in the same way as fjords. As regards the latter a difficulty remains: how can they be explained by analogy with the subalpine lakes if the glacier concerned flowed into the sea? For a long time it has been pointed out that the glacier continues to exert downward pressure on its floor so long as the depth of the trough below sea level does not exceed nine-tenths of the total thickness of the ice. As to the rock bar which marks the seaward limit of the fjord, its level is unlikely to be less at its lowest point than that of the sea at the glacial maximum, since this varied from 100 m to 250 m below present sea level. The bar was probably the point at which icebergs calved, the area where the glacier broke up at tidewater under the triple effect of melting, tides and wave action. Detached and carried away as floating bergs, these glacier fragments would no longer be capable of erosion of bedrock. The rise in the floor of the trough under the extremity of the glacier might be explained by this change in dynamics. Since the icebergs carry away the boulders with which the glacier was laden, no morainic ridge is formed. A fjord owes less to deposition than do piedmont lakes.

There remains one last point of importance to be considered in relation to the formation of fjords. Sea water freezes a little below zero owing to its salt content. As a result, meltwater is not so important in the calving of icebergs into a very cold sea. The action responsible is that of the waves and the tides which break up the ice. For this reason fjords end at the general line of the coast though the threshold may be prolonged a little further than the headlands which enclose it. Judging from the size of the trough, only the most powerful glaciers have advanced further out and then only a little. Thus, overdeeping of fjords implies a pre-existing valley, an inlet which shelters the glacier tongue.

(c) **The Irregularities of the Troughs and Their Origin** The origin of rock bars and rock basins and all the irregularities which cause troughs to depart from the ideal form, has still to be explained. The factors responsible for them may be considered in three main groups.

(i) *The influence of structure* This is considered of prime importance by the Grenoble school and indeed it has played a fundamental part in many cases, as in the Oro massif in Corsica, entirely formed of granitic rocks, which supported a local glaciation of small dimensions during the Würm.

Again, one must stress the importance of jointing in the removal of blocks of compact rocks by glacier ice: not only their density and that of shatter belts, but also, as we have seen, their arrangement. Some joint systems do not help because the blocks jam when pressed in a down-glacier direction. Castellated rocks produced by chemical weathering and later merely polished by ice may in this way survive above steep slopes. The importance of jointing to some extent allows the two hypotheses, the tectonic and the glacialist, to be reconciled as far as the extreme deepening in the piedmont zone is concerned. Both fjords and subalpine lakes have been moulded by glaciers and cannot be explained as tectonic trenches, pure and simple. However, the oblique direction of the majority of Norwegian fjords with their right angle bends (e.g. Trondhjem and Hardanger Fjords) coincides closely with the structural pattern, the major Palaeozoic trend lines or later lines of weakness. A final question concerning the influence of joints: considering the load represented by a very thick ice sheet, to what extent could the resulting pressure on the substratum affect the development of jointing? The existence of isostatic movements indicates the magnitude of the forces involved and the idea may not be so far-fetched that the presence of ice sometimes increases the extent or frequency of joints, which it subsequently uses to its own advantage. It is not unreasonable to suggest that such positive retroaction has operated in the case of certain very large ice streams, as in the fjords of Norway, Labrador and Greenland. A thickness of ice in excess of 1000 m would increase the fissuring of the bedrock so that plucking would continue to be active in spite of the increase in plasticity by pressure. This increased plasticity would not prevent melting due to friction and the consequent plucking resulting from rapid changes in velocity. The concentration of thick icestreams along fault-guided valleys increases the possibility of deepening these valleys and transforming them into particularly deep troughs which in turn concentrate the ice still more.

(ii) *The influence of the ice streams* has been stressed mainly by the glacier bed school, especially Blache. The central idea is that the ice moves along the former fluvial drainage net which it modifies considerably according to its own laws. Of course this concept applies only to valley glaciers. The inlandsis lie almost entirely outside its sphere except where subglacial relief is strongly marked in the marginal zone of separate ice lobes. Blache very rightly stresses the differences in supply between glaciers and rivers which might occupy the same basin. Although annual rainfall varies considerably with altitude, the influence of height on glacier growth is much greater. Not only are there variations in snowfall with height but there is also a fall in temperature which seems to play the essential role in ablation.

Confluence, transfluence and diffluence all modify locally the discharge of valley glaciers and their capacity to erode. They thus help to complicate the shaping of the glacier bed. Confluence is accompanied by a sharp increase in the volume of ice which would explain hanging valleys. Zones of convergence are almost always marked by a widening of the glacier bed. In deglaciated regions, these form the upper valleys just below the cirque level. Confluence may result in other landforms such as the trough's end, where the main graded trough ends upstream in a semicircular rock face, at the top of which the troughs of tributary glaciers join. This feature seems to be related to the junction of two glaciers of nearly equal discharge at an acute angle. In such a case, a confluence spur is sometimes produced, in the form of a narrow rocky ridge with very steep sides formed by the two side walls of the troughs. Occasionally the crest of this ridge displays roches moutonnées.

Diffluence and transfluence result in the main glacier losing volume so that its capacity to erode further downstream is reduced. This is very unusual, however, as they generally affect powerful glaciers where a slight variation in discharge makes little difference. Their main effect is to produce lateral troughs hanging with respect to the main glacier from which they have branched. Diffluent and transfluent troughs usually hang at both ends above the main valley. Onde has called steps due to diffluence and transfluence *verrous de déperdition glaciaire*, rock bars of ice wastage, where the divergent ice was thick, and *verrous d'expansion*, rock bars of expansion, where it was thin. This distinction presumes a knowledge of the ice thickness which is not always easy to obtain.

(iii) *The influence of polycyclic relief* has been invoked by de Martonne. It forms part of his theory of glacial landforms. De Martonne believed that a glacier accentuates the irregularities of the profile of the river valley it occupies. Glacial erosion is exclusively a function of pressure. While accentuating any pre-existing breaks of slope in the long profile, the glacier would preserve the cross profile. The trough would coincide with the incised part of the talweg; valley benches would survive as the trough shoulders. The Grenoble school has strongly attacked this theory and completely rejects it. It must be admitted that the reconstructions of such polycyclic valleys, made principally in the Alps by supporters of de Martonne's theory, are often contradictory. Nevertheless, the former polycyclic relief has influenced the development of glacial forms (e.g. in the Carpathians, Norway and Labrador). De Martonne's theory of glacier dynamics which concerns mainly the development of the long profile, is worthy of attention. Rate of flow, thickness and adhesion are indeed the three variables which determine the work of a glacier. These are effectively controlled in different ways by the topography of the glacier bed. Paradoxically, glaciers moving on steep slopes would effect little work so long as they are thin, since the surface is crevassed by shearing. On thick glaciers an increase in slope leads to the appearance of tensile flow at depth; but the pressure of the ice, by increasing plasticity, excludes shearing. The plucking of blocks is still possible, however, and this would explain the steep distal side of some rock bars, where the original slope was steep enough. At the foot of such steep slopes, flow is compressive, and this, added to the increased pressure due to the greater thickness, results in a much more vigorous erosion. These conditions would be particularly favourable to abrasion and plucking under the effect of the tangential component of pressure.

Conclusion

In attempting to sum up the geomorphological effects of glaciation it is tempting to compare the sum of erosion and deposition in a glacier basin with that of a river basin. In mountainous areas, the results are of comparable magnitude. The mud deposited by the Muir Glacier in Alaska represents an average lowering of the surface by 20 mm. The outlet glaciers in Spitzbergen carry a debris load corresponding to an annual lowering by 0·1–20 mm. On the Aletsch Glacier the figure is 0·5 mm a year. The maximum figures given above are similar to those of rivers in the Apennines, Algeria, Java and Burma. As to the Aletsch Glacier, it does exactly the same work as the upper Rhône above Lake Geneva. It must be borne in mind, however, that these measurements of glacial erosion are much more subject to chance than those for rivers because they are, of necessity, for outlet glaciers.

To understand the morphological action of glaciers, some important points must be kept in mind.

(i) The action of ice on solid rock seems to require a load of rock debris, the necessary tools of abrasion. The latter is a very slow process.

(ii) The more rapid and effective process of glacial erosion is plucking. This presupposes certain lithological conditions (unconsolidated rock or previously fragmented rock).

(iii) Glaciers are guided in their movement by former relief. This influence is all important in valley glaciers.

(iv) Glaciers do modify relief. Between the pre-existing relief and their own action, several antagonistic forces come into play. Amongst these are lithological conditions, the regime and the nourishment of the glaciers in question. It is therefore not surprising that the behaviour of glaciers varies so widely.

The work of ice combines with that of running water in a variety of ways. The chief differences are as follows.

(i) Preliminary fragmentation, which allows the removal of debris, is in general entirely mechanical, being due either to frost or to tectonic shattering. It liberates only silt or coarser debris.

(ii) The transport of materials by ice takes place with unlimited competence, competence being the determining factor much more than capacity load, which in river transport is never reached and impossible to reach.

The resistance of rocks to glacial erosion is often very different from their resistance to fluvial erosion. Readily weathered rocks break down in wet climates especially if it is hot. They may be very resistant to glacier action if they are not frost-susceptible and massive. Rocks which are slow to weather, with widely spaced joints, and not fissile, may be very resistant to river work, like the greenstones at le Queyras. But the glacier carries them away easily. Where it is possible to delimit accurately two basins, a comparison of the rock types (counted in relation to debris size) in both morainic and alluvial deposits in the same area, with the relative importance of the corresponding outcrops, is very informative. It enables a quantitative value to be given for the resistance of rocks in relation to a morphoclimatic environment, following the method suggested for river alluvium. Such studies will help us to escape sterile controversy and make a true evaluation of the great variations which occur owing to factors which are too complex to be contained within the confines of abstruse theories.

CHAPTER 4

The Ice Margin

APART from the Antarctic ice sheet, all existing glaciers end in a zone of melting. A new factor in addition to those of glacier dynamics, comes into operation, the action of meltwater. The change in glacier dynamics near the ice front is in itself enough to establish a distinctive zone. Where the glacier ends on dry land it passes from an active to a passive stage. The most striking feature of the ice margin is the depositional landscape, terminal moraines in the case of valley glaciers, marginal moraines in the case of ice sheets, are often very imposing. Their hilly relief blocks valleys.

Melting increases towards the front. Water is formed, collects and begins to have a morphogenetic effect. It becomes steadily more powerful, escaping completely from the ice and forming a proglacial stream. The ice margin is, above all, a zone of transition, where the work of ice is replaced by that of meltwater. It is the major stages in this transition, characterized by a different quantitative balance between the two groups of opposed factors, which form the main subdivisions of this chapter. These are first, the zone of melting where the water concentrates into small streams on the ice, that is the frontal area where the ice is disappearing; secondly, the zone of terminal moraines, and finally the proglacial zone where meltwater collects to form rivers or sheets of water.

(A) THE ZONE OF MELTING

Englacial water flows within the ice, subglacial below the ice in contact with the bedrock, superglacial on the surface of the ice, and marginal water flows along the ice edge, either on rock or on alluvium. Englacial water often flows between ice walls. But all water in this zone though originating on the surface of the glacier makes its way down through the ice, eventually reaching the rock bed.

(I) Water in Contact with the Ice

It is impossible to understand relief if an analysis of the processes is not made first. Before studying the landforms it is absolutely necessary to decide the precise origin and role of water in contact with the ice, in so far as it is capable of observation.

(1) Direct Evidence

This water may originate in three ways: it may result from the melting of ice or snow, from rain falling on the glacier, on rain and snow melt from the surrounding land.

Marginal water is only found in zones of rapid ablation, chiefly in mountain areas in association with valley glaciers (e.g. the ice dammed lakes, Märjelen See on the margin of the Aletsch glacier). Some examples are also known from ice sheets. Water from the glacier, mainly in the form of meltwater, forms part of their supply. In summer, according to slope, water on the Alpine glaciers forms pools and streams which are incised into the ice. On the Gorner glacier they are 2–3 m wide and by late summer they are sunk 2–3 m into the ice. On the margin of very large glaciers these meltwater streams become really large as on the Greenland icecap margin where streams are sunk in ice-walled canyons many tens of metres wide and 30–40 m in depth. A considerable number of these streams seem to recur each year in the same place. Superglacial streams are always seasonal and disappear during the cold season. The intense cold prevents them from forming in Antarctica.

It is on the Alaskan glaciers, whose lobes are advancing because of unusually heavy precipitation locally, without any relation to temperature changes, that superglacial streams are achieving their most spectacular results. It is true that the ice is often dead and sometimes covered with forest. Large rivers are formed, which rework the moraines, rounding the pebbles, forming terraces of alluvium and even leaving minor lacustrine deposits on the ice itself. But this is a special case, closely related to the presence of dead ice. Owing to the climate, surface melting is very rapid, causing a concentration of debris on the surface as ablation moraine which now protects the ice. The superglacial streams flow on this moraine and rework it.

Usually, superficial streams do not remain on the glacier surface. After a more or less lengthy subaerial course, they soon plunge into shafts or crevasses called *moulins*. Sometimes the water swirls and eddies into it, at other times it falls into an open shaft similar to a limestone swallow hole. The water makes its way through the mass of the ice and tends to reach the subglacial rock floor as much by the melting of the ice it causes, as by mechanical erosion. Englacial water has been found even in winter in construction work under the ice, as at the Mer de Glace and at Mont Collon. In the Alps this is the origin of the winter discharge from the glacier tongues. This discharge of water, though small, is constant and comes from the melting of the ice in contact with the rock bed. Obviously this does not occur in cold glaciers since the temperature of the bedrock below the thinning glacier tongue is below zero. In the Antarctic practically no water comes from the outlet glaciers.

(2) Indirect Evidence

This is the only evidence available for the earlier phases of the glacier work. It forms two types. First there are the microforms found particularly on bedrock, such as potholes. These have been found especially in Scandinavia, infilled by retreat moraines, which seems to suggest that they were formed at the ice margin just before the glacier disappeared. It is most probable that interglacial potholes could survive a periglacial phase of the ice advance and then a period of glacial erosion. This type of survival is very rare and is not always a reliable index for dating. The second type of indirect evidence is provided by the shape of pebbles. The morphometry of strictly glacial material has already been analysed. Materials laid down by meltwater both from modern glaciers and from Quaternary deposits (identified by other criteria) show the following characteristics.

1. The pebbles are at least as well rounded as those of subaerial rivers. The median of those in deposits which have been most severely worked by meltwater may reach 0·300–0·400.

2. Most of the pebbles are only slightly flattened, like those of ground moraine and unlike those of ordinary rivers; the medians lie around 1·55–1·6 for compact rocks.

3. Compared with stones found in typical ground moraine, their shape implies sorting. Above a certain size, which varies from case to case, no further rounding of the pebbles takes place. Their ice moulded shape survives unaltered. It is tempting to equate this limit, which can also be observed in river deposits, with the competence of the current.

The laws governing the shaping of pebbles by glacier meltwater are very close to those applying to river pebbles in potholes, rotation producing a marked rounding, but only a slight degree of flattening. The only pebbles to display a comparable rounding are those in river potholes which are trapped and not replaced. In nearly every case, obvious differences prevent any confusion. Some direct observations are confirmed by this relationship; glacial water flow is comparable with that of karst water eddying down shafts, siphoned under pressure and widening the walls of the fissures which close again gradually under the pressure of the ice. These facts must be kept in mind in order to understand the morphological effects.

Sometimes a deposit will consist only of waterworn stones but more often they are mixed with stones shaped solely by ice, as for example in some basal till near the margin, or in terminal moraines and the lateral moraines of some major glacier. Here they are a sure indication of the intervention of meltwater in the morphogenesis, and may thus be a means of identifying surface features or deposits whose form has become unrecognizable. Water-worn pebbles found in a glacial deposit help to fix the point on the glacier at which melting becomes important. In the Quaternary ice sheets, they indicate the region where a polar or intermediate type gives way to a temperate glacier in space, as much as in time.

Sometimes, englacial water causes a degree of size sorting particularly noticeable in the fine fraction, or a reduction in the silt and clay in the moraine which then has a predominantly sandy matrix. This sorting is very irregular and may only affect pockets in the middle of an unstratified mass. Indeed the washed sands from a subglacial tunnel or englacial may be seen intermixed with till due to a subsequent advance of the ice or to collapse resulting from melting.

(II) The Morphological Action of Meltwater

The role of meltwater was formulated at an early stage. Some tend to exaggerate its importance, such as Bruhnes and Girardin who attributed the bulk of glacial work to it. The progress of techniques in sedimentology has made it possible now to lift this question out of the realm of hypothesis and imagination and to settle it by the analysis of processes. Nowadays, firm criteria enable the work of meltwater to be assessed and the improvement in techniques suggest this will be done with increasing precision. For some time German and Scandinavian authors have realised the importance of meltwater in constructing certain landforms such as osar. Recent work has fully confirmed this. The explanation of other forms such as marginal lakes is more hypothetical. Generally, it is more difficult to identify erosional than constructional forms. For the latter, direct evidence is provided by the materials, while for the former, a relationship must be established.

(1) Constructional Forms

The most important of these are osar. Their original definition is in terms of form. They are narrow elongated hills often with a fairly constant height, so that they resemble dykes. The term is vague. It is still in use, though frequently somewhat modified in meaning. Other terms are also used, *osar*, *esker* and *kame*, thus creating considerable confusion.

Kames. By far the majority of workers use this term for a marginal deposit laid by subaerial water in contact both with the ice and with the rock slopes overlooking it. Topographically, the kame is flatter, often with a level top. In agreement with the majority, I would classify kames as marginal features. It should be noted that Polish authors, particularly from Torun, use the term kame to describe deposits formed in ponded water partly between masses of stagnant ice and partly on top of them. Deltas built by superglacial streams are frequent among kames. The material is usually sandy with rounded pebbles.

Eskers. With eskers the confusion is even more marked. Kame and esker are used indiscriminately by some authors. Flint prefers esker to os, while Woldstedt regards them as different landforms. In his opinion, an os is more elongated and more continuous. An esker is short and narrow, and round-topped. The confusion is so great that it would be better to cease using the two words in a different sense. I will use the word *osar* as a general term and distinguish several types.

The topographic character of osar remains vague. Chabot describes them as long narrow hills, often sinuous, with constrictions and expansions and limited depressions after which they reform. Their trace forms more or less parallel lines and is sometimes anastomosing. Very often the os form has been modified, for example in Sweden, by the Late Glacial Sea, or by the melting of buried blocks of ice. The slope of their sides may also vary greatly, being as steep as 20° or sometimes more gentle, (5–10°). Their length is equally variable; in central Sweden, osar may stretch for many hundreds of kilometres, with only short breaks. Others are much shorter and are only a few kilometres in length. However, among typical osar there is always a definite relationship between length, breadth and height. Large osar are always narrow for they are never more than 400–700 m wide but their height may reach 40–50 m. Small osar, 200–300 m in length and 40–50 m in width, reach between 10 and 20 m in height. A second characteristic of osar is their well worn, graded, sorted and stratified materials. In Sweden, they distinguish between gravelly osar formed of pebbles whose long axes are between 5 and 20 cm long (and almost never longer), and sand osar, from which pebbles are almost completely absent. Of course, intermediate types exist whose material is size-sorted and forms successive beds of different grain size, exactly as in fluvial deposits. But they differ from river gravels in the arrangement of the beds. They are almost never horizontal but usually dip strongly. Dips of 10° are not uncommon, and they may even reach 20° or more. Sometimes the bedding is domed, with a dip diverging from the axis of the os. It even happens that the slope of the side of the os coincides with the dip of the beds. The morphology of the os is then very typical, very elongated, somewhat sinuous, narrow and steep sided.

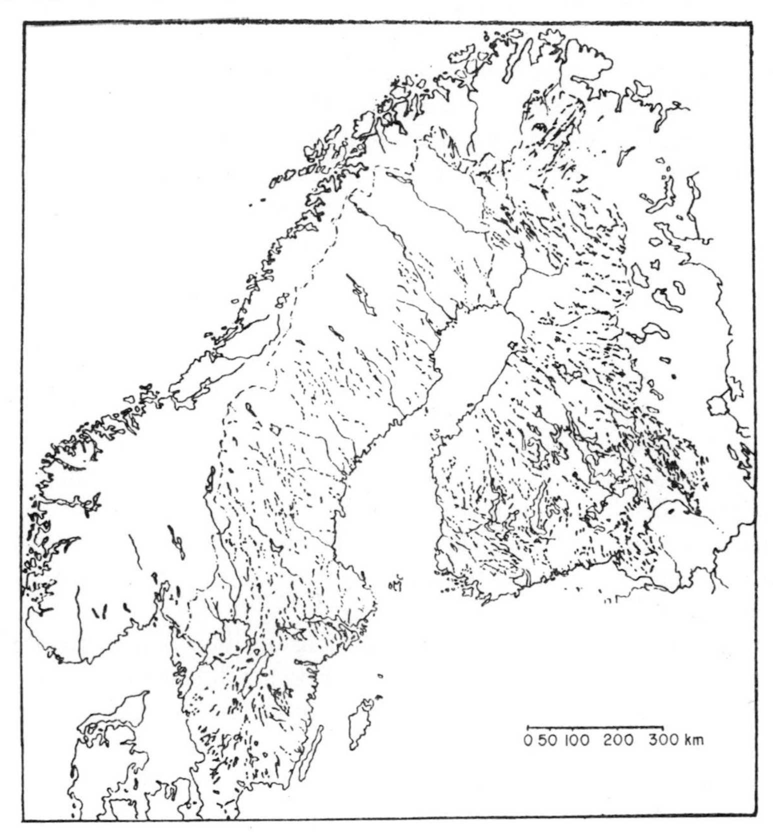

FIG. 28 Pattern of osar in Scandinavia (*after Flint*)

Owing to their linear shape and composition, osar are attributed to glacial meltwater. Almost all writers agree on this, but on the details of the mechanism, opinions differ. De Geer envisaged them as successive deltaic deposits accompanying the steady retreat of the ice sheet during the Late Glacial. This interpretation is contradicted by a study of the bedding, which ought to be divergent from a series of points representing the former heads of the deltas. Tanner attributes the osar to various subglacial streams which furrowed the ice cap during its retreat. At the present time, this view is largely accepted. Woldstedt has stressed the fact that osar are necessarily retreat features. Since they are well stratified, the ice must have been nearly motionless in order not to disturb the deposits during an advance. Osar presuppose ice that is dead, or nearly so, together with a great intensity of subglacial drainage, periods of retreat offer optimum conditions for their formation. In Sweden osar often lie directly on ground moraine and are overlain by marine deposits of the Yoldia Sea. Osar are aligned parallel to subglacial channels which are controlled most often by the general slope of the ice sheet, which is in turn determined by its former direction of flow.

It is on the subject of the actual conditions of deposition that opinions differ most. One view is that osar are deposited on the surface of the ice or within it, and are later let down by melting. Others believe that they are deposited *in situ* on the bed of the glacier by subglacial streams. Of course these two theories are not mutually exclusive. Osar could very well be formed in either way. They should then be differentiated by their structure. Only the osar formed in situ on the glacier bed could retain the original bedding. In the others the bedding would be severely disturbed by collapse, its fluvial origin could then only be recognized by the sorting of the pebbles and above all, by their shape.

Again, some osar are deposited on the bed of the glacier and are later preserved by a cover of ablation moraine during the final melting of the ice. They then lack a distinctive form but may be recognized in sections and exist because of lithological factors; their washed material, for example, will solifluct less easily than the enclosing moraine; their pebbles may cause rapids on streams.

The mechanics of deposition varies considerably. Some osar are deposited near the front of an ice sheet during a halt stage. They are then short and not very high, their distal end passes into proglacial deposits, especially into the heads of cones. Others, somewhat irregular in form, have been considered by de Geer to mark a spasmodic retreat. Flint has suggested that in some cases they may represent annual deposits. Other examples such as the great osar of central and northern Sweden have been deposited during rapid retreat in subglacial channels, sometimes on rock in the middle of dead ice, whose only function was to provide retaining

9 *Carboniferous varvites (Proglacial), 2 km west of Itu, São Paulo, Brazil*
Striking regularity of Proglacial deposits in water (lacustrine or marine?). More shaley and more sandy beds alternate. Some beds show oriented ripple marks, passing into oblique stratification which indicates current direction (débâcles).

walls. They may also be formed in stream channels on the surface of the ice and subsequently be let down during melting. This type is probably very rare, for the surface ice of the inlandsis is clean and unlikely to supply the material for rapid deposition.

Just as drumlins indicate ice advance or stability, so osar are retreat features which are better defined if the retreat is rapid. For this reason they belong essentially to the area of the inlandsis.

(2) Erosional Forms

To identify these forms, instead of direct observation, we must resort to the correlation of deposits. This cannot always be done with the same degree of accuracy. Although constructional forms occur, especially in areas glaciated by an ice sheet, erosion forms have been recorded as often in areas of valley glaciation. There are several types.

In glaciated valleys narrow canyon-like gorges occur. Brunhes has stressed their importance and believed them to be subglacial, he went so far as to attribute to them the chief role in the moulding of the glaciated landscape. Other writers, particularly de Martonne have interpreted these gorges which trench the trough floor as being due to postglacial erosion, and indeed these gorges are often infilled by alluvium. It is quite true that there are many narrow gorges cut into the floor of glacial troughs which have been subsequently buried by alluvium. In some cases, however, the infill has proved to be outwash so it would appear that the gorge is not postglacial. A more detailed examination of what is sometimes a little hastily called 'alluvium', often shows it to be the deposits of subglacial streams. A noteworthy case is that in the gorge of Guil, upstream from La Maison du Roy (upper Durance). In all this area the present stream is cutting a gorge, often epigenetically, in undulating rock furrowed by subglacial channels. These are filled by moraine, often consisting of debris which has been worn and sorted by meltwater. At one place, morainic blocks have fallen into a laminated deposit of silt and fine sand laid down in a quiet backwater. It seems that the erosion of this gorge and the laying down of the related deposits must have taken place subglacially. The subglacial hypothesis of Brunhes applies in some cases at least.

Subglacial erosion is a proven fact. Onde and de Blache, among geographers of the Grenoble school, have held that a considerable number of the gorges incised in rock bars have been formed beneath the glaciers by the action of meltwater (e.g. the Mer de Glace, Fig. 29).

Along the edge of former icecaps, related forms can be seen whose form

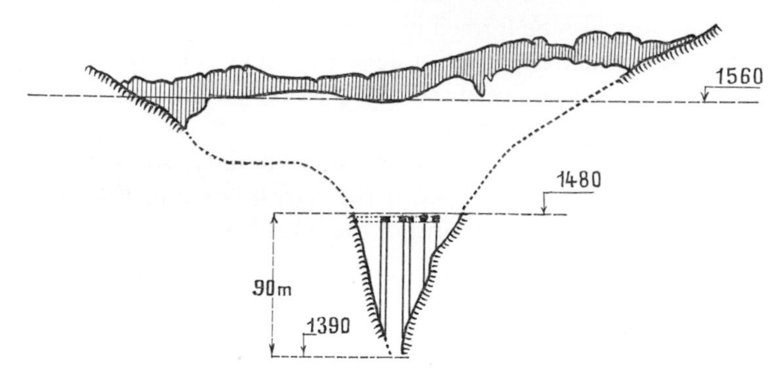

FIG. 29 Section through the tongue of the Mer de Glace, based on a tunnel at 1480 m and borings (*from Ract-Madoux and Renaud*)

The lined area shows the reduction in the glacier between 1922 and 1944; the barbed lines show the known rock slopes; the packed lines, hypothetical slopes.

No exaggeration of vertical scale. Note the V-gorge in the floor of the trough, occupied by ice.

differs because of a difference in morphological environment. German authors have observed a long time ago, finger lakes sometimes tens of metres deep, perhaps tens of kilometres long and aligned approximately perpendicular to the edge of the inlandsis. Often the present lakes are related to the heads of old proglacial cones situated on their continuation several kilometres downstream. Both Polish and German authors almost unanimously believe them to be the work of subglacial meltwater. It has been shown that the basins containing the lakes occur only in a narrow zone marginal to the ice sheet. They are most frequent in embayments between two ice lobes, just where meltwater would be expected to concentrate in greatest volume.

Often the bottom of the lake basin rises several tens of metres towards the marginal moraine, forming a distinct reverse slope in the talweg of the subglacial tunnel between the lake and the head of the proglacial cone. It may well be due to flow under pressure. The tunnels were almost entirely eroded in unconsolidated rocks such as sands, gravels, moraines or clay.

(B) THE FRONTAL ZONE

The complete disappearance of the ice at the front of the glacier, by

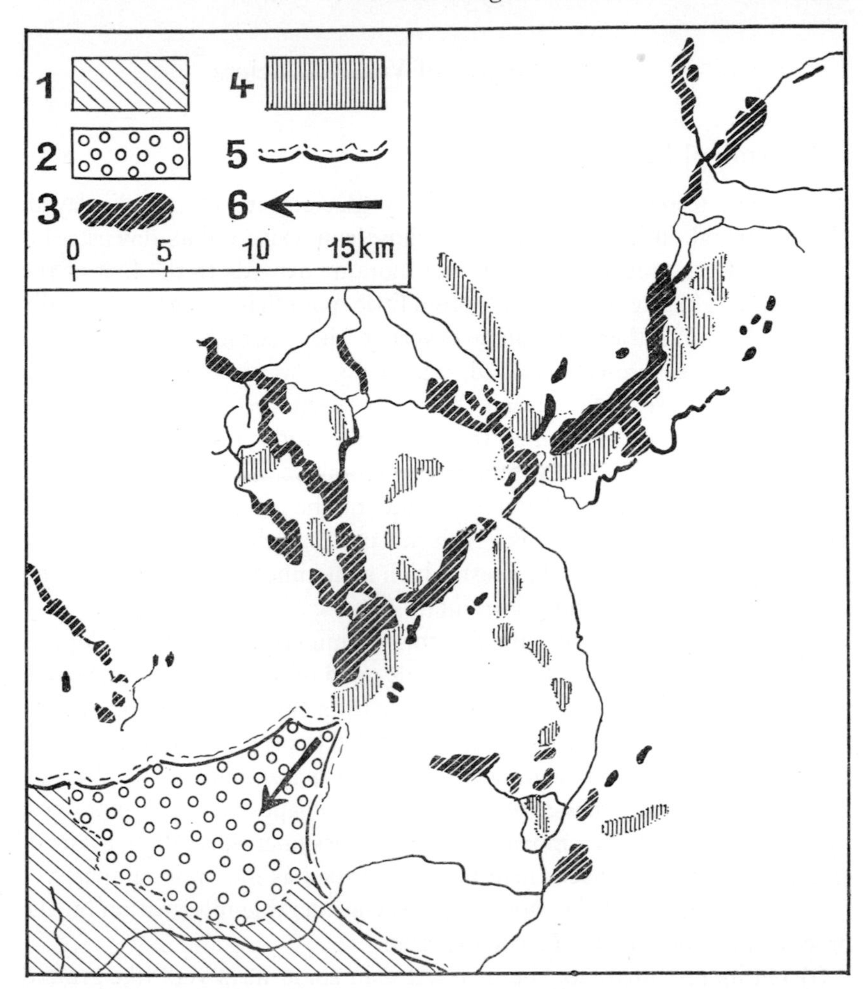

FIG. 30 Subglacial channels: the Havel lakes (*after Woldstedt*)

1. Urstromtal, a proglacial channel 2. Proglacial cone, at the exit of a subglacial tunnel 3. Lakes marking various confluent subglacial tunnels 4. Deposits of subglacial channels, with well rounded pebbles 5. Ice sheet margin 6. Direction of flow.

melting, forms the basis of a significant zone, characterized by a change of process, from glacier transport with which water cooperates in the marginal zone, though in a subordinate capacity, to transport by water alone, which characterizes the proglacial zone. This distinctive zone is the scene of considerable morphogenetic activity, mainly depositional. The main landforms are the moraines, frontal and marginal.

(I) The Margins of Valley Glaciers

(1) Terminal Moraines

The recent terminal moraines of valley glaciers are clearly displayed. Their general outline is a half oval whose convexity points downstream like that of the tongue. Laterally, the moraine extends to the foot of the valley side. The lateral moraine is often little more than a veneer, generally not thick and rather irregular, covering the bedrock. The terminal moraine is often crescent shaped, narrowing towards the sides, though not in every case. The reverse has even been recorded, where large amounts of debris are supplied from the valley sides in the lower part of the glacier, giving unusually large lateral moraines. The terminal moraine looks rather like the front of an embankment. The proximal slope, exposed by the retreat of the glacier, is a little steeper than the distal slope. There are many large blocks on the crest which sometimes lie parallel to it and sometimes show no preferred orientation.

It is not difficult to account for this asymmetry. The distal slope is formed along the ice edge from materials piled up as they were deposited, they may have been washed by meltwater from the surface of the ice. On the crest of the arc, the thrust of the ice tended to orient the blocks parallel to its front. On the proximal face, the materials accumulated on the surface of ice which later melted *in situ*. The linear shape of terminal moraines, their resemblance to an embankment, their dissymetry, recalling a sort of external glacis, has caused them to be described as morainic ramparts.

The composition of the moraine gives considerable information on the processes responsible for its construction.

(i) On its proximal face the material is in some ways very like ground moraine. Sorting and stratification are rare and indistinct. When present, washed material is in irregular lenses of well washed pebbles without any matrix, very well graded and almost always a little worn. These lenses are the deposits of englacial channels at the end of the glacier.

(ii) On the distal face, the material is very different, although the change may take place over several tens of metres. Bedding and sorting are general, rounding of pebbles more marked. The pebbles form beds, dipping strongly outwards from a certain number of points. They thin progressively downstream and the calibre decreases at the same time. The apexes of these cones correspond to the outlets of glacial streams which shift from year to year. This arrangement suggests deposition by sheet flow on a steep slope, originally the outer face of the moraine. The absence of disturbance in the bedding, the almost complete dominance of unchannelled flow, implies deposition on the edge of, and just beyond the ice limit, and not on dead ice like the inner face.

Downstream, the character of the bedding changes during the passage to the proglacial area. Run-off becomes channelled. In place of parallel bedding, cross-bedded lenses appear with oblique stratification.

The moraine is often broken by a gap at the head of a particularly large proglacial cone which is much flatter than the coalesced cones produced by unchannelled flow. If the gaps are not deep, the basin on the site of the lower end of the glacier tongue (the terminal basin) may be occupied, after the disappearance of the ice, by a lake (moraine dammed lake).

(2) **Lateral Moraines**

The lateral moraines of small valley glaciers have no features of particular interest. But large glaciers, descending well below the snowline, have very varied marginal features with a distinctive topography. Water collects at the edge of the ice in contact with solid rock especially as the cross profile of the ice surface is more convex, and screes on the slopes are less frequent and less capable of forming a talus of debris at their foot. The action of the water is shown in the deposits; the material in the lateral moraine becomes more rounded.

When the material transported along the glacier margin is relatively abundant, and the glacier is a sufficiently stable base level, kames are formed. When the ice melts, the kames remain as terraces, *kame terraces*. Their morphology is quite different from river terraces. The surface of a kame is more hummocky and irregular, often showing the form of coalesced cones, rapid changes in altitude and sharp depressions. These are due to the instability of the local base level formed by the ice mass, subject to melting, stream erosion, and sometimes doming. The face of a kame terrace is generally steep, giving the appearance of a bench hanging on the side of the valley. Most often this is due to a slide when the ice against which the materials rested, finally melted. Kame terraces are very common in France though often not recognized. I have mapped some fine examples on the Orgelet sheet (of the French Geological Survey) in Jura and seen others near Saint-Nizier on the flank of Vercors above the Grenoble gap.

Alongside the effects of deposition, the effects of erosion are being produced. A type of channel may be cut by marginal streams into the border of the mountain mass overlooking the glacier. These drainage channels form notches whose depth varies with the stability of the glacier, the resistance of the rock and the volume of water. Their downstream end is sometimes marked by a deltaic kame deposit. The relations between relief and the surface form of the glacier makes these channels more common on the margins of valley glaciers in the mountains. There are many fine examples in Lorraine in the Vosges.

(II) The Margins of the Ice Sheets

Some of the features already examined in connection with valley glaciers are found on the margins of ice sheets, but not in the same numbers. The sheer size of an ice sheet, its tendency to extend out on to the plains far from the mountain massif which forms the core of the glaciation, alters the character of the marginal features. The marginal zones of valley glaciers and ice sheets cannot be directly compared. The same processes are at work but there are many transitional forms.

(1) Transitional Types

Two are typical: ice caps and outlet glaciers of an ice sheet. In an area of strong relief, the outlet glaciers of an ice sheet form distinct valley glaciers. In such a situation, the thinning margin of the ice sheet is more easily influenced by relief. On the flanks of mountains which are ice-free, accumulations of kames and even ice-dammed lakes are found. The ice tongues move down the valleys which are transformed into more or less typical troughs. The effect of such a development on the drainage and the formation of terraces is considerable.

Ice caps are a different matter. By definition, their margin is scarcely affected by relief.

(2) Distinctive Features of the Ice Sheet Margin

Moraines bordering an ice sheet reach a considerable height, much higher than the terminal moraines of valley glaciers, in consequence of the much greater volume of ice and the steep marginal gradient. In Greenland they reach 400 m in height, though it is impossible to say if they are plastered on a core of bedrock.

Another characteristic of an ice sheet margin is its complexity in plan. A good example is the Fennoscandian inlandsis. The distinction between lobes and tongues is a matter of scale. Lobes mark massive advances which do not form salients. Their total width may reach 200 km but they extend only some 50 km ahead of the general margin. A study of erratics has proved them to correspond to large ice streams within the main sheet. The relief of the border zone depends on the irregularities of the ice front. Marginal morainic systems form wide garlands following the outline of the ice lobes. On the site of the lobes themselves, the ground moraine often forms depressions with higher ground on either side. This has influenced the development of postglacial drainage. In detail however, the relief has been controlled by ice tongues.

In the re-entrants where the ice tongues join the main mass of the ice sheet, moraines are replaced by proglacial deposits. Subglacial tunnels are located at the junction of two ice tongues and are continued downstream by proglacial cones.

(C) The Proglacial Zone

This is dominated by the action of running water which forms an organized net at the foot of the terminal moraines by the concentration of unchannelled run-off on the outer slopes of the moraine. Ready-made englacial streams also join. Because of its origin this flow has certain characteristics which control its morphogenetic action.

(I) Characteristics of Flow

These result from the source of supply, which is related entirely to ablation of the ice, even in the case of marginal streams which flow along the ice edge. Their flow is determined by the possibilities of infiltration through the ice mass, which depend on its thermal condition.

(1) Variation in Discharge

The rhythm of melting causes variations in the volume of stream flow. Some variations are periodic others occasional. Periodic variations may be seasonal or diurnal.

Obviously, seasonal variations occur only in regions where there is an adequate seasonal contrast in temperature. These are considerable in both temperate and cold regions. In the Alps, the ratio between the monthly discharge of meltwater streams in summer and winter is between 10 and

20:1. In Greenland, flow almost completely ceases in winter but in summer meltwater forms great torrents.

Diurnal variations mainly affect the glacier streams of non-polar regions, the temperate and the hot zones. Occasional variations are superimposed on seasonal variations and despite their infrequency, have a considerable morphogenetic significance, because of their size. Two types are particularly common: the escape of water from marginal lakes (e.g. Märjelen See) and glaciovolcanic floods which are particularly frequent in Iceland. The latter are caused by a volcanic eruption underneath the ice. The ice melts very rapidly above the vent and the water rushes down the slopes, both under the ice and over it.

The size of variations in discharge of outwash streams causes corresponding changes in their competence to move the load of debris in transit. The reshaping of the material is continuous and considerable, sometimes progressive during periods of moderate flow when the streams are confined to their channels, but at other times, heavy and rough, with catastrophic flooding and unchannelled flow. When the flow is regular and channelled as in a normal system, it is called fluvioglacial. Proglacial is a more general term covering all types of flow, *débâcles* as well as fluvioglacial. Owing to the nature of their supply, fluvioglacial rivers have a distinctive character. The heavy load of alluvium supplied by the moraines, which lack vegetation because of the low temperatures, lead to shifting channels, which are almost always braided. The frequent changes in discharge give transport by saltation a predominant role with important consequences for pebbles. This is indicated by high indices of roundness and flatness, greater than those for ordinary alluvium, and an unusually strong preferred orientation, the large majority of the long axes being perpendicular to the current. Since the stream channels are anastomosing, bedding is very well developed with alternating lenses of varying grain size.

(2) The Discharge of Water and Sediment

Changes in water discharge are all the more important as flow is generally large.

The mean discharge of glacier streams (the average discharge compared to the area of the basin) is always large and much greater than that of neighbouring non-glacial streams. The importance of this mean is due to the concentration of flow in a small part of the year because of the holding capacity of the ice, and to the low evaporation, small subglacial percolation and the complete lack of vegetation.

From where they leave the glacier, proglacial streams are carrying a large load. Part at least is a very fine rock flour. The lack of sorting in morainic debris makes it easier for the streams to pick up a load, as a considerable fraction is below their competence. In contrast to rivers whose load is a function of their gradient, glaciers are able to carry debris even on a very gentle slope.

Next, the more important proglacial deposits must be considered.

(II) The Surface Form of the Deposits

(1) Simple Forms

Proglacial deposition may take many different forms according to the conditions of stream flow. In part, fluvioglacial deposition is due to heavily laden rivers subject to large and frequent changes in discharge, whose gradient decreases downstream. The importance of floods, especially seasonal floods, leads to instability of the bed. The major bed, filled in summer, differs greatly in width from the minor bed of winter. The frequency of braided channels is the result of a heavy load and the absence of vegetation to stabilize the banks.

A very important and very different type of deposit is due to catastrophic floods. The resemblance to torrential mudflows and wadi floods is very strong. The powerful current sweeps material of all sizes before it, almost without sorting, the force of the flood leads to deposits being reworked on a large scale and a surface scouring until the capacity load is reached. The morphology is spread out in a sheet, pell-mell, the tops of the largest blocks protruding through the surface. In well-defined valleys, the sheet fills the floor, forming a generally flat surface with a steep gradient.

In less dissected country like Iceland, sheet flows produced by catastrophic floods are not contained within a valley. They spread out across the whole surface of the region to form a true glacis. This is uniform in its upper parts and passes into a complicated system of distributaries in the hollows downslope. At the lower limits alluvial cones are sometimes built into the sea.

Glaciolacustrine deposits are formed where the relief prevents the escape of the proglacial drainage. As the material has mainly settled out from suspension it is silty or clayey, occasionally sandy. It is finely bedded. The most common facies is varved clays. Frequently, deltas along their margins mark the outlets of the major subglacial streams. Their material is, of course, much coarser and shows steeply dipping foreset bedding. When drained, the lake floor is strikingly flat, but often shows partly buried ridges.

Glaciomarine deposits are well developed in Scandinavia where the margin of the icesheet stood in the sea from time to time. As the sea was shallow and almost closed, the deposits are very similar to lacustrine sediments. A very different type of deposit occurs in a sea crowded with icebergs. A land-derived mud is spread on the sea floor, containing a mixture of varying proportions of material derived from subaerial denudation together with organic debris and a fine fraction of morainic origin. The series of beds does not show any consistent sorting. Some are finely bedded sands and silts derived by settling from material carried in suspension. Others are coarser, sandy and gravelly, and unbedded, material that has been dropped in bulk by icebergs. Sometimes large blocks have fallen into and deformed the underlying beds. I have studied similar material in the proglacial deposits of the Precambrian at Chapada Diamantina (Bahia, Brazil). Without a detailed knowledge of recent deposits, it is impossible to interpret correctly, 'old glacial deposits' from the Palaeozoic or Precambrian rocks whose study has scarcely begun in many countries and which have an economic importance (diamonds in Bahia).

All these basic forms combine to make regional patterns.

(2) Regional Patterns

There are many differences between an ice sheet and a valley glacier owing to differences in the relief pattern. The limit of the ice sheet is continuous for long distances. Its moraines are marginal. On the other hand the proglacial drainage of valley glaciers does not follow the edge of the ice but flows out from it and the proglacial zone consists of valley trains perpendicular to the mountain front.

(*a*) The proglacial landforms of the Quaternary ice sheets have been particularly well studied in central Europe and in the U.S.A.

The ice mass of the inlandsis, which reached a thickness of 1000–2000 m some tens of kilometres from its margin, influenced the drainage in two ways simultaneously. First, it blocked the preglacial drainage of the region; secondly, it formed the source of a proglacial drainage system. All along the margin of the inlandsis there is abundant proglacial water whose flow is controlled by the relationship between the ice front and the pre-existing relief. Channels which follow the ice margin and carry meltwater could be termed proglacial channels.

Each stable position of the ice front is indicated by a system of proglacial channels, each leading into the next and each some hundreds of kilometres long and 10–20 km wide.

Along the ice front, well differentiated cones related to the outlet of englacial streams alternate with glacis spreading down from the morainic ridge. The cones usually have a marked slope and well sorted material. Both the glacis, or apron, and the cones built against border moraines, form a gentle, fairly regular slope to the side of the periglacial channels following the ice margin. The deposits, which come almost entirely from one side, push the axis of the channel outwards, for the run-off from periglacial areas is much smaller. The result is a sapping of bedrock on the outer bank of the proglacial channel.

Finally, immense variations occur in discharge and load. The channel floor is spread out over 2 or 3 km and is braided. It has often experienced successive downcutting and aggradation so that it generally has accumulation and erosion terraces.

(*b*) Piedmont proglacial features are particularly well developed in Bavaria and Switzerland, in Bas-Dauphiné, at the foot of the central Pyrenees, in Alaska, in Patagonia and in some parts of Siberia.

Unlike the central European type of inlandsis margin, the general arrangement of the drainage is radial. The piedmont was occupied by separate tongues or lobes each giving rise to a main stream receiving meltwater from the ice front, from subglacial streams and from marginal channels. The radial pattern, related to both the general slope of the piedmont and the position of the different ice tongues, plays a very important part in the evolution of the proglacial relief. This is the work of fluvio-glacial streams in which longitudinal transport is dominant, and the exact opposite of the lateral proglacial channels of the ice sheets. Proglacial

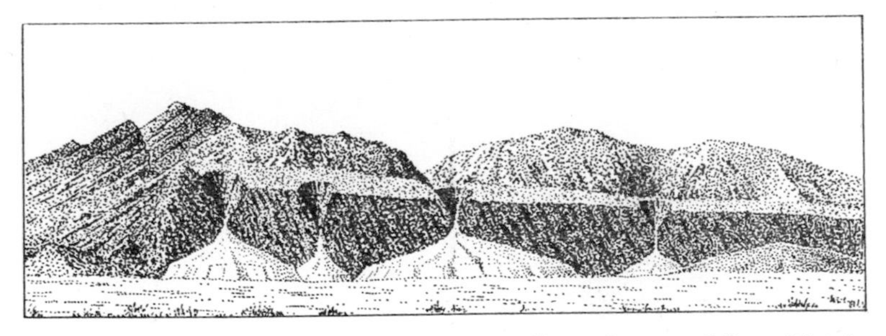

FIG. 31 Fluvio-glacial terrace, Hecho valley, Aragon (*from Nussbaum, Pirineos, 1949, p. 504*)

Dissected fluvio-glacial complex. Note the marked down-stream slope from the outer face of the terminal moraine.

materials are sorted in a downstream direction, which means that fluvioglacial valleys are infilled more rapidly upstream than downstream. This infill also increases both in thickness and width. The result is a complex landscape characterized by elongated residual interfluves, formed of the piedmont deposits. A radial valley system dissects this pattern. Sheets of alluvium, which sometimes coalesce, are often locally thick enough to conceal the former relief.

Variations in discharge and load cause both the development of aggradation and erosion terraces along fluvioglacial valleys. These features are all reduced in scale downstream as the importance of fluvioglacial materials and the variations in flow decrease.

When defined in terms of one particular process, that is the action of meltwater, the ice margin zone possesses a dynamic unity. It nevertheless has a significant diversification in relief which depends on the importance of meltwater in the combination of conflicting forces at work in the glacial environment.

CHAPTER 5

The Morphogenetic Effects of Multiple Glaciation

THIS study would be incomplete without a consideration of the changes in the glaciers during the million or so years of the Quaternary era. Rhythmic changes in the extent of the glaciers, the 'glacial sequences', have controlled the development of the landforms (advance and retreat features). This influence of time can be considered on two scales, and as often happens, the difference in scale entails not only quantitative but also qualitative modification. On the scale of local features, the relief is produced chiefly by an alternation of processes related to advance and retreat, which modify it to a varying degree. On a regional scale the relief evolves chiefly in harmony with forces closely connected with glaciation, eustatic changes of sea level and isostatic movements.

THE DIRECT CONSEQUENCES OF MULTIPLE GLACIATION

Since, in the marginal zone, a direct conflict exists between processes characteristic of ice and those characteristic of meltwater, it is essential to distinguish carefully between the morphogenetic effects of continuous advance and those of deglaciation.

(A) THE INFLUENCE OF CONTINUED ICE ADVANCE

The study of this problem is more difficult than that of recessional features. Indeed it is rare to find a glacier advancing today in any region where direct observation is possible. As to Quaternary features, they are often destroyed or profoundly modified by the later advance, and are difficult to identify.

(1) The Landforms of Ice advance

These are push moraines, which form asymmetrical hills with convex summits, arcuate in plan, but with interruptions filled by proglacial deposits. However, when fresh, push moraines have several typical features. Their slopes are always more steep and their profile more convex than those of other moraines; sometimes there is even a slight break in slope between the moraine and the proglacial deposit at its foot.

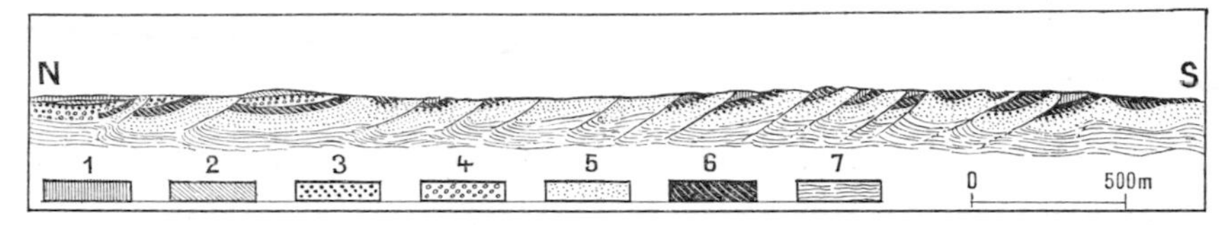

FIG. 32 Pseudo-tectonic structures in a push moraine. Itterbeck area, N.W. Germany (*after Richter, Scheider, Wager*)

1. Later deposits 2. Ground moraine 3. Periglacial sands 4. Pre-saale gravels 5. Micaceous sands of the upper Tertiary 6. Glauconitic sands of upper Oligocene 7. Middle Oligocene.
Vertical scale not exaggerated. Ice moved from left (north) to right (south).

The push moraine is not connected with a melting glacier tongue. There is no large volume of meltwater likely to spread material reworked from its mass.

The structure of push moraines is very typical and is the best basis for their identification. It consists of thrust blocks of beds which have been pushed and more or less tilted by the ice as it advanced. Push moraines are most common in connection with ice sheets but they also occur with valley glaciers.

(2) The Problem of Stadials

Quaternary marginal and terminal morainic deposits are arranged in roughly concentric arcs, with gaps between the arcs. This pattern is as common with valley glaciers as with ice sheets.

Some authors believe that each of these systems of terminal moraines represents a glacial stadial, each glaciation having successive stadials. Each arc, or series of arcs, deposited by the ice in an area it formerly covered would thus mark a stage in its retreat. More detailed study suggests that these terminal moraines are not recessional features but, on the contrary, represent a readvance. However, the formation of these morainic arcs does not depend solely on the movement of the glacier; it is related to the ever-changing balance between the two opposing forces responsible for morphogenesis at the ice margin. In theory, several different cases could arise. Ice alone, or almost alone, could be responsible, with water in a very subordinate position or even entirely lacking owing to climatic conditions. In this case it would not remove material shed by the ice, so that this would build up to form a well marked terminal moraine. At the other end of the scale, water could predominate and the ice melt *in situ* without being able to accomplish any transport. There is then much sorting of debris which tends to be spread out, considerable development of ablation moraines, characteristic of ice in rapid retreat, and ultimately the formation of a rock glacier. In this case there is no distinct terminal moraine. Deposits are typically recessional. It is also possible to have a state of relative equilibrium, (which may have many peculiarities in detail), where there is a balance between material brought up by the ice and its removal by meltwater. This occurs during a period of stillstand. The formation of the moraines then depends on a group of factors. If the ice is clean, with little debris, moraines are poor or missing. If on the other hand, the ice is loaded with so many large blocks that it is beyond the capacity of the meltwater to remove them, a moraine will be formed.

The controlling factor in this situation is climate. On it depends both the glacier budget and the rhythm of ablation. It is clear that moraines are not necessarily formed; they are often missing and their absence is not always due to their subsequent destruction. Well developed systems of end moraines generally belong to phases of advance or to readvance during retreat. Their formation is closely controlled by regional and local conditions. When an increase in nourishment occurs, a 'bulge' in the glacier is produced, which travels towards the front as a wave moving more quickly than the ice. It results in a thickening of the ice which modifies the conditions of flow, increasing appreciably the pressure on the underlying rock. This increased thickness leads to increased shearing and an increase in debris in the glacier. It is conceivable that such a temporary growth of the glacier, producing a slight advance of the snout, might be accompanied by a marked increase in the arrival of debris at the front.

The size of the end moraine is also a function of the morphoclimatic zones. Thus, in the Andes in Venezuela, end moraines are extraordinarily large, forming very distinctive ramparts, while outwash deposits are very poorly developed and contain only small pebbles. Their unusual development must be due to the absence of well-defined thermal seasons and to a rhythm of daily melt incapable of supplying large volumes of water. The small discharge is not competent to move more than a small fraction of the debris supplied by the glacier so that it accumulates in situ as terminal moraines.

The same variations in balance between the two opposed agents, ice and meltwater, control the formation of fluvioglacial landforms. Penck believed that fluvioglacial deposits are formed during the glacial maximum. In reality, the problem is much more complex and conditions vary from valley to valley. Many valleys appear to have been extensively infilled during the retreat of the glaciers when water, stored as ice and rapidly released, washes down a large volume of ablation moraine. At any particular point in front of the glacier, the effect of the ice recession can be seen in the ever-decreasing calibre of the outwash debris. From the time meltwater leaves the glacier, it effectively sorts its load by depositing the coarser material progressively as its gradient decreases, the two phenomena being linked by autocatalysis. As the glacier moves further away, smaller debris reaches the point under consideration. When other factors do not disturb the process, this relationship could help to correlate moraines with outwash deposits. A check must be made by means of erratic counts, heavy minerals etc.

(3) The Morphological Effects of Ice Advance

The return of glaciation is accompanied by a severe disturbance of the morphoclimatic balance. One system is substituted for another, one set of processes for another. A remoulding of relief follows, marked by the appearance of glacial forms, including not only those due to ice itself but also those developed by nivation and other processes caused by the cold climatic conditions accompanying the ice advance.

The phases of advance are of fundamental importance. Some glacial processes are developed very rapidly during the growth of the ice. The remoulding of the relief tends to proceed much faster than the norm. However, this readaptation brings into operation a whole series of opposing forces resulting from the resistance of the rocks or the tendency of some glacial processes to work in opposition to each other. At the beginning these have little effect. The rock, in particular, has been loosened or shattered by processes operating in advance. Nevertheless, they build up progressively and the action of glacial processes becomes less and less efficient. For this reason, the dynamic balance between different processes tending to develop glacial landforms and the resistance offered to them,

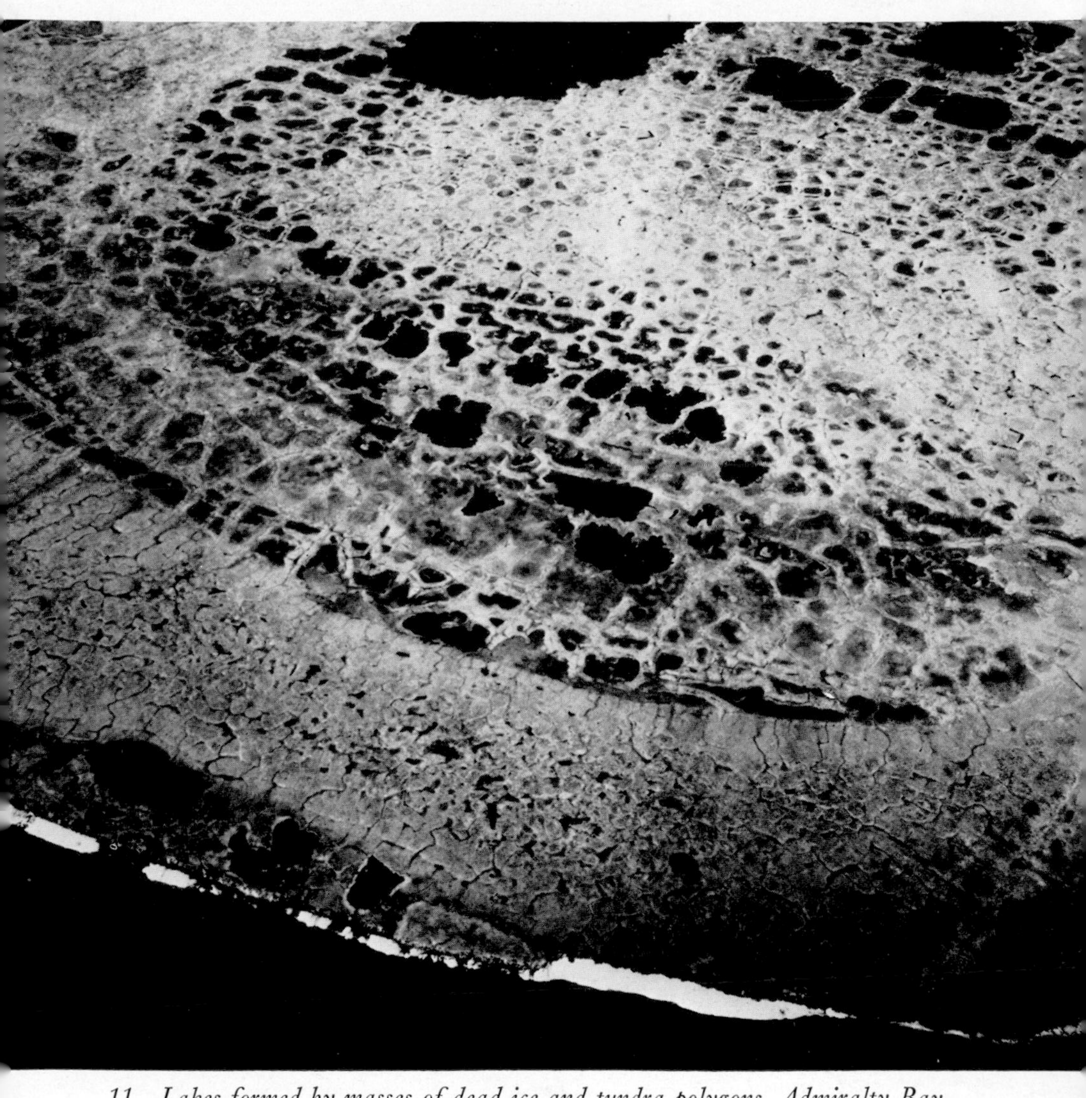

11 *Lakes formed by masses of dead ice and tundra polygons. Admiralty Bay, Oarlock Island, Alaska*

12 Rock glaciers in Alaska

can be extremely variable, differing from one glacier to another and from one period to the next. This explains the wide range of glacial forms and the frequency of a typical relief – only slightly 'glaciated'.

One of the processes belonging strictly to the ice advance is periglacial deep shattering, the theory of which was proposed by Demorest and developed by Boyé. During the advance, far in front of the centres of glaciation, cold conditions occur well ahead of the occupation of the area by ice. As has been proved many times, permafrost develops and extends downwards for tens or even hundreds of metres. Water freezing in rock joints widens them. When the area has been buried by ice, the ground is protected from further loss of heat by radiation, and the permafrost melts. This releases blocks which have been loosened by frost and allows them to be incorporated in moraines. This hypothesis explains the huge moraines deposited by some glaciers in Antarctica, such as those of New Swabia, during a phase of advance when the ice itself is clean.

(B) Landforms of Deglaciation

The importance of the factors is now reversed. Melting is taking place rapidly and the ice disappearing *in situ*. The ice is no longer active; its main function is to deposit the material it contains where it melts. Running water is the active agent. The marginal zone moves back continuously, averaging some hundreds of metres a year for the ice sheets of the Late Glacial period.

(1) Retreat Landforms

These are due to special conditions at the ice margin; dead ice, a superabundance of meltwater and, most often, a rapid retreat of the ice front. With this in mind, our study will begin with a description of existing features; then the time factor will be introduced and we shall turn to the landforms of the Late Glacial.

(a) Existing Phenomena The excellent monograph by Sharp on the superglacial debris of Wolf Creek Glacier, in the Yukon, will serve as an example. At the foot of Mount Hood in the Saint Elias Range, this glacier is formed of dead ice for the last 15 km of its tongue and descends to around 1300 m. It is a very large valley glacier in a region of dry continental climate. It is entirely covered in its lower part, by ablation moraine, composed of former englacial debris concentrated on the surface by melting. The average thickness of the ablation moraine is about 0·6 m. This is believed to result from the melting of a bed of ice at least 150 m thick. Compared with the surface moraines of an active glacier, this cover contains many rounded pebbles – well sorted and stratified deposits indicating the dominant action of meltwater.

Differential melting has produced repeated inversions of relief. Water is concentrated in hollows on the surface which tend to collect debris. In the following year these deposits delay the melting of the ice so that the former channel is gradually transformed into a ridge, thus inverting the relief. Other ridges which develop correspond to the crevasse pattern. Meltwater builds deltas in lakes and carries into pools and lakes muds which are laid down as stratified deposits. These deposits are all temporary, they will be reworked, as the glacier surface is lowered by ablation, both by meltwater or by solifluction and later will be affected by collapse and settling. They bury the underlying ground moraine, depositing on top of it, a layer of ablation moraine which differs considerably in character.

Sharp's observations in Alaska have a general application. Other research workers have observed similar features elsewhere.

In dry climates with a large range of temperature, such as Tibet, the Punjab or the Pamirs, glacier tongues disappear beneath debris of all kinds and are completely buried. During retreat, no end moraines are formed; instead there is an accumulation of angular debris which is washed and partly reworked by meltwater. It seems very similar to the deposits produced in the Andes of Santiago dating from the close of the Würm, described by me. This type of glacier, buried under its own debris, is the exact opposite of those described above.

The Swedes have also drawn attention to ice-cored moraines whose irregular surface is ridged and hummocky. They appear comparable in many ways to those just described.

(b) **Lateglacial Features** The very rapid retreat of the ice sheets gave rise to more complex phenomena. The recession, considered in time as well as in space, was accompanied by additional complications, particularly the glacio-eustatic rise in sea level. It is therefore important to distinguish between the sequence of events in a terrestial and a marine environment.

The landforms of retreat on land evolve under the dominant influence of running water. This not only modifies the character of the superglacial material changing it to ablation moraine, it is also responsible for the erosion of the bedrock (glacial drainage channels; Fr. *canyons de récession*). These proglacial *retreat gorges* are very unevenly distributed. They may occur in groups or be quite absent. They seem to be less common where the ice was strongly crevassed and heavily charged with debris. Meltwater was lost in the crevasses and reworked the debris instead of attacking the solid rock.

Retreat gorges have been described chiefly in Sweden, Great Britain and Canada, where there has been much discussion on them.

They consist of short channels, usually some hundreds of metres in length, sometimes a kilometre, incised in resistant rock apparently quite at random, on the flank of a ridge or across the end of a crest line, for example. Their depth rarely exceeds about ten metres. Swedish workers have been able to show that they can be formed very quickly and do not require more than a season for the shortest, or more than 5 or 6 years for the longest channels. They result from flow between the ice margin and a nunatak and their irregular topographic situation is explained by the occupation of the lower ground by ice. Others were cut by waters draining from ice-margin lakes. They can be differentiated from subglacial channels by their weaker development, shorter length and by their position. Subglacial gorges are generally developed on low ground where meltwater tends to collect.

Retreat features developed in a marine environment are obviously different because running water no longer has the dominant role. The landforms are those of submarine deposition with some distinctive features. At the mouths of the major subglacial and superglacial channels, fine debris is carried into the sea to form deltas. Further from the shore there is a steady deposition of silt which veneers the ground moraine already laid down, filling the depressions. Owing to the rhythm of seasonal melting, a stratification akin to varves is developed.

More distinctive features are the series of low ridges, only a few metres high, lying parallel to the former ice front. De Geer called them annual moraines in the belief that in winter, when melting ceased, the ice sheet advanced again for some tens of metres. In the following summer renewed melting caused the morainic debris to be deposited forming a ridge. Hoppe rejects this hypothesis on the grounds that an advance depends on the speed of the ice and the rate of melting, and it is improbable that the annual retreat would be constant. He believes the ridges to be submarine terminal moraines deposited between the calving of one iceberg and the next. Their fairly regular spacing would be due to the size of the bergs which does not vary greatly. The theory also explains the absence of these ridges along stretches of the old shoreline where the sea was shallow enough to allow the ice to rest on the bottom, preventing the formation of bergs.

(2) Dead Ice Features

They belong to an advanced stage of deglaciation where the ice consists only of discontinuous masses buried completely under debris. There is no fresh supply of ice, hence the term 'dead ice'. The ice is, naturally inactive.

Masses of fossil ice are one of the elements of dead ice. They are not necessarily glacial in origin and are also found in a periglacial environment. During rapid retreat, masses of ice in hollows are protected by ablation moraine; they may survive tens of years after being separated from the ice front. Examples may be seen at present in Alaska; a hollow in the glacier bed or a thick cover of debris offers favourable conditions. The relief produced by the melting of the ice masses is one of depressions, which is sometimes wrongly called pseudo-karst. On the site of each block a basin is formed which remains for a considerable time, depending on the depth and the amount of material being deposited in it. On ground moraine and clay-rich ablation moraine, slipping and solifluction soon modify the edges of the basin and fill it rapidly. On the other hand, if the drift is gravelly the sides of the hollow remain steep and infilling is very slow.

Rock glaciers offer another example of the geomorphological work of dead ice. These are glaciers whose nourishment has ceased and which have become buried under debris derived from the surrounding slopes. The outer face of a rock glacier lobe is an unstable talus sloping at 35–40°. It is affected by the internal thrust of its ice core owing to displacement by plasticity. Humid conditions lead to severe frost shattering. Rock glacier moraines are generally characterized by completely unworn material, by the frequent frost-shattered forms, and by the rarity, sometimes the absence, of a clayey matrix; they form only where frost shattering is intense. Under such conditions fine material is not produced. They are essentially a feature of mountain regions though masses of dead ice are found, especially in the piedmont zone, in areas of inlandsis or large valleys

Rock glaciers are common today in the high valleys that were heavily glaciated during the Quaternary such as the San Juan Mountains, Alaska, the Engadine, west Greenland, and the southern Alps in France. Climate plays an important part in their development and dry mountain areas with a continental climate are most suitable. Rock glaciers have been noted mainly on the floors of valleys enclosed by high mountains or at their mouth; generally they have the shape of a valley glacier. Their cross profile is convex. In plan they show transverse arcuate ridges, between 10 and 100 m apart, convex downstream and sorted according to the size of the blocks. These regular transverse ridges and the very steep frontal slope differentiate them clearly from block flows which are entirely due to solifluction. They are nourished by avalanches whose snow melts in summer and filters through the debris reaching the buried ice where it refreezes. This increases the ice mass and enables it to more or less maintain the delicate equilibrium which makes rock glaciers ephemeral features. In the 8000–10 000 years of Postglacial time alone, several successive generations have been distinguished in Haut-Ubaye and in the Queyras.

(3) Modifications of Fluvial and Other Processes

The importance of the remodelling of relief during the change-over from a system of glacial erosion to a fluvial morphogenetic system has long been stressed. For some there is nothing in common between the two systems, for others the difference is purely quantitative, the glacier bed not being on the same scale as the river bed. Personally, I believe that the two reasons, invoked are not necessarily mutually exclusive. It is to the credit of the Grenoble school that they have insisted that certain fluviatile forms belong to the glacial morphogenetic system and develop during the glacial recession and not during the interglacial.

Proglacial rivers are intensely active during deglaciation owing to the large volume of meltwater and loose morainic debris liberated from the ice. The conditions of their work are by no means the same in areas of mountain glaciation and in an ice sheet. The valley directs the flow of the water in the former, and the channels form rivers right at the ice front. In the marginal zone of the glacier itself, meltwater is more abundant than during phases of stability, it is also more active and the work of remodelling begins even under dead ice. The conditions under which melting takes place control the site of the river; in middle latitudes, on the floors of deep troughs running east–west, where the difference in insolation between the two sides is at a maximum, gorges are cut not along the central axis but at the foot of the shaded slope where the ice tongue has survived longest. Frequently these gorges have been buried under recent alluvium. It is during deglaciation that an abrupt change in the morphoclimatic equilibrium enables new processes to work at great speed; in this case, fluvial processes. As on the edge of a retreating ice sheet, immediately behind the front, meltwater is able to cut gorges in a few years, while a short distance away deposition is general.

A short distance from the ice, aggradation during retreat is very rapid, as may be verified in front of glaciers heavily charged with morainic debris and at present in retreat.

Not only the longitudinal profile but also the cross profile of the valley is modified. The sides of a trough, even in weak or unconsolidated rocks, may be kept steep by the lateral pressure of the ice. After the ice has melted, if the trough wall has been oversteepened, it will be unstable. Various processes will operate to reduce the slope angle of the trough side; the most rapid of these is slipping. In the Late Glacial period, several landslips in the Alps were exceptionally large. On the Upper Rhine at Flims a slip has blocked the valley for a distance of 7 km, and to a depth of 400 m; its volume has been calculated at 15 million cubic metres. It was formed from a large slice of the mountainside which was composed of marls and shales dipping towards the trough. The steep walls of troughs also set in motion other processes requiring fairly steep slopes, such as avalanches. In the Rabbi valley, moraines with clayey or silty matrix, perched at different heights along the sides of the valleys, often above a steep slope, give rise to mudflows and muddy torrents and, if the vegetation cover is scanty, to gullying.

Working mainly to the detriment of freshly deposited moraines, these processes modify their character considerably. Moraines lying on mountain slopes are often washed, at least on the surface, by run-off which has removed some part of their fine matrix. Very often, solifluction and slipping has destroyed their original stratification, and changed the orientation of the embedded blocks. In deeply sunk valleys with steep sides, kame terraces have become unrecognizable because of this. It is necessary to distinguish carefully between moraines which have suffered solifluction or landslipping, or have been washed, and those still *in situ* and undisturbed, if mistakes are to be avoided, not only in interpretation, but also in assessing their potential in soil formation, agricultural production and construction work.

Acting on the surface, all these processes rapidly modify the initial glaciated landscape. Large masses of debris accumulate at the foot of trough sides and encumber the floor so that it may be difficult to recognize the trough as such. This abundant supply of debris down the slopes helps to explain the rapidity and intensity of Late Glacial deposition.

Little by little, the intensity of the new processes begins to lessen. Great landslides become fewer. The more unstable masses have long since given way. Present-day slips usually have a more indirect origin.

Mudflows and muddy torrents are mostly activated by streams cutting into unconsolidated deposits. This destruction by water of morainic material begun at the close of the active phase of deglaciation, and the decrease in the supply of debris from the slopes by mass movement, reduces the load carried by the rivers, particularly in their lower valleys and in the piedmont.

Very often, the Würm valley train has been dissected into terraces and trenched by gullies. This dissection is made difficult by the size of the Würm material determined by the increased competence of rivers swollen during deglaciation. Indeed the dissection is often only in the early stages and is limited to the washing out of material fine enough not to exceed the competence of the rivers. The course material remains encumbering the river bed and the water finds its way through it. On the whole, post-glacial dissection is represented by a slight incision and a very wide flood plain scattered with boulders through which anastomosing channels wander. As a result of this incision the stream may reach the foot of the valley side which is actively undercut. It is thus often accompanied by significant lateral erosion. Braided flow during phases of glacial aggradation, lateral and vertical erosion during interglacials, combine to alter the course of the river, especially in the piedmont zone with its slighter relief.

Like the phase of glacial advance, the phase of deglaciation is marked by a great increase in morphological activity. Both follow a sharp change in the morphoclimatic balance which leads to a change in process. The new processes are particularly active at the height of deglaciation when they cause a rapid reshaping of landforms. Later, as during the onset of glaciation, their activity decreases. The Quaternary era was, from the geological point of view, marked by extreme instability and a rapid succession of glacial and interglacial periods repeated several times. For this reason, it has been a period of marked morphogenesis. This is why, in such a limited period, erosion and deposition have been so intense. The result is a very great diversification of relief, especially in areas at the limits of glaciation, for they have undergone the greatest changes in morphogenetic process.

CHAPTER 6

The Indirect Consequences of the Glaciations

FROM the viewpoint of geology, the periods of glaciation, both Quaternary and older, have exerted a strong influence on the development of the earth's surface. They have set in motion abrupt and powerful changes in its equilibrium which have caused changes in sea level, biological changes, and isostatic reactions; in their turn, the consequences of glaciation affect the evolution of the landscape. Isostatic movements and glacioeustatic oscillations in world sea level have affected the development of relief, and the changes in equilibrium which they introduce are the indirect morphodynamic consequences of glaciation. The biogeographical changes, and especially the changes in plant limits, have influenced one of the main factors of climatic geomorphology: the resistance of the vegetation cover to erosion. But it is not possible to put in the same system all the processes affecting morphogenesis set in motion by glaciation. The degree of contemporaneity with the phases of glaciation varies. The world-wide changes in the volume of the seas are exactly in phase with the changes in the volume of ice. Isostatic readjustment, on the other hand, follows several millennia later; this delay appears to be between 5 and 20 millennia, since the postglacial uplift of the Canadian and Fennoscandian shields is still very much in progress, 8000 to 10 000 years after the deglaciation.

Biogeographical consequences are also out of phase. Climatic changes which cause variations in the extent of the ice have two consequences which are very much out of step with one another. First, there is a rapid change in the area covered by different plant species and associations which helps to upset the equilibrium of the morphoclimatic environment. During the advance of the ice the forest zone recedes before the tundra and the tundra before the subpolar or periglacial desert. During the recession (Alaska today, the Russian plain in the Late Glacial), the area uncovered by the ice is rapidly colonized by the forest. This oscillation in vegetation boundaries has been, for some years or even for some centuries, in phase with the major climatic changes. Because of the infinite variety of living things, the biogeographical results of glaciation are not limited to this. There is another set of consequences which takes effect only after a lapse of time and which is not in phase with glaciation, the appearance of new species. Since glaciation is a primary geological change, it strongly influences biological evolutionary development.

Only one consequence of glaciation which has had the strongest and most direct geomorphological repercussions, the glacio-eustatic oscillation of sea level and the isostatic readjustments, will be discussed here. Modifications in the distribution of living things are a problem of general climatic geomorphology.

(A) Glacio-eustatic Changes

The locking up of large masses of water on the continents in the form of ice is, in the last analysis, achieved mainly at the expense of the oceans and the seas. The glacio-eustatic sequence consists of a fall in sea level accompanying the advance of the ice and a rise of sea level during deglaciation. Throughout the Quaternary this has caused repeated changes in the base level of river erosion and marine erosion which have been of great significance. It is important to analyse its character and consequences.

Glacio-eustatic oscillations depend directly on changes in the volume of the ice and are synchronous with them. However, there are some factors working to counter them. The most important is the isostatic response of the bottom of the ocean basins. A recent estimate of the volume of water in existence today in the form of ice is that of Cailleux:

	Surface	*Volume*	*Depth of Water*
Antarctica	13 000 000 km^2	32 000 000 km^3	80 m
Greenland	1 650 000	3 400 000	8·7
Other glaciers	450 000	100 000	0·3

The depth of water is calculated solely with reference to the surface of the oceans. This estimate corresponds fairly well to the maximum volume which has been suggested for the Antarctic ice as a result of recent geophysical exploration. The previous values were considerably lower and would allow for a depth of water of only 30–40 m.

If existing ice were to melt completely, and no other factors were to offset this, sea level would rise about 90 m. During the Quaternary glaciations, however, sea level has been lower than today. Considering the estimated volume of the ice sheets, the figure for the glacial maximum would be at least 50 m lower, and between 150 and 230 m lower at most. A large fall would explain a number of points concerning submarine topography. Often subaerial deposits are found on the continental shelf. It is important therefore to arrive at a figure for the size of these glacio-eustatic changes. A study of submarine relief confirms the values usually allotted by glaciologists to the volume of the Quaternary ice, but these are a rough approximation and should be corrected for general isostatic readjustment. Water contained in the continental ice sheets comes originally from the sea. Owing to reduced pressure on the sea floor it tends to rise by isostasy, the compensating movement of magma at depth. Assuming the density of the magma to be between 2·74 and 3·34, the upward movement would be 30 to 36% of the depth of water removed. The resulting fall would be 70 to 64% of this same depth. To sum up, the Würm shoreline may be put at 50–100 m below the present and during the glacial maximum 70–130 m below. Isostatic readjustment, being out of phase with the glacio-eustatic oscillation, plays a very important part in the pattern of the sea level changes. During the Würm deglaciation, which took place in a short time, the transgression was also very rapid because isostatic readjustment was not yet fully in operation. Subsequently it became slower and slower with secondary fluctuations due partly to the variable retreat of the ice. Thus a stillstand of the sea at −25 m is recorded on the continental shelf in the Persian Gulf and off Venezuela and a level of +1 m to +2 m is widespread and well preserved throughout the intertropical belt would correspond to the Postglacial Climatic Optimum. Known as the Dunkirk sea level (*Dunkerquien*), this often plays an important geomorphological role, as the maximum of the Flandrian Transgression.

Similarly, a slowing down in the regression caused by each glaciation must have taken place owing to the effects of isostatic compensation. A full appreciation of it must await more careful exploration of the continental shelf. However, it is clear that glaciation has had a considerable indirect influence on the formation of certain major submarine features, on sedimentation and on coastal morphogenesis.

These glacio-eustatic fluctuations of sea level are, however, only one factor of this morphogenesis, they control especially its geographical limits. In some regions, a series of former beaches can be seen, the highest being the oldest. The Pliocene beach is often more than 120 m, and that of the older Quaternary about 100 m above the present beach. To get conditions comparable with those of the Pliocene, one must suppose that the existing ice sheets have melted. Sea level should then rise by 60 m. Since the Pliocene, therefore, there has been a relative upward movement of the land of 120 less 60 m approximately. This might be due to loss of weight owing to erosion or to an epeirogenic movement whose cause is unknown. The fact that, between these heights the change in sea level has not been continuous but has fluctuated, is evidently the result of the glacial fluctuations. In even more areas, the last interglacial beach is higher than the present, by 3–10 m, or even 15 m. The difference may be explained either as being a fraction of the slow rise of the earth's crust, or because deglaciation in the Riss–Würm (Interglacial) would have been a little more extensive than at present. The small difference in sea level indicates that the Antarctic ice sheets at least still had a very considerable volume, not very different from today. However, in some areas, all these relative movements have been increased, cancelled out, or even reversed, by tectonic deformation.

The Riss-Würm Interglacial period was followed by a regression in cold climatic conditions which have furnished proof of the deterioration of climate ahead of the ice advance. In fact, when sea level was at about its present level, the growth of the glaciers was not yet very considerable and the newly born ice sheets would still have been unable to lower the temperature appreciably in Brittany or Picardy where indications of a cold climate are clear. In areas which are stable, tending to rise, or even to sink slightly, the Pre-Flandrian Regression (that is, of the last glaciation or Würm), caused large parts of the continental shelves to emerge. Where the former sea floor has been affected by subaerial processes, which have deeply weathered the rocks, the sea, during the succeeding transgression (the Flandrian), had at its disposal a large volume of loose debris, including alluvium left by rivers and, especially on the continental margins of periglacial regions, aeolian sands. During the transgression, these were gradually carried back to the coast where they played a considerable part in the smoothing of the coast line by deposition. This explains why the rock types found on the beaches, in many cases do not wholly correspond to the source of present-day materials; there are for example many flint pebbles on the east coast of the Ile d'Yeu (off Vendée), which is entirely composed of schists. This has considerable bearing on the search for coastal mineral deposits, such as on the west coast of Africa. The now submerged continental shelf shows evidence of subaerial denudation dating from the period of regression.

Repeated changes in sea level left little enough time for the sea to shape the coastline during the periods of relative stability. In comparatively stable areas, the present coast and that of the Riss-Würm Interglacial, because of the small difference in their height, occur in practically the same sites. Generally, the sea has been limited, in the Holocene, to a partial exhumation of the interglacial beach and the Würm terrestrial deposits which cover it. In tropical seas, on the other hand, the Flandrian Transgression has assisted the growth of coral reefs, or at least that part above present sea level.

Changes in sea level have caused both vertical and horizontal displacements of base level which have affected fluvial processes. Theoretically, these changes should have given rise to eustatic terraces. There would then have been downcutting during the ice advance and aggradation during glaciation. A complete theory of terrace development has been founded on this concept, each interglacial sea level having produced a terrace at about the same height above the talweg as the interglacial beach is above the modern. It is only in the upper part of the valleys which the headward erosion of the glacial periods would not have had time to reach, that the terraces are no longer distinguishable (Baulig). In fact, such a simple case is unusual because glacio-eustatic changes occur with other factors which often outweigh them. As well as regional tectonic factors, which may differ from place to place, morphoclimatic factors play a fundamental role. Aggradation is favoured by a large quantity of available debris and by a reduction in the velocity of the stream, downcutting by the opposite conditions. In middle latitudes during cold periods, the eustatic fall in sea level, might, in cases where it steepened the talweg at the mouth, promote downcutting. This effect was largely neutralized by the increase in the load of fluvioglacial or periglacial rivers. Wherever the slope of the stream bed is approximately the same as that of the sea floor, there is no significant increase in gradient, as for example in the lower Po–Adriatic. On the whole, during cold periods, aggradation predominated over downcutting in the lower reaches of rivers in middle latitudes. The area affected by glacio-eustatic downcutting forms only a narrow fringe around the coasts, a little wider in the case of the larger rivers not fed by glaciers. Hasty generalizations are to be avoided, for very often the operation of different factors result in a certain dynamic equilibrium. Many valleys in Brittany and Cornwall have been choked with solifluction deposits right to the present shore line. Streams have been so slow in removing these that Flandrian deposits are absent. In every case, the combination of factors must be carefully examined; changes in sea level which have not taken place at a constant speed during the retreat and advance of the ice, regional tectonic movements, climatic fluctuations and their effect on tectonic movements, or changes in climate and their effect on different rock types. In Vendée, for example, Mme. Ters has been able to show that an important period of downcutting took place towards the end of the Flandrian transgression. This apparently coincided with a transition from a climate favourable to solifluction, and therefore excluding glacio-eustatic incision, to a climate favourable to river work, hence the downcutting. A simple explanation which takes account of only a change of sea level or only a change of climate is inadequate. The problem needs patient analysis of the possible combinations of these factors to establish processes on precise dating (C^{14}, pollen analysis, varve counts, etc.).

(B) Glacio-isostatic Warping

Isostatic movement differs from glacio-eustatic movement in that its effects are both local and affected by a time lag. Apart from the sea bed it affects only those regions which have been covered by an ice sheet or the area immediately surrounding them. Its effects are therefore less general. Since it is out of phase with oscillations of the ice front, its morphological effects are complicated by its varied relationship with glacio-eustatic changes.

In order to understand how these operate, it is necessary to recall the main points concerning isostasy. Gravity measurements on the earth's surface have shown that, very approximately, areas of high land are underlain by lighter material and depressions by heavier material. There is a compensation or isostasy. During geological time, losses in weight due to erosion and increases due to deposition have not resulted in a loss of equilibrium. This implies that, at depth, compensating currents move in the opposite direction to the transport of sediments, or more generally opposite to the movement of surface materials. In particular, the growth or the disappearance of an ice sheet causes a displacement of this nature. The actions and reactions which it engenders may be called glacio-isostasy. The pressure on the substratum of a layer of ice 1500–2000 m thick, like that of Fennoscandia, would be the equivalent of 500–700 m of rock. The effect of this weight would produce an isostatic reaction which leads to a depression of the surface. The growth of an ice sheet being slow, it is possible that the time lag between the development of the ice and the isostatic movement would be small. During deglaciation, on the other hand, the melting of the ice took place rapidly and the pressure exerted by it was suddenly reduced so that isostatic compensation resulted in uplift.

The plasticity of the earth's crust at depth is low and its viscosity very high, so that isostatic compensation takes place only after considerable loss of equilibrium and then very slowly. The speed of deglaciation has been such that, when isostatic compensation was at a maximum, the ice recession was almost finished. This time lag explains why the glacio-eustatic uplift has still not been completed in Fennoscandia and North America.

Quite a number of facts confirm this interpretation. The Scandinavians and Gutemberg have collated them. The movements are limited to areas which have recently undergone a considerable glaciation. Their speed is related to the rate of the retreat in the area. The limits of the areas affected coincide with the maximum extent of the ice and the isopleths of equal speed of deformation today are concentric with the ice margin. It was the same during the older glaciations. Strong negative gravity anomalies are typical of these areas and increase towards the centre where the ice was thickest and the uplift is also still rapid. Generally, these glacio-isostatic deformations are dome-shaped, with a maximum elevation where the ice sheet was thickest.

In Scandinavia where the ice-shed lay east of the mountain divide, the coastal belt of Norrland exhibits the greatest total uplift. At present, the rate of uplift is at a maximum on the bottom of the Gulf of Bothnia and seems to be related to a later deglaciation. The coincidence of a rigid shield with the central area of each of the two northern hemisphere ice sheets of the Quaternary must have influenced the nature of the uplift, which recalls the slow epeirogenesis of the ancient massifs. It is possible, however, that in some cases, limited differential isostatic movements must have taken place locally, which repeat on a smaller scale the overall doming and cause the resurrection of older relief. The tectonic grid pattern of some parts of the Canadian and Fennoscandian Shields would have been accentuated in this way during successive Quaternary glaciations, by causing movement along faults and shatter belts, which in turn facilitated glacial erosion. Areas of folded mountains are the most favourable to these phenomena.

These features have, of course, considerable morphological consequences. Locally, glacio-isostasy is expressed in a relative change of level between land and sea which is superimposed on the more general glacio-eustatic changes. The problem is complicated by the time lag and by regional differences in the rate of isostatic recovery. In the case of the last deglaciation, glacio-eustatic forces, not being out of phase, were dominant at first, so that the Late Glacial was marked at first by submergence. Then isostatic uplift began to make itself felt, becoming more marked and more rapid. In some parts at least, its speed exceeded that of the transgression, as in the Gulf of Bothnia where there was a rise in sea level of 2–4 mm a year and an isostatic uplift of more than 10 mm. In the resulting rise of land in relation to sea level, the general transgression was masked by local uplift and was replaced by a rapid regional regression. This pattern applies only to the central areas of the Quaternary ice sheets where isostatic recovery, still in progress, is on a large scale. In marginal areas, isostatic uplift is less marked.

Where isostatic uplift temporarily exceeded the glacio-eustatic transgression, the morphogenetic conditions have been those of a very rapid regression. Climatic change was complicated by epeirogenic movements. On land, the general tendency was for downcutting. Then a very important factor made itself felt, the great variability in the rate of erosion on different rock formations. The extent of vertical erosion is very considerable on the softest deposits. In the lower part of the Angermannelv valley in Sweden the river has cut out a gorge 50–70 m deep in the marine and deltaic silts and sands of the ice recession at an average speed of about 20 mm a year. This incision has been accompanied by lateral erosion which has created a flight of surfaces whose height is extremely variable, as they are generally due to former meanders. The tendency has been generally towards a reduction in radius of meanders so that the modern river is straighter than its former course. Hjulström believes that meanders are only well developed on soft homogeneous rocks and in sectors where the rate of uplift is moderate. Their decreasing importance over time would in this case be due to the increase in relative uplift at the start of the Postglacial period and in the recent past. This considerable downcutting and lateral erosion by meanders has of course produced superimposition which has resulted in a local reduction in erosion so that local basins are separated by gorges. These thresholds formed of the Precambrian Shield form a base level to each basin so that it develops to some extent independently. During the incision of the gorge, lithological differences are exploited. The grain size of unconsolidated deposits is an important factor. Silt and sand are easily eroded because their grain size is well below the competence of the river. Coarser materials are, on the other hand, superficially washed, the larger debris forms a residual pavement which is very resistant. Their surface may be exhumed later. However, well stratified sedimentary rocks even when quite coherent, are much less resistant than massive crystalline rocks because the bedding allows the undermining and removal of blocks, which helps in the development of the river bed.

The regression also affects coastal evolution. For many years now terraced shorelines which have recently emerged, have been described in Scandinavia, Labrador, Greenland, Spitzbergen and on the coast of Sibera. Headlands cut in solid rock show scarcely a trace. Thus the rather weak wave action developed in the Baltic has not had enough time to erode coherent rock and has only washed its surface.

Conclusion

The importance of the morphogenesis of cold climates is much greater than appears warranted by the 25% of the world's land surface affected today. It enables us to understand events which occurred comparatively recently, only yesterday geologically speaking, in more than 40% of the land surface, including some of the most highly developed areas, the centres of modern civilization, west and central Europe, Russia and North America. The main features of the geomorphological environment of these regions have been inherited from cold periods. Their landforms, their soils and even their vegetation can only be understood by the patient reconstruction, from an analysis of their geomorphology and the study of their superficial deposits, of the events they experienced in the cold periods of the Quaternary. Not only does such a study satisfy scientific curiosity; it may be used in the service of man. The fertile loess soils, soils developed on solifluction deposits, on frost debris and on moraines can only continue to be exploited by man so long as the irreplaceable capital they represent is not frittered away. For these deposits are not in equilibrium with the climate of today. They are being altered and being carried away. It is only by a knowledge of their origin and the exact degree of imbalance now affecting them that agriculturalists can be helped to plan the world's food supply of tomorrow. An inventory of soil resources can only be based on a geomorphological survey which alone is able to ensure an understanding of the development of the soil. The significance of the geomorphological milieu in public works and in the development of hydro-electric power is also very great. It enables a forecast to be made of the conditions likely to be encountered in foundations of buildings, of the stability of the ground, or advice to be given on a choice of site. It has been largely for practical purposes that research workers in Scandinavia, Poland, Holland, Germany and Belgium have developed new methods which in the last thirty years have given us an entirely new conception of the geomorphological forces active during the cold phases of the Quaternary.

FIG. 33 Complex topography of inlandsis: region of Mount Razorback (Labrador)

This knowledge may, in the hands of the geologists, prove to be of invaluable assistance in the interpretation of glacial deposits in older rocks, of Palaeozoic and Precambrian age. These have experienced the same processes, and climatic fluctuations great enough to induce an imbalance in the earth itself and lead to isostatic deformation. It is in such extreme cases that the interplay of different natural forces may be clearly observed. In this lies their general value. They allow a more intimate knowledge of the processes of nature, a better understanding of them and a clearer formulation of their laws, increasing the control of mind over matter and preserving for science its true role, that of the modern fount of wisdom.

Bibliography

General works on cold environment are few, most of those published being devoted to either periglacial or glacial phenomena. The *Chronique arctique* in NOROIS enables one to keep up to date as far as the Arctic is concerned. *Arctic*, (Montreal), *Polar Record* (Cambridge) and the publications of the Arctic Institute of Leningrad perform similar functions and are not limited to geographical aspects.

J. TRICART: 'Géomorphologie glaciaire at périglaciaire', *La Géographie française au milieu du XXe siècle*, Baillère, 1956, p. 53–58, forms a useful summary.

Research techniques and the major problems are outlined in *Arctic Research*, Special Publication No. 2, Arctic Institute of North America, 1955, p. 262.

A very full bibliography, unfortunately confined to the Arctic, and not specifically geographical, may be found in *Arctic Bibliography*, Arctic Institute of North America, Department of Defence, Washington, 1953–5, 5 vols.

A good summary of the problems and history of exploration is given by E. WEGMANN, 'Trois Phases de l'exploration arctique', *Bull Soc. neufchâteloise des Sc. Nat.*, LXXIV, 1951, pp. 107–12.

For examples of zonation and the relations between periglacial and glacial, see J. CORBEL, 'Climats et morphologie dans la Cordillère canadienne', *Rev. canadienne de Géogr.* XII, 1958, pp. 15–45; SOCHAVA, (Geobotanical map of the U.S.S.R.), *Priroda*, No. 10, 1954, p. 36–42; and J. TRICART, 'Accumulation glaciaire, fluvioglaciaire et périglaciaire; l'exemple de la Durance', *Actes IVe Congrès du Quaternaire*, Rome-Pise, 1952, I, pp. 48–56.

Works devoted entirely to glaciers are cited in the bibliographies to Part One and Part Three.

Bibliography

PART ONE CHAPTER I

(1) Distribution of Glaciers

All specialized works deal with the distribution of glaciers.

FLINT, R. F. (1957) *Glacial and Pleistocene geology*, John Wiley, New York, p. 553.

KLEBELSBERG, VON (1948–9) *Handbuch der Gletscherkunde und Glazialgeologie*, Springler, Vienna, **2**, p, p. 1028.

LLIBOUTRY, L. (1965) *Traité de glaciologie, II: glaciers, variations du climat, sols gelés*, Masson, Paris, p. 616.

(a) **On snow**

CORBEL, J. (1960) 'Trois Études de neige: Labrador, Grandes Rousses, Popocatepetl', *Rev. Géogr. Alp.*, **48**, pp. 453–81.

LLIBOUTRY, L. (1964) *Traité de glaciologie, I, glace, neige, hydrologie nivale*, Masson, Paris, p. 427.

PÉGUY, Ch.-P. (1952) *La neige. Coll. Que sais-je?*, P.U.F., Paris, p. 120. This is an important work, fully documented, with a new penetrating approach.

PEARCE, D. C. et GOLD, L. W. (1951) 'The Canadian snow survey, 1947–1950', *U.G.G.I. Ass. Int. Hydr. Sc.*, Brussels, I, pp. 277–304.

WHITTOW, J. B. (1960), 'Some observations on the snowfall of Ruwenzori', *Journ. of Glac.*, **3**, pp. 765–72.

(b) **On the glacier budget**

AHLMANN, H. W. son (1948) 'Glaciological Research on the North Atlantic Coasts', *Roy. Geogr. Soc. Research*, **ser. I**, p. 83. Fundamental work which summarizes the research of the author and his team. Deals with the classification of glaciers. Bibliography.

KIRWANN, MANNERFELT, ROSSBY and SCHYTT, (1949) 'Glaciers and Climatology, Hans W. son Ahlmann's contribution', *Geogr. Ann.*, **31**.

(c) On the mechanism of glacier supply and wastage

The following are among the more recent works; for the earlier, see von Klebelsberg's bibliography.

Symposium (1962) Problems of mass balance studies', *Journ. of Glaciol.*, **4**, no. 33, pp. 251–301.

ANDREWS, R. H. (1964) 'Meteorology and heat balance of the ablation area, White Glacier. Axel Heiberg Isl.', Res, Rep., McGill Univ. Montreal, *Meteor*, **1**, p. 107.

ARNOLD, K. C. (1965) 'Aspects of the glaciology of Meighen Island, Northwest Territories, Canada', *J. of Glaciol.*, **5**, pp. 399–410.

CALLENDAR, G. S. (1952) 'The effect of the altitude of the firn area on a glacier's response to temperature variations', *Journ. of Glaciology*, **2**, no. 10.

CORBEL, J. (1958) 'Aspects régionaux de l'inlandsis groënlandais', *Norois*, **5**, pp. 241–66.

CORBEL, J., (1964) 'Glaciers et climats dans le massif du Mont-Blanc', *Rev. Géogr. Alpine*, pp. 321–60.

DIBBEN, P. C. (1965) 'Heat-balance study on Sorbreen Jan Mayen', *J. of Glaciol.* **5**, no. 42, pp. 793–803.

HATTERLEY-SMITH, G. (1963) 'Climatic interferences from firn studies in Northern Ellesmere Island', *Geogr. Ann.*, **45**, pp. 139–51.

KOERNER, R. M. (1961) 'Glaciological observations in Trinity Peninsula, Graham Land, Antarctica', *J. of Glaciol.*, no. 30, pp. 1063–74.

LLIBOUTRY, L., VALLON, M. et VIVET, R. (1961) Étude de trois glaciers des Alpes françaises, *Publ. A.I.H.S.*, no. 58 (Comm. Neiges et Glaces), pp. 145–59.

MELLOR, M. (1960) 'Temperature gradients in the Antarctic ice sheet', *Journ. of Glaciol.*, **3**, pp. 773–82.

MERCER, J. H. (1961) 'The estimation of the regimen and former firn limit of a glacier', *J. of Glaciol.*, **30**, pp. 1057–62.

MERCER, J. H. (1961), 'The response of fjord glaciers to changes in the firn limit', *Journ. of Glaciol.*, **3**, pp. 850–58.

MORAWETZ, S. 'Schneegrenze, Gletscherablation, Temperatur und Sonnenstrahlung in den Ostalpen', *Petermanns Mitt.*, **105**, pp. 93–104.

MORTENSEN, H. (1952) 'Heutiger Firnrückgang und Eiszeitklima', *Erdkunde*, pp. 145–60.

MULLER, F. (1963) 'Englacial temperature measurements on Axel Heiberg Island Canadian Arctic Archipelago', *A.I.H.S.*, *Public.* **61**, pp. 168–80.

STUART, A. W. (1961) 'Glaciological work of the 1959–1960 U.S. Victoria Land traverse', *J. of Glaciol.*, no. **30**, pp. 997–1002.

WALLEN, C. C. (1948) 'Glacial-meteorological investigations on the Karsa glacier in Swedish Lappland, 1942–8', *Geografiska Ann.*, No. 3–4.

WILSON, C. R., CRAY, A. P. (1961) 'Ice movement studies on the Skelton glacier', *Journ. of Glaciol.*, **3**, pp. 873–8.

ZOTIKOV, I. A. (1963) 'Bottom melting in the central zone of the ice shield on the Antarctic continent and its influence upon the present balance of ice mass', *Bull. A.I.H.S.*, **8**, pp. 36–44.

(d) **Types of glaciers**

AHLMANN, SVERDRUP, OLSSON (1935) 'Scientific results of the Norwegian–Swedish Spitzbergen expedition in 1934', *Geografiska Ann.*, pp. 22–8, 145–218, and (1936), pp. 34–73, 25–244.

BAIRD, WARD et ORVIG (1952) 'The Glaciological Studies of the Baffin Island Expedition', 1950, *Journ. of Glaciol.*, **2**, no. 11.

FRISTRUP, B. (1951) Climate and glaciology of Pearyland, North Greenland, U.G.G.I.', *Ass. Int. Hydrol. Sc.*, Bruxelles, **I**, pp. 185–93.

GALIBERT, G. (1960) 'L'Évolution actuelle des faces nord de la haute montagne alpine dans le massif de Zermatt', *Rev. Géogr. Pyr. S.O.*, **31**, pp. 133–63.

MARKOV, K. K. (1960) 'L'altitude moyenne de l'Antarctide', *Ann. de Géogr.*, **69**, p. 394–402.

MELLOR, M. (1959) 'Ice flow in Antarctica', *Journal of Glaciol.*, **3**, pp. 377–84.

PÉGUY, Ch-P., (1947) *Haute-Durance et Ubaye, esquisse physique de la zone intra-alpine des Alpes françaises de Sud*, Arthaud, Grenoble et Paris.

PÉGUY, Ch-P., CAILLEUX, A., DAVEAU, S., HAMELIN, L. E., LÉGER, M., DURAND-DASTES, F., RUDOLPH, A. M., SHAW, E. M., AHMAD, M., (1958), 'Études sur le glacier de Saint-Sorlin', *Rev. de Géogr. Alpine*, **46**, pp. 405–62.

SCHYTT, V. (1954) 'Glaciology in the Queen Maud Land. Work of the Norwegian-British-Swedish expedition', *Geogr. Rev.*, **44**, pp. 70–87.

WALLEN, C. C. (1951) 'Influence affecting glacier extension in Northern Sweden', U.G.G.I., *Ass. Int. Hydrol. Sc.*, Bruxelles, **1**, pp. 145–53.

WARD, W. H. (1954) 'Glaciological studies in the Penny Highland, Baffin Island, 1953', U.G.G.I., *Ass. Intern. Hydrol. Sc.*, *Ass. de Rome*, **4**, pp. 297–308.

(e) **Glacier oscillations**

AHLMANN, H. W. son, (1953) 'Glacier variations and climatic fluctuations', Isiah Bowman Memorial Lecture, series 3, *Amer. Geog. Soc.*, p. 51.

BELLAIR, P. (1964) 'Inlandsis et problèmes de glaciations. Les données actuelles de l'Antarctique', *Ann. Soc. Géol. Belgique*, **88**, pp. B201–9.

CAILLEUX, A. (1952) 'Premiers Enseignements glaciologiques polaires françaises', *Rev. de Géomorphologie dyn.*, **2**, pp. 1–19. Important study of the ice sheets, leading to a new theory of origin. Excellent bibliography on Greenland.

HEUSSER, C. and MARCUS, M. (1964) Historical variations of Lemon Creek Glacier, Alaska and their relationship to the climatic record, *J. of Glaciol.*, **5**, no. 37, pp. 77–86.

HOBBS, W. H. (1922) *Characteristic of existing glaciers*, New York, Macmillan. Very useful work of reference: well documented.

HOLLIN, J. T. (1962) 'On the glacial history of Antarctica', *Journ. of Glaciol.*, **4**, no. 32, pp. 173–95.

IVES, J. D. (1962) Indications of recent extensive glacierization in North Central Baffin Island (N.W.T.)', *Journ. of Glaciol.*, **4**, no. 32, pp. 197–205.

LAWRENCE, D. B. (1951) 'Glacier fluctuation in North-Western North America within the past six centuries', U.G.G.I., *Ass. Int. Hydrol. Sc.*, Bruxelles, i, pp. 161–166.

MERCANTON, P. L. (1951) 'Rapport sur les variations de longueur des glaciers européens, de 1947 a 1950', U.G.G.I., *Ass. Intern. Hydrol. Sc.*, Bruxelles, i, pp. 107–19.

NANGERONI, G. (1954) 'Appunti per una revisione del catalogo dei ghiacciai lombardi', *Atti Sco. Ital. Nat.*, **43**, pp. 373–407.

OESCHGER, H., RÖTHLISBERGER, H. (1961) 'Datierung eines ehemaligen Standes des Aletschgletschers durch Radioaktivitätsmessung an Holzfunden an weiteren Gletschern', *Z. für Gletscherkunde*, **4**, pp. 191–205.

(2) Extent of Periglacial Phenomena

A very full bibliography on periglacial features in different parts of the world and a good summary on types of ground occur in CAILLEUX and TAYLOR, 1954: *Cryopédologie, étude des sols gelés. Expéd. Polaires Franç. IV*, Hermann, Paris, p. 220. The reader is referred to this bibliography, except for the more important works. See also the reports of the I.G.U. Commission on Periglacial Geomorphology in the *Biuletyn Peryglacjalny*; and TROLL, C. (1944) 'Structurboden, Solifluktion und Frostklimate der Erde,' *Geol. Rundschau*, p. 545–694, a classic on the problem, with a full bibliography. An English translation of the latter by S.I.P.R.E. (Translation 43: October 1958) is available.

(f) Extent of present-day phenomena

COOK, F. A. (1960) Selected bibliography on periglacial phenomena in Canada, *Dept. of Mines and Techn. Surv., Geogr. Branch, Bibliogr. Series*, Ottawa, no. 24, p. 22.

DYLIKOWA, A. (1956) 'Formes contemporaines du type congélifluctif sur le Turbacz (Gorée, Carpathes)', *Biul. Peryglac.*, no. **4**, pp. 339–44.

FURRER, G. (1954) *Solifluktionsformen im schweizerischen Nationalpark: Untersuchung und Interpretation auf morphologischer Grundlage Liestal*, p. 74.

FURRER, G. (1955) 'Die Strukturbodenformen der Alpen', *Geogr. Helvetica*, **10**, pp. 193–212.

JAHN, A. (1951) 'Cryoturbate phenomena of the contemporary and of the Pleistocene periglacial zone', *Acta geologica Polonica*, I, pp. 159–200; Eng. summary, pp. 75–84.

KLAER, W. (1957) 'Beobachtungen zur rezenten Schnee- und Strukturbodengrenze im Hochlibanon', *Zeitschr. für Geom.*, I, pp. 57–70.

LOUIS, H. (1954–5) 'Schneegrenze und Schneegrenzbestimmung', *Geogr. Taschenbuch*, pp. 414–18.

MARSON, F. et al., (1965) *Bibliography on snow, ice and permafrost, with abstracts.* US army, Corps of Engin., Cold Reg. Res. and Eng. Lab., CREEL Rep. 12, p. 287.

(g) Temperature conditions in frozen ground

ANDREWS, J. T., MATTHEW, E. M. (1959/60) Studies in frost-heave cycles at Schefferville, *McGill subarctic res. Lab. Ann. Report.* pp. 6–11.

BRANDTNER, E. (1954) 'Die Bodenfrostverhältnisse des Winters 1962–3 in Bayern, Hessen und Württemberg'. Baden auf Grund von Beobachtungen des Deutschen Wetterdienstes, Ber. 3, *Dt. Landesk.* **13**, no. 1, pp. 50–2.

COOK, F. A. (1955) 'Near surface soil temperature measurements at Resolute Bay, Northwest Territories', *Arctic*, 8, no. 4, pp. 237–49.

COOK, F. A., RAICHE, V. G. (1962) 'Freeze–thaw cycles at Resolute, N.W.T.', *Geogr. Bull.*, no. **18**, pp. 64–78.

GEORGE, P. (1946) *Les Régions polaires*, 1, Collection A. Colin, p. 207, Paris.

RAPP, A. (1960) 'Recent development of mountain slopes in Kärkevagge and surroundings, Northern Scandinavia', *Geogr. Ann.*, **42**, pp. 73–200.

TOUT, D. (1964) 'The climate of Knob Lake', *McGill Sub-Arctic Res. Rep.* **17**, p. 236.

TROLL, C. (1943) 'Die Frostwechselhäufigkeit in den Luft- und Bodenklimaten der Erde', *Meteor. Zeitschr.*, **60**, pp. 161–71.

(h) Types of periglacial environment

ALEXANDRE, J. (1962) 'Phénomènes périglaciaires dans le Basoutoland et le Drakensberg du Natal', *Biul. Peryglac.*, no. **11**, pp. 11–13.

BÜDEL, J. (1948) 'Die klima-morphologischen Zonen der Polarländer. Beiträge zur Geomorphologie der Klimazonen und Verzeitklimate,' *Erdkunde*, II, pp. 22–53.

BÜDEL, J. (1960) 'Die Frostschuttzone Südost-Spitzbergens', *Coll. Geogr., Bonn*, No. **6**, p. 105.

CAILLEUX, A. (1963) *Géologie de l'Antarctique*, SEDES, Paris, p. 203.

CORBEL, J. (1961) 'Morphologie périglaciaire dans l'Antarctique', *Ann. de Géogr.*, **70**, p. 1–24.

CZEPPE, Z. (1966) *The course of the main morphogenetic processes in South-West Spitzbergen*, Uniw. Jagiellonsk., *Prace Geogr.*, **13**, p. 124.

DAVIES, W. E. (1961) 'Surface features of permafrost in arid areas', *Proc. 1st Intern. Symp. Arctic Geol.* (1960), II, pp. 981–7.

DOLLFUS, O. (1965) *Les Andes centrales du Pérou et leurs piémonts (entre Lima et la Pérène), étude géomorphologique.* Trav. Inst. Fr. Ét. Andines, **10**, p. 404.

HÖVERMANN, J. (1962) 'Über Verlauf und Gesetzmässigkeit der Strukturbodengrenze', *Biul. Peryglac.*, No. **11**, pp. 201–7.

KAISER, K. (1965) 'Ein Beitrag zur Frage der Solifluktionsgrenze in den Gebirgen Vorderasiens', *Z. für Geom.*, NS IX, pp. 460–79.

MACKAY, J. Ross (1963) 'The Mackenzie delta area'. N.W.T. *Dept. of Mines, Geogr., Branch*, Mem. **8**, p. 202.

MARKOV, K. K. (1960) 'Zonalité des phénomènes périglaciares en Antarctide', *Biul. Peryglac.*, No. **8**, pp. 43–8.

POPOV, A. I. (1962) 'Periglacial phenomena and the laws of their distribution in the USSR', *Biul. Peryglac.*, no. **11**, pp. 77–83.

POTZGER, J. E., COURTEMANCHE, A. (1955) 'Permafrost and some characteristics of bogs and vegetation of Northern Quebec', *Rev. canadienne de Géogr.*, **9**, pp. 109–14.

RAPP, A., RUDBERG, S. (1960) 'Recent periglacial phenomena in Sweden', *Biul. Peryglac.*, no. **8**, pp. 143–54.

RATHJENS, C. (1965) 'Ein Beitrag zur Frage der Solifluktionsgrenze in den Gebirgen Vorderasiens', *Z. für Geom.* NS IX, pp. 35–49.

RAYNAL, R. (1961) *Plaines et piémonts du bassin de la Moulouya* (*Maroc oriental*), *étude géomorphologique*. Rabat, p. 617.

ROZYCKI, S. Z. (1957) 'Zones du modelé et phénomènes périglaciaires de la Terre de Torell (Spitzbergen)', *Biul. Peryglac.*, no. **5**, pp. 187–224.

SEKRA, J. (1964) 'Results of the geological and geomorphological investigations in the Pamir (Central Trans-Alai), *Antropozoikum* (Praha), A, no. **2**, pp. 158–68 (English summary).

SUSLOV, S. P. (1961) *Physical geography of Asiatic Russia*. English translation by N. GERSCHEVSKI and J. E. WILLIAMS. Freeman, New York–London, p. 594.

TRICART, J. (1963) 'Amorce de roses de pierre actuelle dans les Alpes, près de Sallanches', *Biul. Peryglac.*, no. **12**, pp. 173–4.

WICHE, K. (1962) 'Le Périglaciaire dan le Karakorum de l'Ouest', *Biul. Peryglac.*, no. **11**, pp. 103–10.

PART ONE CHAPTER 2

There are innumerable studies on the extent of the glaciations and on Quaternary periglacial phenomena, as well as on the succession of cold periods. The following list is limited to those which give a good overall picture or are particularly descriptive.

(a) The succession of cold periods

In addition to the general works of VON KLEBELSBERG and FLINT cited at the end of Chapter 1.

BOURDIER, F. (1954) 'Remarques sur les faunes du Quaternaire français antérieures au Würm', *C.R. Somm. S.G.F.*, pp. 76–8.

BULL, C., MCKELVEY, B. C. and WENN, P. N. (1962) 'Quaternary glaciations in Southern Victoria Land, Antarctica', *Journ. of Glaciol.*, **4**, pp. 63–78, no. 31.

FALCONER, G., IVES, J., LOKEN, O., ANDREWS, J. T. (1965), 'Major end moraines in Eastern and Central Arctic Canada', *Georgr. Bull.*, **7**, pp. 137–53.

FLINT, R. F. (1953) 'Recent advances in North American Pleistocene stratigraphy', *Eiszeitalter und Gegenwart*, **3**, pp. 5–13.

GAGE, M. (1965) 'Accordant and discordant glacial sequences'. Intern. Studies Quat., *Geol. Soc. Amer.*, *Special Papers*, **84**, pp. 393–414.

GALON, R., ROSZKOWNA, L. (1961) 'Extents of the Scandinavian glaciations and of their recession stages on the territory of Poland in the light of an analysis of the marginal forms of inland ice', *Przeglad Geogr.*, **33**, pp. 347–64.

GELLERT, J. (1966) 'Morphologie der Eisrandzonen der letzen skandinavischen Vereisung in Mittel- und Osteuropa', *Geogr. Berichte*, **39**, pp. 99–121.

MARKOV, K. K., et al. (1964) Stratigraphie des dépôts quaternaires et géomorphologie de la partie européenne occidentale de l'URSS', *Rep. VIth Inter. Congr. Quatern. Warsaw 1961*, **2**, pp. 161–5.

PENNY, L. F. (1964) 'A review of the last glaciation in Great Britain', *Proc. Yorkshire Geol. Soc.*, **34**, pp. 387–411.

RATHJENS, C. (1954) 'Das Problem der Gliederung des Eiszeitalters in physischgeographischer Sicht', *Münchner geogr. Hefte*, no. **6**, p. 68.

SUGGATE, R. P. (1963) 'New Zealand quaternary chronology', *Rev. Géom. Dyn.*, **14**, pp. 153–9.

SUN TIEN CHING and YANG HUAI JEN (1961) ('The great ice age glaciation in China), *Acta Geol. Sinica*, pp, 233–44.

WOLDSTEDT, P. (1950) *Norddeutschland und angrenzende Gebiete im Eiszeitalter*, Kohler, Stuttgart, p. 464. Fundamental study, with very complete bibliography.

WOLDSTEDT, P. (1950) 'Das Vereisungsgebiet der Britischen Inseln und seine Beziehungen zum festländischen Pleistozän, *Geol. Jahrbuch*, **65**, pp. 621–40.

WOLDSTEDT, P. (1954) *Das Eiszeitalter. Grundlinien einer geologie des Quartärs*, Enke, Stuttgart, p. 374.

WRIGHT, H., RUHE, R. V. (1956) 'Glaciation of Minnesota and Iowa', *The Quaternary of the United States*, Princeton Univ. Press, p. 29–41.

(b) **Palaeoclimatic reconstructions**

'Le Périglaciaire préwurmien. Colloque International, Liège, 9–12 June 1959'. *Congr. et Coll. Univ. Liège*, **17**, 1960, p. 197; *Biul. Peryglac.*, no. **9**, 1960.

BEHRMANN, W. (1948) 'Golfstrom und Eiszeit', *Petermanns Mitt.*, **92**, pp. 154–8. The changes in oceanic circulation produced by glacio-eustatic falls in sea level and their climatic consequences.

BLACK, R. F. (1964) 'Periglacial phenomena of Wisconsin, North-Central United States', *Rep. VI Intern. Congr. on Quatern. Warsaw 1961*, **4**, Lodz., pp. 21–8.

BROWN, E. H. (1966) 'Dry valleys in the chalk scarp of South-East England,' *Biul. Peryglac.*, **15**, pp. 75–8.

BRUNSCHWEILER, D. (1962) 'The periglacial realm in North America during the Wisconsin glaciation', *Biul. Peryglac.*, no. **11**, pp. 15–27.

BÜDEL, J. (1951) 'Die Klimazonen des Eiszeltalters', *Eiszeitalter und Gegenwart*, I, pp. 16–26.

BÜDEL, J. (1950) 'Die Klimaphasen der Würmeiszeit', *Die Naturwissenschaften*, **19**, pp. 438–49. Fundamental. Full Bibliography.

BÜDEL, J. (1953) 'Die "periglaziale" morphologische Wirkungen des Eiszeitklimas auf der ganzen Erde', *Erdkunde*, **7**, pp. 249–65

CAILLEUX, A. (1962) 'Cartes de morphologie périglaciaire quaternaire en Europe', *Biul. Peryglac.*, no. **11**, pp. 129–32.

FIRBAS, F. (1950) 'Die Quatäre Vegetationsentwicklung zwischen den Alpen und der Nord- und Ostsee', *Erdkunde*, **4**, nos. 3–4, pp. 6–15.

GUERASSIMOV, J. R. et MARKOV, K. K. (1952) 'La Paléogéographie du territoire de l'U.R.S.S. durant la période glaciaire', *C.R. XIX Congrès Géol.-Int. Alger*, **15**, pp. 289–304.

KLUTE, F. (1951) 'Das Klima Europas während des Maximums der Weichsel-Würmeiszeit und die Änderungen bis zur Jetztzeit', *Erdkunde*, **5**, pp. 273–83. Fundamental study with full bibliography. Maps.

LAMB, H. H. (1964) 'The role of atmosphere and oceans in relation to climatic changes and the growth of ice sheets on land', In A. NAIRN, *Probl. in Palaeol.*, Wiley, London, pp. 332–48.

POSER, H. (1948) 'Boden- und Klimaverhältnisse in Mittel- und Westeuropa während der Würmeiszeit', *Erdkunde*, **2**. Like the following works by the same author, this article is fundamental. Good bibliography, maps.

POSER, H. (1947) 'Dauerfrostboden und Temperaturverhältnisse während der Würmeiszeit im nicht vereisten Mittel- und Westeuropa', *Die Naturwissenschaften*, no. **1**.

POSER, H. (1947) 'Auftautiefe und Frostzerrung im Boden Mitteleuropas während der Würmeiszeit', *Die Naturwissenschaften*, nos. **8–9**.

RAYNAL, R. (1956) 'Les Phénomènes périglaciaires au Maroc et leur place dans l'évolution morphologique. Rapports de la commission de Morphologie Périglaciaire de l'U.G.I.', *Biul. Peryglac.*, no. **4**, pp. 143–62.

SMITH, H. T. (1964) 'Periglacial eolian phenomena in the United States', *Rep. 6th Intern. Congr. Quaternary, Warsaw*, 1961, pp. 177–86.

SMITH, H. T. U., (1962) 'Periglacial frost features and related phenomena in the United States', *Biul. Peryglac.*, no. **11**, pp. 325–42.

TRICART, J. (1960) 'Corrélation des périodes pluviales et arides au Nord et au Sud du Sahara', 18. *Congr. Int. Geogr. Rio*, (1956), **2**, pp. 594–601.

TRICART, J. (1966) 'Quelques Aspects des phénomènes périglaciaires quaternaires dans la Péninsule Ibérique', *Biul. Peryglac.*, no. **15**, pp. 313–27.

WRIGHT, H. E. Jr., (1961) 'Late pleistocene climate of Europe: a review', *Bull. Geol. Soc. America*, **72**, pp. 933–84.

PART TWO CHAPTER I

(a) Ground frost and permafrost

Permafrost International Conference, proceedings, NAS–NRC, Publ, 1287, 1965, p. 556.

ANNERSTEN, L. (1966) 'Interaction between surface cover and permafrost, *Biul. Peryglac.*, no. **15**, pp. 27–33.

BERTOUILLE, H. (1964) 'Étude d'un réseau actuel de fentes de gel', *C.R. Somm. S.G.F.*, pp. 137–9.

BROWN, R. J. E. (1960) 'The distribution of permafrost and its relation to air temperatures in Canada and the USSR', *Arctic*, **13**, pp. 163–77.

BROWN BECKEL, D. K. (1957) 'Studies on seasonal changes in the temperature gradient of the active layers of soil at Fort Churchill', *Arctic*, pp. 151–83.

CZEPPE, Z. (1966) 'The course of the main morphogenetic processes in South-West Spitzbergen', *Univ. Jagiellonsk., Krakow, Prace Geogr.*, **13**, pp. 124.

DYLIK, J. (1961) 'Quelques Problèmes du pergélisol en Pléistocène supérieur, *Bull. Soc. Sc. Lodz*, **12**, no. 7, p. 21.

DYLIKOWA, A. et OLCHOWIAK-KOLASINSKA, J., (1955) 'Processes and structure in the active zone of perennially frozen ground', *Biul. Peryglac.* (Lodz), no. **2**, pp. 197–203.

IVES, J. D. (1958/59) 'Permafrost investigations in Central Labrador-Ungava', *McGill Sub-arctic res. lab., Annual Rep.*, pp. 32–44.

KACHURIN, S. P., (1962) 'Permafrost science (Geocryology). Soviet Geography', *Amer. Geogr. Soc., Occas. Public.*, no. **1**, pp. 80–4.

KERÄNEN, J. (1950–51) 'On frost formation in soil', *Fennia* (Helsinki), vol. **73**.

LARSONNEUR, C. (1964) 'Quelques Actions du gel sur les sédiments fins', *C. R. Somm. S.G.F.*, pp. 181–3.

MULLER, S. (1945) *Permafrost or permanently frozen grounds and related engineering problems*, U.S. Army Chief of Engineers, Milit. Intelligence Division Office, Special Strategic reports, study no. 62, Washington, p. 232.

PÉWÉ, T. (1966) *Permafrost and its effect on life in the North*. Oregon State Univ. Press., p. 40.

POPOV, A. I. (1956) 'Le Thermokarst', *Biul. Periglac.*, no. 4, pp. 319–30.

POPOV, A. I. (1953) 'Particularités de la lithogenèse des plaines alluviales sous conditions de climat rigoureux', *Izv. Ak. Nauk U.S.S.R.*, Ser. Geogr., no. **2**, pp. 29–41.

TABER, (1943) 'Perennially frozen ground in Alaska', *Bull. Geol. Soc. of America*, pp. 1433–1548.

WILLIAMS, P. J. (1961) 'Climatic factors controlling the distribution of certain frozen ground phenomena', *Geogr. Ann.*, **43**, pp. 339–47.

(b) **The action of freeze thaw in the soil**

ANDERSSON, G. (1907) 'Contribution to the Geology of the Falkland Islands', *Wiss. Ergebn. der schwed. Südpolar Exped.*, Stockholm.

BESKOW, G. (1930) 'Erdfliessen und Strukturboden der Hochgebirge im Licht der Frosthebung', *Geolog. Forh.*, **52**, fasc, 4, pp. 622–38.

BÜDEL, J. (1959) 'Periodische und episodische Solifluktion im Rahmen der klimatischen Solifluktionstypen', *Erdkunde*, **13**, pp. 297–314.

BUTRYM, J., CEGLA. J., DZULYNSKI, S., NAKONIECZNY, S., (1964): 'New interpretation of periglacial structures', *Folia Quaternaria*, no. **17**, pp. 1–34.

CAILLEUX, A., (1943) 'Fissuration de la craie par le gel', *B.S.G.F.*, ser. 5, 13.

CORTE, A. E. (1951) *The frost behaviour of soils: laboratory and field data for a new concept. Part I: Vertical sorting.* U.S. Army Cold Reg. Res. and Engin. Lab., Res. Rep. **85**, p. 22.

CORTE, A. E. (1962) *The frost behaviour of soils: laboratory and field data for a new concept. Part II: Horizontal sorting.* U.S. Army Cold Reg. Res. and Engin. Lab., Res. Rep. **85**, p. 20.

CORTE, A. E. (1962) 'Vertical migration of particles in front of a moving freezing plane', *Journ. Geophys. Res.*, **67**, pp. 1085–90.

CORTE, A. E. (1963) *Vertical migration of particles in front of a moving freezing plane.* U.S. Army Cold Reg. Res., and Engin. Lab., Res. Rep. 105, p. 8.

CORTE, A. (1966) 'Particle sorting by repeated freezing and thawing', *Biul. Peryglac.*, no. **15**, p. 175–240.

CZEPPE, Z. (1966) 'The course of the main morphogenetic processes in South West Spitzbergen', *Uniw. Jagiellonsk., Krakow. Prace Geogr.* no. **13**, p. 124.

DYLIK, J. et KLATKA, T. (1952) 'Recherches microscopiques sur la désintégration périglaciaire', *Bull. Soc. Sc. et Lettres*, Lodz, cl. 3, no. **4**, p. 12.

FITZPATRICK, E. A. (1956) 'An indurated soil horizon formed by permafrost', *Journ. Soil Sci*, **7**, p. 248–254.

GERLACH, T. (1959) 'Needle ice and its role in the displacement of the cover of waste material in the Tatra mountains', *Przeglad Geogr.*, **31**, pp. 603–5.

GODARD, A., HOUEL-GANGLOFF, F. (1965) 'Essais de gélifraction articifiel – les pratiquées sur des calcaires et grès lorrains', *Rev. Geogr. Est.*, **5**, pp. 125–40.

JAHN, A. (1940–46) 'Research on the structure and temperatures of the soils in western Greenland', *Bull. Ac. Polonaise Sc. et Lettres, ser. A., Sc. Math.*, pp. 50–9.

KOZARSKI, S. and ROTNICKI, K. (1964) 'Involutions dans le sable du stade de Poznan au Sud de Gniezno', *Biul. Peryglac.*, no. **13**, pp. 15–52.

LEFFINGWELL, E. (1910) 'The Canning River Region, Northern Alaska', *U.S. Geol. Survey Prof. papers*, **109**, Washington.

MACKAY, J. Ross, (1966) 'Segregated epigenetic ice and slumps in permafrost, Mackenzie delta area, N.W.T.', *Geogr. Bull.*, **8**, pp. 59–80.

MATTHEWS, B. (1960/1) 'Frost-heave cycles at Schefferville, October 1960–June 1961 with a critical examination of methods used to determine them', *McGill subarctic res. lab., Ann. Report*, pp. 112–25.

PÉWÉ, T. L. and PAIGE, R. A. (1963) 'Frost heaving of piles with an example from Fairbanks' Alaska', *U.S. Geol. Surv., Bull., no. 1, 111–1*, pp. 333–407.

RUDBERG, S. (1964) 'Slow mass movement processes and slope development in the Norra Storfjäll area, southern Swedish Lappland', *Z. für Geom. Suppl. 5*, pp. 192–203.

TABER, S., 'Frost heaving', *Journ. of Geol.*, **37**, no. 5, pp. 428–61.

WATERS, R. S. (1965) 'The geomorphological significance of pleistocene frost action in south-west England', *Essays in Geogr., Austin Miller*, Univ. of Reading, pp. 39–57.

WIMAN, S. (1963) 'A preliminary study of experimental frost weathering,' *Geogr. Ann.*, **45**, pp. 113–21.

(c) Biochemical action

BERTOUILLE, H. and CAILLEUX, A. (1966) 'Dépôts calcaires, fentes et ferruginisations quaternaires près de Paris', *Tijdsch. Kon. Nederl. Aardr. Gen.*, **83**, pp. 208–19.

CAILLEUX, A. (1965) 'Quaternary secondary chemical deposition in France', *Geol. Soc. America. Spec. Paper* **84**, p. 125–312.

DOUGLAS, L. A., TEDROW, J. C. (1959) 'Organic matter decomposition rates in Arctic soil', *Soil Sc.*, **88**, pp. 305–12.

DOUGLAS, L. A., TEDROW, J. C. (1960) 'Tundra soils of Arctic Alaska', *7th Intern. Soil Sc. Congr., Madison.*

HILL, D. E., TEDROW, J. C. F. (1961) 'Weathering and soil formation in the Arctic environment', *Amer. Journ. of Sc.*, **259**, pp. 84–101.

MACKAY, J. R. 'A subsurface organic layer associated with permafrost in the Western Arctic', *Dep. of Mines, Geog. Paper* **18**.

TEDROW and CANTLON (1958) 'Concept of soil formation and classification in Arctic Regions', *Arctic*, p. 166–179.

PART TWO CHAPTER 2

It is impossible to classify references according to the paragraph headings in the text as many of them consider the microform and its distribution together. A systematic arrangement is therefore adopted.

(a) Ground with closed patterns and ice wedge structures

Recent work later than that in the bibliography of Cailleux and Taylor:

CHURCH, R. E. et al., (1965) *Origin and environmental significance of large-scale patterned ground, Donnelly Dome Area, Alaska.*, U.S. Corps of Eng. Col. Reg. Res. and Eng. Res. Rep., 159.

COOK, F. A. (1959) 'Some types of patterned ground in Canada', *Geogr. Bull.*, no. **13**, 73–9.

CORBEL, J. (1954) 'Les Sols polygonaux. Observations, expériences, genèse', *Revue de Géom. dynamique*, no. **2**, pp. 49–58.

CORBEL, J. (1964) 'Sols polygonaux et sols striés de la Baie du Roi', *Spitzberg, Audin, Lyon*, pp. 287–304.

DYLIK, J. (1956) 'Coup d'œil sur la Pologne périglaciaire', *Biul. Peryglac.*, no. **4**, pp. 195–238.

DYLIK, J. (1963) 'Nouveaux Problèmes du pergélisol pléistocène', *Acta Geogr.*, Lodz, no. **17**, p. 93.

DYLIK, J. (1966) 'Problems of ice-wedge structures and frost-fissure polygons', *Biul. Peryglac.*, no. **15**, pp. 241–91.

DYLIK, J. (1966) 'Traces fossiles de l'évolution descendante des polygones des fentes de gel', *Tijdschar. Kon. Nederl. Aardr. Gen.*, **83**, pp. 227–37.

FURRER, G. (1955) 'Die Strukturbodenformen der Alpen', *Geogr. Helvetica*, **10**, pp. 193–212.

JOHNSSON, G. (1959) 'True and false ice-wedges in Southern Sweden', *Geogr. Annaler*, **41**, pp. 15–33.

LACHENBRUCH, A. (1960) 'Thermal contraction cracks and ice wedges in permafrost', *U.S. Geol. Surv.*, Prof. Paper 400 B, pp. B 404–B 406.

LACHENBRUCH, A. (1962) 'Mechanics of thermal contraction cracks and ice wedge polygons in permafrost', *Geol. Soc. of America*, Special Papers, **70**, p. 69.

PÉWÉ, T. L. (1959) 'Sand-wedge polygons (Tesselations) in the McMurdo Sound Region, Antarctica. A progress report', *Amer. Journ. of Sc.*, **257**, pp. 545–52.

PÉWÉ, T. L. (1962) 'Ice wedges in permafrost, Lower Yukon river area near Galena, Alaska', *Biul. Peryglac.*, no. **11**, pp. 65–76.

PÉWÉ, T. (1965) 'Ice wedges in Alaska. Classification, distribution and climatic significance', *Proc. Permafrost Intern. Conf.*, NAS–NRC, Publ. 1287, pp. 76–81.

PÉWÉ, T. L. (1966) 'Palaeoclimatic significance of fossil ice-wedges', *Biul. Periglac.*, no. **15**, pp. 65–73.

PISSART, A. (1963–4) 'Contribution expérimentale à la connaissance de la genèse des sols polygonaux', *Ann. Soc. Géol. Belgique*, **87**, no. 7, pp. 213-23.

MACKAY, J. Ross (1953) 'Fissures and mud circles on Cornwallis Island, N.W.T.', *Canadian Geogr.*, no. **33**, pp. 31–7.

(b) Stripes and Garlands

BROCKIE, W. (1965) ' "Patterned Ground", some problems of stone stripe development in Otago', *Proc. 4th N.Z. Geogr. Conf.*, *N.Z. Geogr. Soc.*, pp. 91–104.

CAINE, T. N. (1963) 'The origin of sorted stripes in the Lake District, Northern England', *Geogr. Ann.*, **45**, pp. 172–79.

KUNSKY, J. et LOUCEK, D. (1956) 'Stone stripes and thufurs in the Krkonose', *Biul. Peryglac.*, no. **4**, pp. 345–9.

LLIBOUTRY, L. (1955) 'L'origine des sols striés et polygonaux des Andes de Santiago (Chili)', *C.R. Ac.*, **240**, pp. 1793–4.

(c) Earth Hummocks and Involutions

DYLIK, J. (1963) 'Periglacial sediments of the S.W. Malgorzata hill in the Warsaw–Berlin pradolina', *Bull. Soc. Sc. Lettres* Lodz, **14**, no. 1, p. 18., fig. 2.

HOPKINS, D. M. et SIGAFOOS, R. S. (1954) 'Discussion; Role of frost thrusting in the formation of tussocks', *Amer. Jnl. Sc.*, **252**, pp. 55–9.

KLATKA, T. (1954) Structures périglaciaires de toundra à Tychow, *Biul. Peryglac.*, no. 1, pp. 148–9.

OLCHOWIK-KOLASINSKA, J. (1962) *Classification génétique des structures de mollisol*, Acta Geogr. Univ. Lodziensis, no. 10, p. 105.

SHARP, R. P. (1942) Soil structures in the St. Elias Range, Yukon Territory, *Journ. of Geom.*, 5, pp. 274–301.

(d) Block Flows

DAHL, H. (1966) Block fields, weathering pits and tor-like forms in the Narvik Mountains, Nordland, Norway. *Geogr. Ann.*, 48–A, pp. 55–85.

FEZER, F. (1953) Schuttdecken, Blockmassen und Talformen im nordlichen Schwarzwald, *Göttinger geogr. Abh.*, no. **14**, pp. 45–78.

KLATKA, T. (1962) Champs de pierre de Lysogory, origine et âge. *Acta Geogr. Lodz*, no. **12**, p. 129, (French summary).

(e) Screes

CAINE, T. N. (1962) *The effect of frost action on low angle scree slopes and on sorted stripes in the Lake District*, M.A. Thesis, Univ. of Leeds.

CORBEL, J. (1954) 'Sols striés et éboulis ordonnés', *Revue de Géom. dynam.*, no. **1**, pp. 31–3.

CZUDEK, T., DEMEK, J., PANOS, V., SEICHTEROVA, H. (1963) 'The pleistocene rhythmically bedded sediments in the Hornomoravsky uval (The Upper Moravian Graben)', *Antropozoikum*, A, no. **1**, pp. 75–97.

DYLIK, J. (1955) 'Rhythmically stratified periglacial slope deposits', *Biul. Peryglac.* (Lodz), no. **2**, pp. 175–85.

DYLIK, J. (1960) 'Rhythmically stratified slope waste deposits', *Biul. Peryglac.*, no. **8**, pp. 31–41

GUILCHER, A. et TRICART, J. (1954) 'La XXXVIe Excursion inter-universitaire: Champagne, Lorraine', *Ann. de Géog.*, **63**, pp. 1–21 and 88–98.

GUILLEN, Y. (1964) 'Les Grèzes litées comme dépôts cyclothémiques', *Z. für Geom.*, Suppl. **5**, pp. 53–8.

GUILLEN, Y. (1964) 'Grèzes litées et bancs de neige', *Geol. en Mijnbouw*, pp. 103–12.

LLIBOUTRY, L. (1956) 'Observation d'éboulis à lits de limon en cours de formation et anciens dans les Andes de Santiago', *C.R. Ac. Sc.*, **423**, pp. 3741–49.

SOUCHEZ, R. (1964) 'Sur, la gélivation des calcaires et la genèse des grèzes litées', *C.R. Ac. Soc.*, **258**, pp. 3741–3.

(f) Hydrolaccoliths

CAILLEUX, A. (1956) 'Mares, mardelles et pingos', *C.R. Ac. Sc.*, **242**, pp. 1912–14.

CAILLEUX, A. (1957) 'Les mares de Sud-Est du Sjarlland (Danemark'), *C.R. Ac. Sc.*, **245**, pp. 1074–6

DYLIK, J. (1964/5) 'L'Étude de la dynamique d'évolution des dépressions fermées à Jozefow, aux environs de Lodz', *R.G.D.*, **15**, pp. 158–71.

HAMELIN, L. E. (1957) 'Les Tourbières réticulées de Québec–Labrador subarctique', *Bull. A.G.F.*, no. **267–8**, pp. 47–8.

HENOCH, W. E. S. (1960), 'String-bogs in the Arctic 400 miles North of the tree-line', *Georg. Journ.*, 116, pp. 335–9.

LINDQUIST, S. MATTSSON, J. O. (1965) 'Studies on the thermal structure of a pals', *Svensk Geogr. Aarsbok*, **41**, pp. 38–49

MAARLEVELD, G. C. (1965) 'Frost mounds. A summary of the literature of the past decade', *Medel. Geol. Stichting*, NS no. **17**, pp. 3–16.

MACKAY, J. Ross (1962) 'Pingos of the pleistocene Mackenzie delta area', *Geogr. Bull.*, no. **18**, pp. 21–63.

MACKAY, J. Ross, (1963) *The Mackenzie delta area*, N.W.T., Dept. of Mines, Geogr. Branch, Mem. **8**, p. 202

MACKAY, J. Ross (1965) 'Gas-domed mounds in permafrost, Kendall Island, N.W.T.', *Geogr. Bull.*, **7**, pp. 105–15.

MÜLLER, F. (1959) 'Beobachtungen über pingos. Detailuntersuchungen in Ostgrönland und in der Kanadischen Arktis', *Meddel. om Grönland*, **153**, no. 3, p. 127, pl. 5.

MÜLLER, F. (1962) 'Analysis of some stratigraphic observations and radiocarbon dates from two pingos in the Mackenzie delta area, N.W.T.', *Arctic*, 15, pp. 279–88.

PISSART, A. (1963) 'Les Traces de pingos du Pays de Gellas (Grande-Bretagne) et du plateau des Hautes Fagnes (Belgique)', *Z. für Geom.*, NS **8**, pp. 147–65.

PISSART, A. (1964–5) 'Les pingos des Hautes-Fagnes: les problèmes de leur genèse', *Ann. Soc. Géol. Belgique*, **88**, pp. 277–89.

PRINCE, H. C. (1961) 'Some reflections on the origin of hollows on Norfolk compared with those in the Paris region', *R.G.D.*, **12**, pp. 110–117.

SLOTBOOM, R. T. (1963) 'Comparative geomorphological and palynological investigation of the pingos (viviers) in the Hautes Fagnes and the Mardellen in the Gutland, Luxemburg', *Z. für Geom.*, NS **7**, pp. 193–231.

SVENSSON, H. (1961–62) 'Observations on palses. Photographic interpretation and field studies in North Norwegian frost ground areas', *Norsk Geogr. Tidsskr.*, **18**, p. 212-227.

TROLL, C. (1962) ' "Sölle" and "mardelles". Glacial and periglacial phenomena in continental Europe', *Erdkunde*, **16**, pp. 31–3.

WIEGAND, G. (1965) 'Fossile Pingos in Mitteleuropa', *Würzburger Geogr. Arb.*, **16**, p. 152.

PART TWO CHAPTER 3

(a) General and regional studies

CORBEL, J. (1953) 'Problèmes de morphologie périglaciaire au Spitzberg', *Rev. Géogr.*, pp. 262–8.

CRUICKSHANK, J. and COLHOUN, E. (1965) 'Observations on pingos and other landforms in Schuchertdal, Northeast Greenland', *Geogr. Ann.*, Ser. A, **47**, pp. 224–36.

CZUDEK, T. (1964) 'Periglacial slope development in the area of the Bohemian Massif in Northern Moravia', *Biul. Peryglac.*, no. **14**, pp. 169–93.

DYLIK, J. A. (1952) 'The concept of the periglacial cycle in Middle Poland', *Bull. Soc. Sc. et Lettres de Lodz*, Cl. III, *Sc. Math. et Naturelles*, III, no. **5**, p. 29.

DYLIKOWA, A. et KLATOWA, N. (1956) 'Exemple du modelé périglaciaire du plateau de Lodz', *Biul. Peryglac.*, no. **4**, pp. 239–53.

HÖVERMANN, J. (1953) 'Die periglaziale Erscheinungen im Harz', *Göttinger geogr. Abh.*, **14**, pp. 7–44.

JAHN, A. (1961) 'Quantitative analysis of some periglacial processes in Spitzbergen', *Univ. Wroclaw, Nauki Przyrodnicze*, Ser. B, no. **5**, pp. 1–34.

PELTIER, L. C. (1950) 'The geographical cycle in periglacial regions as it is related to climatic geomorphology', *Annals Assoc. Am. Geogr.*, **11**.

RAPP, A. and RUDBERG, S. (1964) 'Studies on periglacial phenomena in Scandinavia', 1960–63', *Biul. Peryglac.*, no. **14**, pp. 75–89.

TRICART, J. (1954) 'Premiers Résultats d'expériences de solifluction périglaciaire', *C. R. Ac. Soc.*, **238**, pp. 259–61.

TRICART, J. (1956) 'Étude expérimentale du probème de la gélivation', *Biul. Peryglac.*, no. **4**, pp. 285–318.

TWIDALE, C. R. (1956) 'Vallons de gélivation dans le centre du Labrador', *Rev. Géom. dyn.*, **7**, pp. 17–23.

(b) Altiplanation Terraces

DEMEK, J. (1964) 'Altiplanation terraces in Czechoslovakia and their origin', *Journ. Czech. Geogr. Soc.*, Suppl. for 20th Intern. Geogr. Congf., pp. 55–66.

RICHTER, H., HAASE, G., BARTHEL, H. (1963) 'Die Goletzterrassen', *Peterm. Geogr. Mitt.*', **107**, pp. 183–92.

TE PUNGA, M. (1956) 'Altiplanation terraces in Southern England', *Biul. Peryglac.*, no. **4**, pp. 331–8

WATERS, R. S. (1962) 'Altiplanation terraces and slope development in Vest-Spitzbergen and South West England', *Biul. Peryglac.*, no. **11**, pp. 89–101.

(c) Other types of slope

BAECKEROOT, G. (1957) 'Le Système niche-coulée et son rôle dans le modelé (Monts de Lacaune et Sidobre de Castres)', *Bull. A.G.F.*, nos. **265–6**, pp. 41–7

BÜDEL, J. (1959) 'Periodische und episodische Solifluktion im Rahmen der klimatischen Solifluktionstypen', *Erdkunde*, **13**, pp. 297–314.

COTTON, C. A. and TE PUNGA, M. T. (1955) 'Solifluxion and periglacially modified landforms at Wellington, New Zealand', *Trans. Roy. Soc. N.Z.*, **82**, 5, pp. 1001–31.

LINTON, D. L. (1964) 'The origin of the Pennine tors. An essay in analysis', *Z. für Geom.*, NS **8**, Sonderheft, pp. 5–24.

PALMER, J. and RADLEY, J. (1961) 'Gritstone tors of the English Pennines', *Z. für Geom.*, NS **5**, pp. 37–52.

RAPP, A. (1960) 'Talus slopes and mountain walls at Tempelfjorden, Spitzbergen. A geomorphological study of the denudation of slopes in an arctic locality', *Skrifter Norsk Polar Inst.*, **119**, p. 96.

RUDBERG, S. (1962) 'A report on some field observations concerning periglacial geomorphology and mass movement on slopes in Sweden', *Biul. Peryglac.*, no. **11**, pp. 311–23.

SOUCHEZ, R. (1966) 'Réflexions sur l'évolution des versants sous climat froid', *Rev. Géogr. Phys. et Géol. Dyn.*, NS **8**, pp. 317–34.

TIVY, J. (1962) 'An investigation of certain slope deposits in the Lowther Hills, Southern Uplands of Scotland', *Inst. of Brit. Geogr. Trans. and Papers*, **30**, pp. 59–73.

(d) Asymmetrical valleys

GRIMBÉRIEUX, J. (1954–5) 'Origine et asymétrie des vallées sèches de Hesbaye', *Ann. Soc. Géol. Belgique*, **78**, pp. B 267–86.

HELBIG, K. (1965) 'Asymmetrische Eiszeittäler in Süddeutschland und Österreich', *Würzburger Geogr. Arb.*, **14**, p. 108.

MYCIELSKA, E. and NOWAKOWSKA, T. (1955) 'The asymmetry of periglacial covers in the Izera Mts.', *Biul. Peryglac.*, Lodz, no. **2**, p. 225.

OLLIER, C. D. and THOMASSON, A. J. (1957) 'Asymmetrical valleys of the Chiltern Hills', *Geogr. Journ.*, **123**, p. 71–80.

PIERZCHALKO, L. (1954) 'Le Problème des vallées dissymétriques et le développement de la géomorphologie climatique', *Czasopismo Geogr.*, pp. 359–72.

WEINBERGER, L. (1954) 'Die Periglazial-Erscheinungen im österreichischen Teil des eiszeitlichen Salzach–Vorland–Gletschers', *Göttinger Geogr. Abh.*, no. **15**, p. 17–90.

PART TWO CHAPTER 4

(a) The action of running water

ARNBORG, L. and WALKER, H. (1964) 'Water discharge and suspended load in an arctic river', *20th Intern. Geogr. Congr., London, Abstracts*, pp. 83–4.

Brown, J. E. (1956) 'Observations on the break-up in the Mackenzie River and its delta in 1954', *Journ. of Glac.*, **3**, pp. 133–40.

Henoch, W. E. S. (1960) 'Fluvio-morphological features of the Peel and lower Mackenzie Rivers', *Geog. Bull.*, (Ottawa), no. **15**, pp. 31–45.

Lavrushin, Y. A. (1964) 'Principle features of the alluvium of plain rivers in the subarctic belt and the periglacial regions of continental glaciations', *Rep. 6th Intern. Congr. Quaternary, Warsaw 1961*, **4**, Lodz., pp. 111–20.

Mackay, J. Ross (1956) '*The Anderson River map area, N.W.T.*' Geogr. Branch, Mines and Techn. Surveys, Mem. 5, p. 137.

Rudberg, S. (1963) 'Geomorphological processes in a cold semi-arid region', *Prelimin. Rep. Axel Heiberg Isl. Res. Rep., McGill Univ. Montreal*, pp. 139–50.

Schenk, E. (1956) 'Windorientierte Seen und Windablagerungen in periglazialen Gebieten Nordamerikas', *Erdkunde*, **10**, pp. 302–6

(b) Wind action (excluding loess)

Cailleux, A. (1960) 'Actions du vent quaternaires préwurmiennes en Europe', *Biul. Peryglac.*, no. 9, pp. 73–81.

Dylik, J. (1951) 'The loess-like formations and the wind-worn stones in Middle-Poland', *Bull. Soc. Sc. et Lettres de Lodz*, Cl. III, Sc. Math. et Nat., III, no. 3.

Maréchal, R. and Maarleveld, G. (1955) 'L'Extension des phénomènes périglaciaires en Belgique et aux Pays-Bas', *Med. Geol. Stichting*, NS, no. **8**, pp. 77–86.

Markov, K. K. (1956) 'Nature du milieu géographique des regions périglaciaires à la lumière des données paléobotaniques', *Biul. Peryglac.*, no. **3**, pp. 99–106.

Maruszczak, H. (1964) 'Problème de l'action éolienne dans la zone périglaciaire pléistocène à la lumière des indices granulométriques', *Biul. Peryglac.*, no. **14**, pp. 257–73.

Pissart, A. (1966) 'Le Rôle géomorphologique du vent dans la région de Mould Bay (Ile Prince Patrick, N.W.T., Canada)', *Z. für Geom.* NS X, pp. 226–36.

(c) Loess

Brunnacker, K. (1956) 'Regionale Bodendifferenzierungen während der Würmeiszeit', *Eiszeitalter und Gegenwart*, **7**, pp. 43–8.

Dylik, J. (1954) 'The problem of the origin of loess in Poland', *Biul. Peryglac.*, no. **1**, pp. 125–31.

Gellert, J. F. (1962) 'Das Lössproblem in China. Neuere Forschungen, Diskussionen und eigene Beobachtungen', *Petermanns Geogr. Mitt.*, **106**, pp. 81–94

Hempel, L. (1955) 'Frostbodenbilding und Lössanwehung in der Würmeiszeit auf Muschelkalk und Buntsandstein bei Göttingen', *Ak. Wiss. Litt.*, Math-Naturw., no. **2**, p. 13–42.

KADAR, L. (1960) 'Climatical and other conditions of loess fromation', *Trav. Inst. de Geogr. Univ. de Debreczen*, no. **43**, pp. 17–24.

LIEBEROTH, I. (1962) 'Die jungpleistozänen Lösse Sachsens im Vergleich zu denen anderen Gebiete', *Petermanns Geogr. Mitt.*, **106**, pp. 188-98.

(d) Coastal development

BROCHU, M. (1961) '*Déplacement de blocs par la glace le long du St Laurent*, Min. Mines et Rel. Techn., Geogr. Paper No. **3**. p. 27.

DIONNE, J. C. (1962) 'Note sur les blocs d'estran du littoral Sud du St Laurent', *Can. Geogr.*, **6**, pp. 69–77

NICHOLS, R. L. (1961) 'Characteristics of beaches formed in polar climates', *Amer. Journ. of Sc.*, **259**, pp. 694–708.

NORRMAN, J. (1964) 'Lake Vattern, investigations on shore and bottom morphology', *Geogr. Ann.*, no. **1/2**, p. 238.

SUNDBERG-FALKENMARK, M. (1957) 'Studies on lake-ice movements', *U.G.G.I. Ass. Int. Hydrol. Sc.*, *Ass. De Toronto*, **4**, pp. 266–278.

TABER, S. (1950) 'Intensive frost-action along lake shores', *Amer. Journ. of Sc.*, **248**, pp. 784–93.

PART THREE CHAPTER 1

Among the general works which may be referred to throughout Part III, there are several journals exclusively devoted to glaciology which should be consulted by anyone who wishes to keep up to date: the *Journal of Glaciology* (Cambridge) has résumés in French and German; it is interested mainly in glacier flow, but also deals with the glacier budget and glacial morphology. The *Zeitschrift für Gletscherkunde und Glazialgeologie* (Innsbruck), deals especially with glacier regime and budget, and the Quaternary. Before 1954, the *Zeitschrift für Gletscherkunde* (Berlin), had similar interests. The *Comptes Rendus* of the congresses of the I.U.G.G., (especially since 1945) contains much information of a high standard generally, but especially on glaciological matters. On accumulation forms of the Quaternary, there are numerous papers in *Eiszeitalter und Gegenwart* (Hanover), with the accent on glacial geology. The journals and works cited at the end of the Introduction might also be used.

L. LLIBOUTRY: *Le Traité de glaciologie*, 2 vols, Paris, 1964 and 1965, gives an excellent general account, with new ideas, of glacier dynamics. The author is a geophysicist but geomorphological aspects are outlined.

J. TRICART and A. CAILLEUX: *Le Modelé glaciaire et nival*, S.E.D.E.S., Paris, 1962 (volume III of Traite de Géomorphologie).

(a) The physical properties of snow and ice

AHLMANN, H. W. son (1935) 'Scientific results of the Norwegian–Swedish Spitzbergen expedition in 1934: The stratification of the snow and firn on Isachsen's Plateau', *Geografiska Ann.*, **17**. Good account of the characteristics of snow and of the névé of an intermediate type glacier.

HUGHES and SELIGMAN (1938) 'The temperature, melt water, movement and density increase in the névé of an alpine glacier', *Monthly Not. Roy. Astronomical Soc., Geophysical Suppl.*, **4**, no. 8. Good study of the origin of névé on an Alpine type glacier. A follow-on to the work of Ahlmann.

HUGHES, PERUTZ and SELIGMAN (1941) 'The structure of a temperate glacier. Research made at the Jungfraujoch. Publ. no. 4 of the Jungfraujoch Research Party, 1938', *Geogr. Journ.*, **96**.

SCHYTT, V. (1949) 'Re-freezing of the melt-water on the surface of glacier-ice, *Geografiska Ann.*, **31**.

SHUMSKII, P. A. (1964) *Principles of structural glaciology: the petrography of fresh-water ice as a method of glaciological investigations*, trans. by D. Kraus. Dover, New York. p. 497.

STREIFF-BECKER, R. (1936) 'Zwanzig Jahre Firnbeobachtung', *Zeitschr. für Gletscherkunde*, **24**. Basic information on the névé of the Hintereisferner.

(b) The dynamics of glacier flow

Essential recent theory and important data are found in:

ALLEN, C., KAMB, W. MEIER, M., SHARP, R. P. (1960) 'Structure of the Lower Blue Glacier, Washington', *J. of Geol.*, **68**, pp. 601–25.

ANDERSON, B. G. (1963) *Preliminary report on glaciology and glacial geology of the Thiel Mountains, Antarctica. U.S. Geol. Surv., Prof. Paper*, **475** *B*, pp. 140–3.

BATTLE, W. R. B. (1951) 'Glacier movement in North-East Greenland, 1949', *Journ. of Glaciol.*, I, pp. 559–63.

BELLAIR, P. (1963/4) 'Inlandsis et problèmes de glaciations. Les données actuelles de l'Antarctique', *Ann. Soc. Géol. Belgique*, **87**, pp. B201–9.

DEMOREST, M. (1942) 'Glacier regimens and ice movement within glaciers', *Amer. Journ. of Science*, **230**, pp. 31–66.

DEMOREST, M. (1943) 'Ice sheets', *Bull. Geol. Soc. Amer.*, **54**, pp. 363–400.

FINSTERWALDER, S. (1950) 'Some comments on glacier flow', *Journ. of Glaciol.*, I, pp. 383–8. Résumé of the author's work.

FISHER, J. E. (1952) 'Extrusion flow, comments on Dr Nye's paper', *Journ. of Glaciol.*, II, pp. 51–3.

HAEFELI, R. (1952) 'Observations on the viscous behaviour of ice in a tunnel in the Z'Mutt glacier', *Journ. of Glaciol.*, II, pp. 94–9.

KAMB, B. and LACHAPELLE, E. (1964) 'Direct observations of the mechanism of glacier sliding over bedrock', *Journ. of Glaciol.*, V, no. 38, pp. 159–72.

KING, C. A. and LEWIS, W. V. (1961) 'A tentative theory of ogive formation', *Journ. of Glaciol.*, II, pp. 913-39.

LEWIS, W. V. (1949) 'Glacial movement by rotational slipping', *Geografiska Ann.*, **31**.

LLIBOUTRY, L. (1958) 'Glacier mechanics in the perfect plasticity theory', *Journ. of Glaciol.*, III, no. 23, pp. 162–9.

LLIBOUTRY, (1958) 'La Dynamique de la mer de Glace, et la vague de 1891–95 d'après les mesures de Joseph Vallot', *U.G.G.I., Symposium Chamonix*, 16–24 Sept. 58, pp. 125–38.

LLIBOUTRY, L. (1966) 'Bottom temperatures and basal low-velocity layer in an ice sheet', *J. Geophys. Res.*, pp. 2535–43.

MATHEWS, W. H. (1959) 'Vertical distribution of velocity in Salmon Glacier, British Columbia', *Journ. of Glaciol.*, III, no. 26, pp. 448–54.

MATHEWS, W. H. (1964) 'Water pressure under a glacier', *Journ. of Glaciol.*, V, no. 38, pp. 235–40.

MATTHES, F. E. (1942) 'Glaciers', *Hydrology* (Physics of the Earth, no. 9), McGraw-Hill, New York, pp. 149–219.

MEIER, M., RIGSBY, G. and SHARP, R. P. (1954) 'Preliminary data from Saskatchewan Glacier. Alberta, Canada', *Arctic*, **7**, pp. 3–26.

MEIER, M. F. (1960) 'Mode of flow of Saskatchewan Glacier, Alberta, Canada', *U.S. Geol. Surv., Prof. Paper* **251**, p. 70.

MILLECAMPS, R. (1956) 'Sur les directions d'écoulement superficial d'un tronçon de la mer de Glace', *C.R. Ac. Sc.*, **242**, No. 3,

NYE, J. F. (1952) 'The mechanics of glacier flow', *Journ. of Glaciol.*, II, pp. 82–93.

NYE, J. F. (1959) 'The deformation of a glacier below an ice fall', *Journ. of Glaciol.*, III, pp. 387–408.

OSTENSO, N. A., SELLMAN, P. V., PÉWÉ, T. L. (1965) 'The bottom topography of Gulkana Glacier, Alaska Range, Alaska', *Journ. of Glaciol.*, V, no. 41, pp. 651–60.

RACT-MADOUX and REYNAUD (1951) 'L'Exploration de glaciers en profondeur. Travaux de la mer de Glace', *La Houille blanche*, numéro special A.

SELIGMAN, G. (1941) 'The structure of a temperate glacier', *Geogr. Journ.*, **97**.

SELIGMAN, G. (1947) 'Extrusion flow in glaciers', *Journ. of Glaciol.*, I, pp. 12–21. An interesting discussion follows this article (pp. 18–21).

SELIGMAN, G. (1948) 'Joint meeting of the British Glaciological Society, the British Rheologists Club and the Institute of Metals', *Journal of Glaciol.*, I, pp. 231-40. Very important discussion.

SELIGMAN, G. (1949) 'Research on glacier flow', *Geografiska Ann.*, **31**.

SHARP, R. P. (1948) 'Constitution of valley glaciers', *Journ. of Glaciol.*, I, pp. 174–5 and 182–9. Of first-rate importance for ice streams.

SHARP, R. P. (1954) 'Glacier flow: a review', *Bull. Geol. Soc. America*, **65**, pp. 321–38.

SHARP, R., EPSTEIN, S., VIDZIUNAS (1960) 'Oxygen-isotope ratios, in the Blue Glacier, Olympic Mountains, Washington, U.S.A.', *J. of Geophys. Res.*, **65**, pp. 4043–59.

WALLENSTEIN, G. (1957) 'Movement observations on the Greenland ice sheet', *Journ. of Glaciol.*, III, pp. 207–10.

WILSON, R. C. (1959) 'Surface movement and its relationship to the average annual hydrological budget of Lemon Creek Glacier, Alaska', *Journ. of Glaciol.*, III, pp. 355–61.

(c) Theories of glacial erosion

BLACHE, J. (1952) 'La Sculpture glaciaire', *Rev. Géogr. alpine*, **40**, pp. 31–124. Résumé of the different theories, then an examination of the moulding of the beds of local glaciers in relation to the theories of the Grenoble school (the glacial bed school). No bibliography.

BOYÉ, M. (1949) 'Importance du défonçage dans l'élaboration des formes glaciaires', *C.R. Ac. Sc.*, **229**, pp. 723–4. Outlines the author's theory.

CAILLEUX, A. (1952) 'Polissage et surcreusement glaciaire dans hypothèse de Boyé,' *R.G.D.*, no. 5, pp. 247–57.

DEMOREST, M. (1937) 'Glaciation of the Upper Nugssuak Peninsula. W. Greenland', *Zeitschr. für Gletscherkunde*, **25**, pp. 36–56. Discusses a very active glacier which appears to fulfill a protective role.

DEMOREST, M. (1939) 'Glacial movement and erosion: a criticism', *Amer. Journ. of Science*, **237**, p. 603. Useful summary and references especially to American work. Contains his own novel views.

FITZPATRICK, E. A. (1963) 'Deeply weathered rock in Scotland, its occurrence, age and contribution to the soils', *J. of Soil Sc.*, **14**, p. 33–43.

GODARD, A. (1965) 'Recherches géomorphologiques en Écosse du Nord-Ouest', Public. Fac. Lettres Strasbourg, p. 701.

HARLAND, W. B. (1957) 'Exfoliation joints and ice action', *Journ. of Glaciol.*, III, no. 21, pp. 8–10.

HOLMES, C. D. (1949) 'Glacial erosion and sedimentation', *Bull. Geol. Soc. Amer.*, **60**, pp. 1429–36.

KLIMASZEWSKI, M. (1964) 'On the effect of the preglacial relief on the course and magnitude of glacial erosion in the Tatra Mountains', *Geogr. Polonica*, **2**, pp. 116–21.

KOECHLIN, R. (1944) '*Les Glaciers et leur mécanisme*', Lausanne, Rouges & Co., 177 p. Attempts to state glacier flow in terms of that of water. Has some geomorphological errors.

LINTON, D. L. (1962) 'Glacial erosion on soft-rock outcrops in Central Scotland', *Biul. Peryglac.*, no. **11**, pp. 247–57.

LLIBOUTRY, L. (1955) 'L'Incorporation des éboulis dans la glace', *C.R. Ac. Sc.*, 240, pp. 1623–4.

LOUIS, H. (1952) L'Érosion glaciaire', *A.I.H.S.*, *Public.*, No. 59 (Symp. de Bari), pp. 219–25.

MARTONNE, E. de, (1910 and 1911), 'L'Érosion glaciaire et la formation des vallées alpines', *Ann. de Géogr.*, **19**, 1910, pp. 289–317, and **20**, 1911, pp, 1–29. Gives in a more condensed form the author's theory from his *Traité de géographie physique*, vol. II.

MATTHES, F. E. (1930) 'Geologic history of the Yosemite valley', *Geol. Survey Prof. Paper*, no. 160, 137 pages. Discussion of several theories mainly American. It is completed by the author's paper of 1942, cited above (b).

PIPPAN, T. (1965) 'Glazialmorphologische Studien im norwegischen Gebirge unter besonderer Berücksichtigung des Problems der hochalpinen Formung', *Die Erde*, **96**, pp. 105–21.

RAY, L. L. (1949) 'Alpine glaciation', *Bull. Geol. Soc. Amer.*, **60**, pp. 1475–84.

SÖLCH, J. (1935) 'Fluss- und Eiswerk in den Alpen zwischen Ötztal und St. Gotthard', *Petermanns Ergänz.*, nos. 219 and 220. From a regional study, a full statement of the author's views emerges.

SÖLCH, J. (1938) 'L'Érosion glaciaire', *Congr. Intern. Geogr. Amsterdam*, I, p. 41–47.

SOUCHEZ, R. (1966) 'The origin of morainic deposits and the characteristics of glacial erosion in the Western Sör-Rondane, Antarctica', *Journ. of Glaciol.*, VI, no. 44, pp. 249–54.

SOUCHEZ. R. (1966) 'Réflexions sur l'évolution des versants sous climat froid', *Rev. Géogr. Phys. et Géol. Dyn.*, NS, **8**, pp. 317–34.

TRICART, J. (1963) 'Aspects et problèmes géomorphologiques du massif du Hohneck', *Le Hohneck*, *Soc. Philom. Als. Lorr.*, pp. 43–62.

PART THREE CHAPTER 2

A. Rudimentary Forms

This question is not fully dealt with by any of the text-books cited at the beginning of this book.

(a) Avalanches

There are two basic studies on their mechanics but they are rarely mentioned by geomorphologists: that of PÉGUY, already cited, and that of

BÜCHER, E. (1948) '*Beitrag zu den theoretischen Grundlagen des Lawinenverbaues*', Kummerli und Frei, Berne. Examines the mechanics of avalanches, and discusses the construction of defences against them. The opening theoretical discussion is the best available avalanche dynamics.

SULZLEE, C. (1950) 'Rapport sur la mission d'étude effectuéé auprès de l'Institut pour l'étude de la neige et des avalanches de Weissfluhjoch sur Davos', *La Houille blanche*, V, numero special B., pp. 699–708. Good study of the methods used by the Swiss to determine the initiation of avalanches.

BERGER, H. (1964) 'Vorgänge und Formen der Nivation in den Alpen', *Buch. Landesmuseums Kärnten*, **17**, p. 88.

MARKGREN, M. (1964) 'Chute slopes in Northern Fennoscandia', *Lund Studies in Geogr.*, no. A27, 2 vols., 136 and 147 p., 37 and 41.

PEEV. C. (1959) 'Der Einfluss den Hangneigung und Exposition auf die Lawinbildung', *Geogr. Berichte*, **12**, pp. 138–50.

POGGI, A. and PLAS, J. (1965) 'Conditions météorologiques critiques pour le déclenchement des avalanches', *A.I.H.S.*, *Public. 69* (Symposium Avalanches), pp. 25–34.

RAPP, A. (1959) 'Avalanche boulder tongues in Lappland', *Geogr. Ann.* **41**, pp. 34–48.

RAPP, A. (1960) 'Recent developments of mountain slopes in Kärkevage and surroundings, Northern Scandinavia', *Geogr. Ann.* **42**, pp. 73–200.

(b) Other snow-induced mechanical processes

For frost-shattering around snowpatches and accompanying solifluction see references to cirques; for asymmetrical valleys see the bibliography in *Le Modelé périglaciaire* by the author.

CAILLEUX, A. (1962) 'Études de géologie au détroit de McMurdo (Antarctique)', *Com. Nat. F. Recherch. Antarctique.*, no. 1, p. 41.

COOK, F. A., RAICHE, V. G. (1962) 'Simple transverse nivation hollows at Resolute, N.W.T., *Geogr. Bull.*, no. 18, p. 78–85.

GUILCHER, A. et CAILLEUX, A. (1950) 'Reliefs et formations quaternaires du Centre-Est des Pays-Bas', *Rev. de Géomorphol. dyn.*, **1**, pp. 128–43.

(c) Chemical processes

LINDNER, H. G. (1930) 'Das Karrenphänomen', *Petermanns Mitt.*, Ergänzungsheft, no. 208. The most detailed study, with very full bibliography.

RATHJENS, C. (1951) 'Der Hochkarst im System der klimatischen Morphologie', *Erdkunde*, **5**, pp. 310–15.

WILLIAMS, J. E. (1949) 'Chemical weathering at low temperatures', *Geogr. Rev.*, pp. 129–35. An important study with extensive bibliography.

(d) Cirques

The best summary is still that by C. A. COTTON in *Climatic Accidents in Landscape Making, Whitcombe and Tombs*, which has full references.

ANDREWS, J. T. (1965) 'The corries of the Northern Nain-Okak Section of Labrador', *Geogr. Bull.*, **7**, pp. 1129–36.

BATTLE, W. R. (1960) 'Temperature observations in bergschrunds and their relationships to frost shattering', *Royal Geogr. Soc. Res. Series*, no. **4**, pp. 83–95.

BOYÉ, M. (1952) 'Névés et érosion glaciaire', *Rev. de Géomorphol. dyn.*, **3**, pp. 20–36.

CHEVALIER, M. (1955) 'Le Relief glaciaire des Pyrénées du Couserans: 1: Les cirques', *Rev. Géogr. Pyr. et S.O.*, **25**, pp. 97–124.

DEGE, W. (1940) Über Schneefleckenerosion. Einige Beobachtungen in Nordnorwegen und auf Spitzbergen', *Geog. Anzeiger*, **41**, no. 8, pp. 8–11.

FLINT, R. F., DIDALGO, F. (1964) 'Glacial geology of the East flank of the Argentine Andes between lat. 39°10′S and 41°20′S.', *Bull. Geol. Soc. America*, **75**, pp. 335–52.

GALIBERT, G. (1956) 'Le Relief de la montagne dans les massifs de Luchon et des monts Maudits', *Rev. Géogr. Pyr. et S.O.*, **27**, pp. 41–73.

GROOM, G. (1959) 'Niche glaciers in Bünsow Land, Vestspitzbergen', *Journal of Glaciol.*, III, pp. 369–76.

JOHNSON, D. (1941) 'The function of melt-water in cirque formation', *Journ. of Geomorphology*, **4**, pp. 253–62.

LEWIS, W. V. (1939) 'Snow-patch erosion in Iceland', *Geogr. Journ.*, **94**, pp. 153–61.

LEWIS, W. V. (1940) 'The function of melt-water in cirque formation', *Geogr. Review*, **30**, pp. 64–83.

LEWIS, W. V. (1949) 'The function of melt-water in cirque formation: a reply' *Geog. Review*, pp. 110–128.

LEWIS, W. V. (1960) 'Norwegian cirque glaciers', *Royal Geogr. Soc. Res. Series*, no. **4**, 104 p.

MCCALL, J. G. (1960) 'The flow characteristics of a cirque glacier and their effect on glacial structure and cirque formation', *Roy. Geogr. Soc. Res. Ser.*, no. **4**, pp. 39–62.

MILLER, M. M. (1961) 'A distribution study of abandoned cirques in the Alaska–Canada Secondary Range', *Proc. 1st Intern. Symp. Arctic Geol.*, 1960, **2**, pp. 833–47.

MINATO, M., HASHIMOTO, S. and KOBAYASHI, K. (1952) 'Zur Karrbildung im Hidaka- und Hida- Gebirge, Japan', *Actes IV Congr. Quat.*, Rome-Pise, I, pp. 131–5.

TEMPLE, P. H. (1965) 'Some aspects of cirque distribution in the west-central Lake District, Northern England', *Geogr. Ann.*, *Ser.* A, **47**, pp. 185–93.

THOMPSON, H. R. (1950) 'Some corries of North-West Sutherland', *Proc. Geol. Assoc.*, **61**, no. 2, pp. 145–56.

PART THREE CHAPTER 3

A. Deposits and Erosional Alterations

Among general works, those of von Klebelsberg and Flint are the best on this topic. The chapter in Flint devoted to deposits is excellent. An outstanding and succint account of the various criteria for distinguishing glacial deposits, along with a good bibliography, is Wegmann, E. (1951) 'Subkambrische Tillite in der herzynischen Faltungszone, *Geol. Rundschau*, **39**, pp. 221–34.

BRUNNER, H., FRANZ, H. J. (1960) 'Arbeitsmethoden in der Glazialmorphologie', Teil I *Geogr. Ber.*, no. **17**, pp. 259–78.

BRUNNER, H., FRANZ, H. J. (1961) 'Arbeitsmethoden in der Glazialmorphologie', Teil II, *Geogr. Ber.*, no. **18**, pp. 44–66.

On the morphometry of morainic blocks, see the tables in

CAILLEUX, A. et TRICART, J., '*Initiation à l'étude des sables et des galets*', 3 vols., S.E.D.E.S., 5 pl. de la Sorbonne, Paris, 1959–60, and also

ARNEMAN, H. F., WRIGHT, H. E. (1959) 'Petrography of some Minnesota tills', *Journ. Sedim. Petrol.*, **29**, pp. 540–54.

HOLMES, C. D. (1960) 'Evolution of till-stone shapes, central New York', *Bull. Geol. Soc. Amer.*, **71**, pp. 1645–60.

TRICART, J. et SCHAEFFER, R. (1950) 'L'Acquisition de l'indice d'émoussé des galets sous l'effet des systèmes d'érosion', *Rev. de Géom. dyn.*, I, pp. 151–79.

(a) On fabrics

In addition to A. Cailleux and J. Tricart (1959–60), see:

LUNDQUIST, G. (1948) 'Blockensorientering i olika jordarter', *Sver. Geol. Unders*, ser. C, no. **497**, p. 29. Very detailed study made intelligible by numerous illustrations.

RICHTER, K (1932) 'Die Bewegungsrichtungen des Inlandeises, rekonstruiert aus den Kriten und Längsschen der Geschiebe', *Zeitschrift für Geschiebeforschung*, **8** (Berlin), basic discussion.

HOLMES, C. D. (1941) 'Till fabric', *Bull. Geol. Soc. of Amer.* **52**, pp. 1299–1354. Detailed study.

(b) On push moraines

KELLER, G. (1954) 'Drucktexturen im eiszeitlichen Sedimenten', *Eiszeitalter und Gegenwart*, **4–5**, pp. 158–71.

SCHULZ, W. (1959) 'Die Schuppenstruktur des Jungpleistozäns im Bereich der aktiven Steilufer Mittelusedoms', *Ber. Geol. Ges.*, Berlin, **4**, pp. 215–232.

The following are examples of the application of lithological methods to the study of glacial problems; some give summaries of these methods with useful bibliographies:

ALIMEN, H. (1953) 'Pétrographie des nappes alluviales de la Bigorre, essai de corrélations et de chronologie', *B.S.G.F.*, Ser. 6, **3**, pp. 377–91.

ANDREWS, J. T. (1963) 'The cross-valley moraines of North-Central Baffin Island; a quantitative analysis', *Geogr. Bull.*, no, **20**, pp. 82–129.

BLANC, J. (1951) 'Les Formations quaternaires du dôme de Rémollon et des environs du confluent Durance-Ubaye (Études granulométriques)', *Bull. Soc. Préhist. Fr.*, pp. 324–33.

DYLIKOWA, A. (1952) 'De la méthode structurale dans la morphologie glaciaire', *Bull. Soc. Sc. Lettres*, Lodz, C1. **3**, pp. 1–18.

DYSON, J. L. (1952) 'Ice-ridged moraines and their relation to glaciers', *Amer. Journ. Sc.*, **350**, pp. 204–12.

HOPPE, G. (1957) 'Problems of glacial morphology and the ice age', *Geogr. Ann.*, **1**, pp. 1–18.

HOPPE, G. (1963) 'Subglacial sedimentation, with examples from Northern Sweden', *Geog. Ann.*, **45**, pp. 41–9.

KARCEWSKI, A. (1963) 'Morphology, structure and texture of the ground moraine area of West Poland', *Soc. Amis Sc. Poznan. Publ. Sect. Géol. et Géogr.*, **4**, no. 2, pp. 112.

RUHE, R. and GOULD, L. (1954) 'Glacial geology of the Dakota county area, Minnesota', *Bull. Geol. Soc. America*, **65**, pp. 709–32.

TRICART, J. (1960) 'Le Taux de concentration en quartz dans diverses formations glaciaires de Fennoscandie', *Geogr. Ann.* **42**, pp. 201–6.

VIVIAN, H. (1965) 'Glaces mortes et morphologie glaciaire', *Rev. Géogr. Alpine*, **53**, pp. 371–402.

(c) On striae The following show methods of study:

LÉGER, M. (1958) 'Observations sur les striés glaciaires (glacier de Saint-Sorlin)', *Rev. Géogr. Alpine*, **46**, pp. 441–5.

SVENSSON, H. (1957) 'Plastic casts in the examination of glacial striation', *Geol. Föreningens i Stockholm Förhandl.*, 79.

B. The Moulding of the Bed of the Ice Sheet

General works avoid the problem and give little data. Only the fjords and ice margins are studied. One must depend on scattered references.

(a) **On erosion forms**

The essential studies are the following:

JAHNS, R. H. (1943) 'Sheet structure in granites: its origin and use as a measure of glacial erosion in New England', *Journ. of Geol.*, **11**, pp. 71–98.

On drumlins:

BROCHU, M. (1962) 'Étude statistique sur les striés glaciaires de la région de Fort-Churchill', *Geogr. Bull.*, no. **18**, pp. 108–11.

CHORLEY, R. (1959) 'The shape of drumlins', *Journ. of Glaciol.*, III, pp. 339–44.

EBERS, E. (1937) 'Zur Entstehung der Drumlins als Stromlinienkörper', *Neues Jahrb. für Mineralogie*, **78**, B, pp. 200–40. Detailed study; abundant references.

HEIDENREICH, C. (1964) 'Some observations on the shape of drumlins', *Can. Geogr.*, **8**, no. 2, pp. 101–7.

JAATINEN, S. (1960) 'The glacial morphology of Åland, with special reference to the quaternary deposits', *Fennia*, **84**, pp. 5–38.

JEWTUCHOWICZ, S. (1956) 'Structure des drumlins aux environs de Zbojno', *Acta Geogr. Univ. Lodziensis*, no. **7**, p. 74, 39 fig.

JUDSON, S., BARKS, R. E. (1961) 'Microstriations on polished pebbles', *Amer. Journ. of Soc.*, **259**, pp. 371–81.

REED, B. et al. (1962) 'Some aspects of drumlin geometry', *Amer. Journ. of Sc.*, **260**, pp. 200–10.

SYNGE, F. M. (1950) 'The glacial deposits around Trim, Co. Meath', *Proc. Royal Irish Ac.*, **53**, sect. B., no. 10, pp. 99–110.

VERNON, P. (1966) 'Drumlins and pleistocene ice flow over the Ards peninsula, Strangford Lough area, County Down, Ireland', *J. of Glaciol.*, VI, no. 45, pp. 401–9.

(b) **On the erosion forms due to inlandsis**

Descriptions, photographs and discussion of the problems will be found in:

ANSON, W. W., SHARP, J. I. (1960) 'Surface and rock-head relief features in the northern part of the Northumberland coal-field', *Univ. of Durham. Dept. of Geogr. Res. Ser.*, no. 2, p. 23.

BROCHU, M. (1954) 'Lacs d'érosion différentielle glaciaire sur le bouclier canadien', *Rev. de Géomorphol. Dynamique*, no. **6**, pp. 274–9.

CORBATO, C. B. (1965) 'Thickness and basal configuration of Lower Blue Glacier, Washington, determined by gravimetry', *J. of Glaciol.*, V, no. 41, 637–50.

DAHL. R. (1965) 'Plastically sculptured detail forms on rock surfaces in Northern Nordland, Norway', *Geogr. Ann.*, **47** A., pp. 83–140.

DAVIS, W. M. (1920) 'A roxen lake in Canada', *Scottish Geogr. Mag.*, **41**, pp. 65–74.

GJESSING, J. (1965/6) 'On plastic scouring and subglacial erosion', *Norsk Geogr. Tidsskr.*, **20**, pp. 1–37.

HOPPE, G. (1957) 'Problems of glacial morphology and the ice age', *Geogr. Ann.*, **39**, pp. 1–17.

JAHN (1947) 'Studies on jointing of rocks and glacial microrelief in Western Greenland', *Ann. Univ. Mariae Curie-Sklodowska*, Lublin, sect. B, II, pp. 47–99, no. 3.

JOHNSSON, G. (1956) *Glacial morphology in Southern Sweden*, Lund, p. 407.

LINTON, D. (1952) 'The signification of tors in glaciated lands', *Proc. XVIIth Geogr. Congr.*, Washington, 1952 (1957), pp. 354–7.

LINTON, D. (1957) 'Radiating valleys in glaciated lands', *Tijds. Nederl. Kon Aardriks Gen.*, **74**, pp. 297–312.

LINTON, D. (1949) 'Watershed breaching by ice in Scotland', *Trans. and Papers, The British Inst. of Geogr.*, **15**, pp. 1–16.

LINTON, D. L. (1963) 'The forms of glacial erosion', *Trans. and Papers, The British Inst. of Geogr.*, **33**, pp. 1–28.

MICHOT, J., SOUCHEZ, R. (1965) 'La Composition minéralogique des moraines, preuve de l'érosion glaciaire régressive en Antarctique', *C.R. Ac. Sc.*, **261**, pp. 4155–8.

TANNER, V. (1934) 'Outlines of the geography, life and customs of Newfoundland–Labrador', *Acta Geographica*, **8** (Helsinki). Text short but very good photographs: full bibliography.

(c) On glaciated valleys

There are many publications. The following illustrate the different viewpoints and the different types of valley:

AHLMANN, H. W. son (1919) 'Geomorphological studies in Norway', *Geografiska Annaler*. Excellent study of fjords.

AHLMANN, H. W. son (1941) 'Studies in North-east Greenland, 1939–40', *Geografiska Annaler*, pp. 148–82. Discusses the problem of fjords.

BLANCHARD, R. *Les Alpes*, Grenoble, Arthaud, 7 vol., passim. Many examples and photographs. Represents the work of the Grenoble school on Alpine glacial phenomena.

CAROL, H. (1947) 'The formation of roches moutonnées', *Journ. of Glac.*, I, pp. 57–9.

CHEVALIER, M. (1954) 'Le Relief glaciaire des Pyrénées du Couserans; II: Les vallées', *Rev. Géogr. Pyr. et S.O.*, **25**, pp. 189–220.

GUTENBERG, B., BUWALDA, J. P., SHARP, R. P. (1956) 'Seismic explorations on the floor of Yosemite valley (California)', *Bull. Geol. Soc. America*, **67**, pp. 1051–78.

HEIM, A. (1919) 'Vergleichendes über Fluss- und Gletscherwirkung', in *Geologie der Schweiz*, I, pp. 356-79, Leipzig. Exponent of antiglacialism. Many illustrations.

JENNINGS, J. N., AHMAD, N. (1957) 'The Legacy of an ice-cap. The lakes of the Western part of the Central Plateau of Tasmania', *The Australian Geogr.*, **7**, no. 2.

KOECHLIN, R. (1944) *Les Glaciers*, Lausanne, Lerouge. Expounds one version of the glacier bed theory.

LAUTENSACH, H. (1912) *Die Übertiefung des Tessingebietes*, Leipzig and Berlin. Detailed monograph on piedmont lakes.

LJUNGER, E. (1949) 'East-West balance of the Quaternary ice-caps in Patagonia and Scandinavia', *Bull. Geol. Inst., Uppsala*, **33**, pp. 13–96. Piedmont Lakes and troughs. Important bibliography.

ONDE, H. (1951) 'Les Verrous glaciaires, essai de classification', *Pirineos*, **7**, pp. 5–33.

PIPPAN, T. (1965) 'Gletschermorphologische Studien im Norwegischen Gebirge unter besonderer Berücksichtung des Problems der hochalpinen Formung', *Die Erde*, **92**, pp. 105–21.

TRICART, J. (1953) 'Les Séquences morainiques et l'hypothèse du défonçage périglaciaire d'après l'exemple de La Mure (Isère)', *Geol. Bavarica*, no. **19**, pp. 195–200.

PART THREE CHAPTER 4

Works in French or English are less numerous than for the preceding chapters. The best documented of all the ice margins is that of the Fennoscandian ice sheet, and the majority of the references are in German.

A. The Zone of Ice-Contact Meltwater

On the present occurrence of superglacial water, see the following and their bibliographies:

ANGEBY, O. (1952) 'Recent, subglacial and lateroglacial pothole erosion (evorsion)', *Lunds studies in Geogr.*, ser. A, no. **3**, pp. 14–24.

CORBEL, J. (1955) 'Crevasses et rivières sous-glaciaires', *Rev. Géogr. Lyon*, **30**, pp. 237–48.

RENAUD, A. (1936) 'Les Entonnoirs du glacier de Gorner', *Mémoires de la Soc. helvétique des Sc. Nat.*, **71**, mém. no. 1. Very detailed study; excellent descriptions.

STREIFF-BECKER, R. (1951) 'Pot-holes and glacier mills', *Journal of Glaciology*, I, no. 9.

(a) Ice-dammed lakes

Interesting and little known examples occur in:

ARNBORG, L. (1955) 'Ice-Marginal lakes at Hoffelsjökull', *Geog. Ann.*, **37**, pp. 202–28.

THORARINSSON, S. (1940) 'The ice-dammed lakes of Iceland', *Geogr. Ann.*, **15**, pp. 122–49.

LIESTØL, O. (1955–6) 'Glacier lakes in Norway', *Norsk Geogr. Tidskr.*, **15**, pp. 451–2.

LINTON, D. (1951) 'Unglaciated enclaves in glaciated regions', *Journ. of Glaciology*, I, pp. 451–2. An example of the features of marginal drainage of a continental glacier, but very condensed.

MATHEWS, W. H. (1965) 'Two self-dumping ice-dammed lakes in British Columbia', *Geogr. Rev.*, **55**, pp. 46–52.

STONE, K. H. (1963) 'The annual emptying of Lake George, Alaska', *Arctic*, **16**, pp. 26–40.

(b) On osar

There are a number of works, mainly Scandinavian. Only the most accessible and those with the most important bibliographies are cited here:

ANDERSEN, S. A. (1931) 'The waning of the last continental glaciers in Denmark, as illustrated by varved clay and eskers', *Journ. of Geology*, **39**, pp. 609–24. Shows the relations with rapid ablation of dead ice.

BERGDAHL, A. (1953) 'Marginal deposits in South Eastern Sweden, with special reference to the oses', *Lund Studies in Geogr.* ser. A., no. **4**, p. 24.

BOERMAN, W. E. (1948–49) 'Eskers and Kames', *Przegald Geograficzny*, **22**, pp. 49–58. Good summary, especially of terminology; very useful, but short, bibliography.

CHADWICK, G. H. (1928) 'Adirondacks eskers', *Bull. Geol. Soc. of America*, **39**, pp. 923–9. Very useful regional monograph.

FLINT, DEMOREST, WASHBURN (1942) 'Glaciation of Schickshock Mountains, Gaspe Peninsula', *Bull. Geol. Soc. of Amer.*, **53**, pp. 1211–30. Distinguishes between several types of *esker* on grounds of origin.

HOPPE, G. (1961) 'The continuation of the Uppsala Esker in the Bothnian sea and ice recession in the Gävle area', *Geogr. Ann.*, **43**, pp. 329–35.

KELLER, G. (1952) 'Beitrag zur Frage Oser und Kames', *Eiszeitalter und Gegenwart*, II, pp. 127–32.

NIEWIAROWSKI, W. (1965) 'Conditions of occurrence and distribution of kame landscapes in the Peribalticum within the area of the last glaciation', *Geogr. Polonica*, no. **6**, pp. 7–18.

OSBORNE, F. F. (1950) 'Marine crevasse fillings in the Lotbinière Region, Quebec', *Amer. Journ. of Science*, **248**, pp. 874–90. Submarine osar.

(c) On subglacial tunnels and marginal channels

DERBYSHIRE, E. (1961) 'Subglacial col gullies and the deglaciation of North-East Cheviots', *Trans. and Papers, British Inst. of Geogr.*, **29**, pp. 31–46.

DREHWALD, H. (1955) 'Zur Entstehung der Spillways in Nord-England und Süd-Schottland', *Köllner Geogr. Arb.*, no. **8**, p. 82.

GALON, R. (1965) 'Some new problems concerning subglacial channels', *Geog. Polonica*, no. **6**, pp. 19–28.

JONSSON, J. (1955) 'On the formation of frontal glacial lakes', *Geog. Ann.*, **37**, pp. 229–33.

MAJDANOWSKI, S. (1949) 'The southern limit of the Baltic glaciation in European Plain in the light of the extent of lake-channels', *Bull. Soc. Amis des Sc. et Lettres Poznan*, ser. B., pp. 185–208.
PEEL, R. F. (1956) 'The profile of glacial drainage channels', *Geog. Journal*, **122**, pp. 483–87.
SCHYTT, V. (1956) 'Lateral drainage channels along the Northern side of the Moltke Glacier, Northwest Greenland, *Geogr. Annaler*, **38**, p. 64–77.
TRICART, J., (1960) 'A subglacial gorge: la gorge du Guil (Hautes-Alpes)', *Journ. of Glaciol.*, **3**, no. 27, pp. 646–51.
TWIDALE, C. R. (1956) 'Longitudinal profiles of some glacial overflow channels', *Geogr. Journal*, **122**, pp. 88–92.
WOLDSTEDT, P. (1950) *Norddeutschland und angrenzende Gebiete im Eiszeitalter*, Köhler, Stuttgart, p. 464. Contains numerous examples.

B. The Frontal Zone

This has been the subject of many studies, especially in relation to ice sheets. Among general works the best are in Flint and von Klebelsberg.

(a) On moraines

See the references to the previous chapter and that to Woldstedt (1950), cited above, and its extensive bibliography.

GRIPP, K. (1938) Endmoränen, *C.R. Congr. Intern. Geogr.*, Amsterdam, II, section 2a, pp. 215–28. Good summary, mainly concerned with ice sheets.
HORBERG, L. (1954) 'Rocky mountain and continental pleistocene deposits in the Waterton region, Alberta, Canada', *Bull. Geol. Soc. Amer.*, **65**, pp. 1093–1150.
LÜTTWIG, G. (1954) 'Alt- und mittelpleistozäne Eisrandlagen zwischen Harz und Weser', *Geol. Jahrbuch*, **70**, pp. 43–125.
RICHTER, K. (1936) 'Gefügestudien im Engebrae, Fondalsbrae und ihren Vorland-sedimenten', *Zeitschr. für Gletscherkunde*, **24**, pp. 22–30. Excellent monograph on a valley glacier terminal system.

(b) On the form of terminal moraines

References are more numerous. The following is a selection:

ALIMEN, H. (1950) 'Les Formations glaciaires et fluvio-glaciaires de la vallée de l'Ousse (versant Nord-Pyrénéen)', *Bull. Soc. Géol. Fr.*, 5° sér., **20**, pp. 107–20. Excellent monograph: might serve as a model.
BRAVARD, Y. (1963) *Le Bas-Dauphiné, recherches sur la morphologie d'un piémont alpin*. Grenoble, Allier, p. 504.
FALCONER, G. IVES, J., LOKEN, D., ANDREWS, J. T. (1955), 'Major end moraines in Eastern and Central Arctic Canada', *Geogr. Bull.*, **7**, pp. 137–53.

GALON, R. (1961) 'Morphology of the Notec-Warta (or Torun-Eberswalde) ice marginal streamway', *Ac. Sc. Pologne, Geogr. Studies*, **29**, p. 129.

GOLDTHWAIT, R. P. (1951) 'Formation of moraines of Barnes Ice Cap', *Proc. 2nd glaciological conference*, Arctic Inst. of North Amer., New York, p. 6–12. Good study of the dynamics of an unusual but instructive case.

HOPPE, G. (1957) 'Problems of glacial morphology and the ice age', *Geog. Ann.*, **39**, pp. 1–17.

HOPPE, G. (1952) 'Hummocky moraine regions, with special reference to the interior of Norrbotten', *Geogr. Annaler*, **34**, p. 1–72.

ILLIES, H. (1952) 'Eisanden und eiszeitliche Entwässerung in der Umgebung von Bremen', *Abh. naturw. Verein Bremen*, **33**, pp. 19–56. Outstanding monograph on the margin of an ice sheet.

JOHN, B. S., SUGDEN, D. E. (1962) 'The morphology of Kaldalon, a deglaciated valley in Iceland', *Geogr. Ann.*, **44**, pp. 347–65.

KLIMASZEWSKI, M. (1960) 'Geomorphological studies of the western part of Spitzbergen between Kongsfjord and Eidembuk', *Univ. Jagellon, Cracovie Prace Geogr.*, N.S., No. 1, p. 166.

OSTREM, G. (1964) 'Ice-cored moraines in Scandinavia', *Geogr. Ann.*, **46**, pp. 282–337.

STRÖMBERG, B. (1965) 'Mappings and geochronological investigations in some moraine areas of South-central Sweden', *Geogr. Ann.*, **47** A, pp. 73–82.

SZURPYCZYNSKI, J. (1963) 'Relief of marginal zone of glaciers and types of deglaciation of Southern Spitzbergen glaciers', *Prace Geogr.*, no. **39**, Varsovie, p. 163.

VIVIAN, H. (1965) 'Glaces mortes et morphologie glaciaire', *Rev. Géogr. Alpine*, **53**, pp. 371–402.

WARD, W. H. (1952) 'The physics of deglaciation in central Baffin Island', *Journ. of Glaciology*, **2**, pp. 9–22. Completes the paper by Goldthwaithe (1951).

WOLDSTEDT, P. (1952) 'Die Entstehung der Seen in den ehemals vergletscherten Gebieten', *Eiszeitalter und Gegenwart*, II, p. 146–53. Work of englacial waters in the lobes of the ice sheet.

C. The Proglacial Zone

Again there are many references, the chief being found in the general works of Flint, von Klebelsburg and Woldstedt. The following give examples and discuss the problems:

ANTEVS, E. (1925) *Retreat of the last ice sheet in Eastern Canada*, Canada Geol. Survey Mem. 146, p. 142, Glacio-marine deposits.

MACCLINTOCK P. (1922) 'The pleistocene history of the lower Wisconsin River', *Journ. of Geol.*, **30**, pp. 673–89. Good monograph of a proglacial channel.

FLINT, R. F. (1936) 'Stratified drift and deglaciation in Eastern Washington', *Bull. Geol. Soc. Amer.*, **57**, pp. 1849–84. Monograph of a proglacial channel.

ILLIES, H. (1952) 'Die eiszeitliche Fluss- und Formengeschichte des Unterelbe-Gebietes', *Geol. Jahrbuch*, **66**, pp, 525–58.

JEWTUCHOWICZ, S. (1953) 'La Structure du Sandre', *Bull. Soc. Sc. Lettres de Lodz*, III/IV, no. 4, p. 23.

SCHAEFFER, I. (1950) 'Über methodische Fragen der Eiszeitforschung im Alpenvorland', *Zeitschr. Deutschen geol. Ges.*, 102, pp. 287–310. Many references on the Bavarian Piedmont.

SERET, G. (1965) 'La succession des épisodes fluviatiles périglaciaires et fluvioglaciaires à l'aval des glaciers', *Z. für Geom.*, NS **9**, pp. 305–20.

SUNDBORG, A. (1954) Map of the Hoffellssandur, *Geogr. Ann.*, **36**, pp. 162–8.

TARR, R. S. (1909) 'Some piedmont phenomena of the glacier margins in the Yakutat Bay Region, Alaska', *Zeitschr. für Gletscherkunde*, **3**, pp. 81–110. Present-day examples.

TARR et MARTIN (1914) *Alaskan glacier studies*, Nat. Geogr. Soc. Washington, p. 498, Indispensable, Abundant illustrations.

WALCZAK, W. (1954) 'The outwash valley of the Nysa river and the pleistocene hydrological changes in the foreland of the Eastern Sudetes', *Polska Ak. N. Inst. Geogr.*, no. **2**, Warsaw, p. 57.

WOLDSTEDT, P. (1956) 'Die Geschichte des Flussnetzes in Norddeutschland und angrezenden Gebieten', *Eiszeitalter und Gegenw.*, **7**, pp. 5–12.

PART THREE CHAPTER 5

These present some difficulty as most of the information on the topics of this chapter is scattered through works devoted to other questions; most is in regional monographs or studies of chronology. The first have almost all been quoted in the bibliography to the last chapter, the second are given below. Only works bearing on the topics treated in this chapter are mentioned, so that the list is incomplete. Reference should also be made to the bibliographies to Chapter 3 and 4 Part III. Flint contains a good résumé of the methods used to reconstruct glacial oscillations from deposits.

MORAWETZ, S. (1952) 'Das Kommen und Gehen der eiszeitlichen Gletscher', *Peterm. Mitt.*, IV C, pp. 21–9. General consideration of the advance and retreat of ice sheets. Good bibliography.

(a) Observations on existing ice

KINZL, H. (1946–9) 'Formenkundliche Beobachtungen im Vorfeld der Alpengletscher', *Veröffentl. des Museum Ferdinandeum* (*Innsbrück*), **26–9**, pp. 61–82. A basic study, dealing mainly with recession forms. Very well documented

SHARP, R. P. (1949) 'Studies of superglacial debris on valley glaciers', *Amer. Journ. of Sc.*, **247**, pp. 289–315. Abundant data on existing deglaciation features of piedmont glaciers. Fundamental.

(b) Advance phenomena, push moraines

BUBNOFF, S. von (1952) 'Zur mechanik glazigener Gesteindeformationen', *Actes IV Congrès Quat.*, Rome-Pise, I, pp. 86–8.

CAILLEUX, A. (1952) 'Polissage et surcreusement glaciaire dans l'hypothèse de Boyé', *Rev. de Géomorphologie dyn.*, pp. 247–57. Theory of trough formation during the advance phase.

FALCONER, G. (1962) 'Patterned ground under ice-fields', *Journ. of Glaciol.*, LV, no. 32, pp. 238–9.

JONG, J. D. de (1952) 'On the structure of the proglacial pleistocene of the Archemerberg (Prov. of Overijssel, Netherlands)', *Geol. en Mijnbouw*, N.S., **14**, pp. 86–96. Good monograph on push moraines, with sections.

KUPSCH, W. O. (1962) 'Ice-thrust ridges in western Canada', *J. of Geol.*, **70**, pp. 582–94.

MACKAY, J. R. MATHEWS, W. H. (1964) 'The role of permafrost in ice-thrusting: a discussion', *J. of Geol.*, **72**, pp. 378–80.

RICHTER, SCHNEIDER, WAGER (1950) 'Die saale-eiszeitliche Stauchzone von Itterbeck-Uelsen (Emsland)', *Zeitschr. deutschen geol. Ges.*, **102**, pp. 60–75. Excellent monograph on push moraines, with sections.

ROSS MACKAY, J. (1956) 'Deformation by glacier-ice at Nicholson Peninsula, N.W.T., Canada', *Arctic*, IX, pp. 218–28.

ROSS MACKAY, J. (1959) 'Glacier ice-thrust features of the Yukon coast', *Geogr. Bull.* no. **13**, pp. 5–21.

ROSS MACKAY, J. STAGER, J. (1966) 'Thick tilted beds of segregated Mackenzie delta area, N.W.T., *Biul. Peryglac.*, no. **15**, pp. 39–43.

(c) Retreat phenomena

BARTOWSKI, T. (1953) 'The role of "buried dead ice" in the formation of the postglacial landscape of Central Great Poland', *Bull. Soc. des Amis des Sc. et des Lettres de Poznan*, ser. B, **17**, pp. 123–52.

BIRD, J. B. (1959) 'Recent contributions to the physiography of Northern Canada', *Z. für Geom.*, **3**, pp. 151–74.

DERBYSHIRE, E. (1962) 'Fluvioglacial erosion near Knob Lake, Central Quebec, Labrador, Canada', *Bull. Geol. Soc. Amer.*, 73, pp. 1111–26.

FRÖDIN, G. (1954) 'The distribution of late glacial subfossil sandurs in Northern Sweden', *Geogr. Ann.*, **36**, pp. 112-34.

GALON, R. (1964) 'On the geomorphology of Northern Poland', *Geogr. Polonica*, no. **1**, pp. 23–39.

HAMELIN, L. (1952) 'Influence de la glaciation sur le tracé en plan du réseau hydrographique, essai de classification des types de tracés', *The Canadian Geogr.*, no. **2**, pp. 17–30.

HOPPE, G. (1950) 'Les Formes de récession glaciaire de Bothnie septentrionale (Suède)', *Rev. de Géomorphologie dynamique*, I, pp. 79–87. Retreat features in a marine environment.

HORBERG. L. (1954) 'Rocky mountain and continental pleistocene deposits in the Waterton region, Alberta, Canada', *Bull. Geol. Soc. Amer.*, **65**, pp. 1093–1150.

IVES, J. D. (1960) 'Glaciation and deglaciation of the Helluva lake area, Central Labrador–Ungava', *Geogr. Bull.* (*Ottawa*), no. **15**, pp. 46–64.

IVES, J. D. ANDREWS, J. T. (1963) 'Studies in the physical geography of north-central Baffin Island, N.W.T.', *Geogr. Bull.*, no. **19**, pp. 5–48.

JEWTUCHOWICZ, S. (1965) 'Description of eskers and kames in Gashamnoyra and on Bungebreen, south of Hornsund, Vestspitsbergen', *J. of Glaciol.*, v, no. **41**, pp. 719–25.

KLAJNERT, Z. (1966) 'Origin of Domaniewice hills and remarks on the mode of waning of the Middle polish ice sheet', *Acta Geogr. Lodziensia*, **23**, p. 134.

KNAUER, J. (1952) 'Diluviale Talverschüttung und Epigenese im südlichen Bayern', *Geologica Bavarica*, no. **11**, p. 32.

LAWRENCE, D. B., ELSON, J. A. (1953) 'Periodicity of deglaciation in North America since the Late Wisconsin maximum', *Geog. Ann.*, 35, pp. 83–104.

MANNERFELD, C. M., son (1949) 'Marginal drainage channels as indicators of the gradient of Quaternary ice-caps', *Geogr. Annaler*, **31**.

NELSON, J. G. (1963) 'The origin and significance of the Morley Flats, Alberta', *Bull. Canadian Petr. Geol.*, **11**, pp. 169–77.

NIEWIAROWSKI, W. (1961) 'Some problems concerning deglaciation by stagnation and wastage of large portions of the ice-sheet within the area of the last glacation in Poland', *INQUA*, *6e Congr. Varsovie 1961*, *Rep. III*, Lodz 1963, pp. 245–56.

TAMMEKANN, A. (1955) 'Salpausselkä. Die Hauptendmoräne Finnlands im Lichte der neueren Forschung', *Geogr. Rundschau*, **7**, pp. 94–100.

THEAKSTONE, W. H. (1965) Recent changes in the glaciers of Svartisen. *J. of Glaciol.*, v, no. **40**, pp. 411–431.

TRICART, J. (1954) 'Périglaciaire et fluvioglaciaire, essai de corrélation du Quaternaire durancien', *Mém. de Centre de Docum. Cartogr.*, **4**, pp. 171–202.

WARD, W. H. (1951) 'The physics of deglaciation in Central Baffin Island', *U.G.G.I.*, *Ass. Int. Hydr. Sc. Bruxelles*, I, pp. 237–45.

On rock glaciers, the primary works are:

WAHRHAFTIG, C. and COX, A. (1959) 'Rock glaciers in the Alaska Range', *Bull. Soc. America*, **70**, pp. 383–436.

CAPPS, S. R. (1910) 'Rock glaciers in Alaska', *Journ. of Geol.*, pp. 359–75. An old monograph which has useful data.

FAURE-MURET (1959) 'Les Rock-streams ou pseudo-moraines du massif de l'Argentera–Mercantour', *C.R. Somm.*, *S.G.F.*, pp. 118–20.

KESSELI, J. E. (1941) 'Rock streams in the Sierra Nevada, California', *Geogr. Rev.*, pp. 203–27.

OUTCALT, S. and BENEDICT, J. B. (1965) 'Photo-interpretation of two types of rock glacier in the Colorado Front Range, U.S.A.', *J. of Glaciol.*, v, no. **42**, pp. 849–56.

PILLEWITZER, W. (1957) 'Untersuchungen an Blockströme der Ötztaler Alpen', *Abh. Geogr. Inst. fr. Univ. Berlin*, **5**, pp. 37–50.

Indexes

SUBJECT INDEX

For the major topics see the subsections of the table of Contents, pp. vii-ix.

INDEX OF LOCALITIES

INDEX TO AUTHORS

Those pages in italic refer to the bibliographies